Regency
Brides
Collection

2 Sparkling Regency Romances

A Bargain with Fate
by Ann Elizabeth Cree

A Kind and Decent Man
by Mary Brendan

Regency Brides

A collection from some of Mills & Boon
Historical Romance's most popular authors

Regency
Brides
Collection

Ann Elizabeth Cree &
Mary Brendan

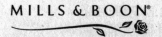
MILLS & BOON®

*MILLS & BOON and MILLS & BOON with the Rose Device
are registered trademarks of the publisher.*

*First published in Great Britain 2004 by
Harlequin Mills & Boon Limited,
Eton House, 18-24 Paradise Road,
Richmond, Surrey TW9 1SR*

REGENCY BRIDES COLLECTION © Harlequin Books S.A. 2004

The publisher acknowledges the copyright holders of the
individual works as follows:

A Bargain with Fate © Annemarie Hasnain 1998
A Kind and Decent Man © Mary Brendan 1999

ISBN 0 263 84083 2

138-1104

*Printed and bound in Spain
by Litografía Rosés S.A., Barcelona*

A BARGAIN WITH FATE
by
Ann Elizabeth Cree

Ann Elizabeth Cree is married and lives in Boise, Idaho, with her family. She has worked as a nutritionist and an accountant. Her favourite form of daydreaming has always been weaving romantic stories in her head. With the encouragement of a friend, she started putting those stories on to paper. In addition to writing and caring for two lively boys, two cats and two dogs, she enjoys gardening, playing the piano and, of course, reading.

Also by Ann Elizabeth Cree
in Mills & Boon Historical Romance™:

★ novels have linking characters
^ novels have linking characters

Chapter One

Whatever was taking the man so long? Rosalyn, Lady Jeffreys pushed a strand of hair off her brow with nervous fingers. She hoped Lord Stamford would soon put in an appearance, or she would be tempted to flee from his house like a common thief.

She had spent the entire morning mustering up the courage to come. If she possessed an ounce of sense, she would have turned coward and jumped back into the hackney carriage the minute she laid eyes on the imposing mansion in St James's Square. Instead, she'd marched up the front steps, determined to confront the notorious Marquis of Stamford.

To her dismay, Lord Stamford's butler not only indicated his lordship would return shortly but insisted on showing her into this intimidating drawing room with its pale green walls and a fireplace with the most elaborate carving she'd ever seen.

The butler had been surprisingly solicitous for such a stiff, dignified man, inquiring if she were warm enough and insisting on arranging her chair near the hearth. She had had some idea that a man of Lord

Stamford's stamp would run a household as wild as his reputation. Instead, the few servants she'd spotted looked respectable enough and went quietly about their business. The drawing room showed no signs of haphazard management. It was furnished in the height of elegance: the mahogany chairs polished to perfection, rich Oriental rugs scattered about the floor. Above the elaborately carved mantelpiece was the portrait of a darkly handsome man, his hair tied back with a riband, his hand on a sword, his cool gaze resting on Rosalyn with a mocking expression.

Rosalyn shifted uneasily. The house seemed unnaturally quiet. She heard no footsteps, no servants' voices—only the relentless ticking of the clock. Another five minutes dragged by. It was quite apparent Lord Stamford did not intend to see her. She was miffed. Rudeness obviously numbered among his many other shortcomings.

Well, she could not sit here forever. She would have to hunt the man down and force him to see her. She stood up so abruptly her reticule slid to the ground. Its contents spilled across the floor.

'Oh, drat!' Rosalyn exclaimed. As she knelt on the carpet, the poke of her bonnet hit the edge of the chair, which knocked it askew. Tears of frustration sprang to her eyes. Could anything else possibly go wrong?

'Lady Jeffreys?'

A pair of shiny black riding boots appeared in her line of vision. She froze. Her horrified eyes travelled up a pair of lean, muscled thighs encased in buckskin breeches, over a dark riding coat covering a broad masculine chest and came to rest on the most wickedly handsome face she had seen in her life. With his lean, dark features and midnight black hair, he could be an arrogant Italian nobleman from a Gothic romance.

His disconcerting gaze swept over her face. She flushed and dropped her eyes. Her fingers trembled as she pushed her bonnet back into place. Never had she felt at such an utter disadvantage.

'It appears you need some help. May I be of assistance?' the man inquired politely.

'No, I…' She snapped into motion, grabbed the last item and shoved it into her reticule. She started to rise, but before she could protest, the man reached down and hauled her to her feet. She backed away, even more flustered.

A small smile of amusement quirked his lips. 'I am Stamford.'

'Lord Stamford?' This man could not possibly be the dissolute gamester she'd expected. Well above average height, his athletic figure proclaimed a man who spent more time in sporting pursuits than hovering around a gaming table. No lines of dissipation marred his fine aristocratic face. But most unexpected of all were the lines of humour lurking about his firm mouth.

Colour flooded her cheeks as the Marquis raised a curious brow.

'Perhaps you expected someone else? You look rather astounded.'

'I was merely surprised. I…I did not hear you come in, my lord.'

'You did seem to be occupied. I am sorry I kept you waiting so long. I usually ride in the mornings and had just returned when I was told you were here. I was not expecting visitors. Have we met before?' His eyes flickered over her face in a coolly amused manner calculated to put her firmly in her place.

She raised her chin. 'No, we have not, my lord.'

'So you do not intend to claim an acquaintance with me?'

'No, why should I? I had not even heard of you until a few days ago.'

'The last lady unknown to me who called on me in this fashion wished to renew an acquaintance which I fear I did not recollect,' he informed her blandly.

Rosalyn stared at him. Whatever was he talking about? Then a shaft of anger shot through her as she perceived his meaning. Did he really have the audacity to imagine she had called on some flimsy pretext merely to make his acquaintance?

Suppressing the desire to let him know exactly what she thought of such arrogance, she said, 'I am not here on a social call but on a matter of business, my lord. There is no other reason I would ever wish to call on you.'

'I beg your pardon, my lady. I usually deal through my agent in business matters. However, in this case...' his lazy gaze slid over her face and down her body '...I shall be delighted to make an exception.'

Her cheeks grew even warmer. She hated her appalling tendency to blush. 'This is a personal matter.'

His dark brows raised a fraction. 'A personal matter? Now I am curious, Lady Jeffreys—especially since you say we have never met.'

'It is not my personal business. It is my brother's.'

'Your brother's?' Surprise flitted across his features. He motioned towards the elegant brocade settee with a careless hand. 'Please be seated and tell me how I can help you.'

He settled his frame in one of the upholstered mahogany chairs arranged near the settee, his dark eyes fixed on her face.

'I am the sister of James Whitcomb,' she began, folding her hands tightly together, wishing he would not stare at her so. 'I believe you know him.'

'I made his acquaintance only a few days ago. Go on.'

'I know that he has lost his estate to you at cards.'

He stretched his muscular legs in front of him and crossed his arms over his chest. Although his expression was still that of the polite host, his eyes hardened almost imperceptibly. 'So, you are here at your brother's request?'

'No, of course not! He would be furious with me if he knew I was here. I pray you will never mention this to him!'

'I wouldn't think of it. I cannot see what business this is of yours, however.'

'What do you mean by that? Of course this affair is my business. He is my brother. It is our family estate!'

'I understood your brother has full title to the property and is free to do with it as he wishes.'

'That is true, of course, but I cannot sit by and watch it lost like this! I think it's quite despicable for you to take away someone's inheritance in such a shabby fashion!'

'Are you perchance implying I cheated, my lady?'

Rosalyn shifted uneasily under his hard gaze. 'No, I don't know that at all! I only meant that it was quite wrong of you to take advantage of such a green boy! I think that—'

'I appreciate your sisterly concern,' he drawled. 'But your brother is hardly a young boy. He was not forced into staking his estate. I did not hold a pistol to his head. He had no business playing for such high stakes if he could not cover them. I am sorry about the loss of your family estate, but I cannot do anything about it.'

Cold fury seeped through her. 'I cannot imagine why you would want another estate. I am certain you must have quite enough.'

Lord Stamford laughed sardonically. He uncrossed his arms and rose from his chair to lounge against the carved marble chimney piece. He idly picked up one of the small ivory figurines adorning the mantel. 'Can one ever have enough estates? I am certain I can think of something to do with the property. But I am still at a loss to know exactly what you hoped to accomplish by coming here today.' He returned the figurine to its place and regarded her with cool indifference.

Rosalyn had never detested anyone more in her life. She swallowed her anger, forcing herself to remain calm. 'I had hoped we could reach some sort of agreement. I cannot pay you the entire price, but I am willing…'

She faltered as a cold, cynical light leapt to his eyes. His gaze, suddenly insolent, raked her face and moved appraisingly down her body, resting for an instant on the soft curve of her breast. She sat frozen.

No man, not even her husband, had ever stared at her in such a manner.

'An agreement? Exactly what sort of agreement did you have in mind, my dear lady? I usually don't bargain my gambling debts away, but I am certain you and I could come to an arrangement that would satisfy both of us. You are not quite in my usual taste, but your figure is satisfactory and you are…pretty enough.'

'I beg your pardon?' For the second time, he'd managed to thoroughly confuse her.

Then his insulting words pierced her consciousness. Humiliation followed by pure outrage washed over her.

She shot to her feet. Her voice shook with suppressed fury. 'You think I am here to offer you…that? I would never do such a degrading thing. I would rather spend my life in debtor's prison or…or hang than come to such a despicable agreement with you!'

She whirled around and swept towards the door. But Stamford reached the door before her; his strong fingers closed over her wrist.

More than a little frightened, she tried to jerk her hand out of his iron grasp. His intimidating nearness, and the warmth of his hand, caused her heart to pound most alarmingly. She could smell the masculine scent of his cologne.

He could not possibly intend to ravish her now! Helplessly, she stared up into his dark compelling eyes surrounded by lashes far longer than any man's should be. His expression, so cold and sardonic only minutes before, was now warm with amusement.

'Please do not leave yet, Lady Jeffreys. I must offer

my most sincere apologies and humbly beg your pardon. I am afraid I misunderstood your intentions. You must give me a chance to redeem myself by telling me what you wanted.' The laughter in his eyes rendered him dangerously attractive.

Her breath caught in her throat. 'I…I must go. Please release me, my lord.'

He instantly dropped her wrist. Gentle fingers caught her chin, tilting her face so he could look into her eyes. 'Don't look so frightened. I promise I won't seduce you in my drawing room. It's not good *ton*, you know.'

How dare he laugh at her after making such an improper suggestion? She slapped his hand away and glared at him. 'I have nothing more to say to you.'

He moved in front of her and rested his broad shoulders against the door and folded his arms over his chest. 'I won't let you go until you tell me what you wanted. I must make up for my despicable behaviour.'

'I cannot say you are behaving any better now,' she snapped.

His eyes danced, totally unrepentant. 'I am afraid I generally don't behave very well. More than one lady of my acquaintance has informed me of that very fact. But please tell me your request.' His mouth curved in a most devastating smile.

She flushed, resenting the implication that he categorised her with all the other women he knew, particularly as she could imagine the sort of female company he kept. But further argument appeared fruitless. He obviously had no intention of letting her go until she did as he bade her. Her shoulders slumped.

'I wanted to discuss some sort of arrangement to pay my brother's debt to you and ask you to return Meryton. I cannot pay you what it is worth, but I can pay something. I have an income from my husband and a small house in London at my disposal. I should like to pay the debt off in instalments…with interest, of course.'

The laughter left his eyes. He said quietly, 'I am sorry, but I cannot fulfil your request, my lady.'

Disappointment surged through her. 'Why not?'

He shrugged. 'The debt is between your brother and me. I do not think he would appreciate your interference. If you wish to come to some sort of an arrangement with him, he may approach me. I would be willing to consider it, but I cannot promise to restore the estate to him.'

'I see.' She prayed she would not burst into tears. 'Please allow me to leave.'

He paused with his hand on the doorknob, the plain gold signet ring he wore reflecting the sunlight filtering in through the brocade curtains. 'Tell me, do you also have a passion for gambling, Lady Jeffreys?'

'Of course not. I am the worst card player in the world.'

He laughed gently. 'It's too bad others are not as honest about their abilities as you.'

He opened the door. She moved past him, ignoring the arm he held out to her. She hastened down the curving staircase to the hallway. His butler sprang to open the door. To her vexation, Lord Stamford trailed her down the steps and followed her to the waiting hackney carriage.

'Are you in London often, Lady Jeffreys?' he asked

conversationally as if nothing had passed between them.

'Rarely,' she replied without looking at him.

He leaned towards her, the sun glinting off his raven hair. 'I thought not. Then you should know it's most improper of you to call on me in this fashion,' he said kindly, but his eyes danced. 'I am surprised your husband allowed it.'

'Not that it is any of your business, my lord, but I am a widow, not a young girl. I can do what I please.'

'Perhaps so, but you should have at least brought a maid with you. My reputation is not the most sterling. Respectable ladies know better than to call on me and certainly not unchaperoned.'

Completely taken aback, she stammered, 'I...I trusted you would behave like a gentleman.'

He grinned at her in a maddening fashion. 'I am afraid you sadly misplaced your trust. I am no gentleman.'

'That's nothing to boast about,' she replied tartly.

'I look forward to our next meeting, Lady Jeffreys.' Without removing his eyes from her face, he captured her hand and raised it to his lips.

Rosalyn jerked her hand away. 'Since I do not move in the same dissipated circles as you, there is not likely to be another meeting.'

He looked startled at that but quickly recovered. 'Shall we make a wager on that, my lady? I think we shall meet again—and soon.'

'Goodbye, my lord,' she said. He merely smiled in his infuriating way and insisted on handing her into the coach.

Rosalyn settled back into the hard cushions. How

she wished she were a man! Planting him a facer or, better yet, running him through with a sword would give her unbounded satisfaction.

Her anger quickly gave away to depression. She had completely failed in her mission. James was no better off; their home had been lost to a stranger. A tear trickled down her cheek, quickly followed by another. She fumbled in her reticule for her handkerchief, grateful she had been too angry to cry in front of the abominable Lord Stamford.

'Oh dear,' she whispered. Could this day possibly get any worse? Her favourite fan was missing, undoubtedly lying in Lord Stamford's elegant drawing room.

'Damn!' Michael muttered as he entered his study. He threw his long frame into the chair in front of his desk, a frown marring his brow. The whole business of this estate was proving to be a blasted nuisance. He'd never meant to gamble Whitcomb out of his estate, but the chance to foil Edmund Fairchilde, a man he disliked, was too tempting. And in spite of himself, he'd felt a flash of pity for the young man, clearly in over his head and about to be ruined, which he surely would be if he fell in Fairchilde's clutches.

To complicate matters, he discovered the Dowager Countess of Carlyn was James Whitcomb's maternal grandmother. Lady Carlyn was a friend of his aunt, Lady Spence. Michael could quite imagine his aunt's words upon learning her nephew had gambled Whitcomb out of his estate. They would hardly be complimentary to Michael's character.

And now Lady Jeffreys. What in the devil pos-

sessed him to insult her in such a fashion? He had
known the instant he first looked into her sweet face
and clear honest eyes, her bonnet charmingly askew,
that she was a lady in every respect.

He spent too much time with the *demimonde*, rendering him far too cynical. Most women of his acquaintance would have no compunction in trading
their charms to pay off a gambling debt. It would not
have been the first time he had been made such an
offer.

He rose, a slight smile lifting the corners of his
mouth. He reluctantly admitted she interested him despite her very real dislike for him. She was quite
lovely in a quiet sort of way. Her prim grey gown
could not completely disguise the soft curves of her
breast and hips or detract from her luxuriant chestnut
hair and large hazel eyes. Michael quite looked forward to their next meeting, although she would most
likely cut him dead, as he undoubtedly deserved.

His thoughts were interrupted by the soft cough of
Watkins, his butler, hovering in the doorway.
'M'lord.'

'What is it, Watkins? Not another unexpected visitor, I trust.'

A feminine voice spoke from behind the butler. 'I
shall show myself in. I do not wish to be told again
that my nephew is not at home.'

Michael inwardly groaned as Lady Margaret
Spence swept into the room, a determined look on her
aristocratic face. He wished Lady Jeffreys to the devil
for her ill-timed visit. He should have been at White's
by now and out of reach of his aunt and her unwelcome business.

He bowed over Lady Spence's gloved hand. 'My dear aunt, I am delighted to see you,' he murmured.

Lady Spence fixed intelligent blue eyes on her nephew's face. 'I doubt it. This is the first time I've managed to catch you at home. I am almost inclined to think you're avoiding me.'

She drew off her kidskin gloves in a businesslike manner and seated herself in the chair near his desk. In her mid-fifties, she possessed the figure and posture of a much younger woman. Today, she was fashionably dressed in a powder-blue round gown with a matching pelisse which set off her greying blonde hair becomingly.

Michael seated himself on the other side of his desk. 'Why would I wish to avoid you? You know I am always pleased to see you. And how is my uncle? I have not yet seen him about town.'

'Frederick is quite well. However, I did not call to exchange pleasantries with you. You know very well why I am here, Michael, so I suggest you stop fencing with me. You cannot avoid this discussion forever.' She impaled him with ice-blue eyes. He sunk back in his chair with all the enthusiasm of a fox run to ground by a pack of hounds.

Nearly an hour later Michael entered the portals of White's. He was shown to a table in the corner of the dining room where he was greeted by a stocky blond man attired in a bottle-green coat and striped waistcoat, his starched cravat elaborately tied in an oriental knot.

'Michael, my boy!' the gentleman exclaimed. 'I

thought you weren't going to show. I've nearly starved waiting for you and was forced to order.'

Michael glanced at his cousin's ample figure and laughed. 'I don't think there's too much danger of that, Charles,' he said pulling up a chair. 'I've been besieged by visitors today. First I had a call from—' he broke off, frowning. 'Never mind. The last caller was my Aunt Margaret.'

'Been after you again about that chit? You'll end up with your neck in the parson's noose before you know it. I'm glad your Aunt Margaret ain't my relative. Don't envy you your father either.'

'They're bad enough apart, but together—I'd rather face a firing squad. I'd have much better odds.' Michael frowned at the glass of dry sherry the waiter set in front of him. 'My aunt came to inform me my bride-to-be will arrive in town within a fortnight. There's been a slight illness in the family that prevents her from coming any sooner. I'll have a reprieve at any rate.'

'Don't see how they can force you into marriage. Good lord, you're thirty, well past your majority,' Charles said.

'Well, would you care to oppose my father?'

'Good point,' said Charles hastily as the waiter brought his meal. 'Don't know how anyone could oppose your parent when he fixes you with that damned devilish stare. Sets me to quaking in my boots every time. I'd marry a woman with a horse-face and freckles before crossing swords with Eversleigh.'

There was silence for a few moments while Charles dove into his food with all the vigour of a man who hadn't eaten for weeks. Michael sipped his sherry in contemplative silence, his long legs stretched out in front of him.

His father, the Duke of Eversleigh, was notorious for his iron-fisted management of his family's personal affairs. Several weeks ago he had summoned Michael to Eversleigh Hall. There, in his formidable study, the Duke had coolly informed his heir it was time he married. Since his son did not seem capable of choosing a suitable bride for himself, a bride had been chosen for him. The young lady was Miss Helena Randall, the granddaughter of a long-standing friend. She was to be presented at Court this season. After a suitable period, unless there were major objections on the part of either party, their betrothal would be announced.

Michael could see any number of objections, starting with the fact he had no desire to marry a girl fresh out of the schoolroom. Argument with his father appeared useless. The Duke wore the implacable expression that meant he'd made up his mind and would brook no opposition. In addition, the Duke's health was poor due to a recent severe bout of pneumonia that nearly claimed his life. Michael hesitated to come to cuffs with his father in his still-weakened condition.

Charles, who always thought better on a satisfied stomach, dropped his fork with a clatter. 'What you need, my boy, is a fiancée!'

Michael eyed him as if he had taken leave of his senses. 'Exactly what I'll end up with if my father has his way. That's what I'm trying to avoid.'

'Would save you a lot of trouble,' said Charles earnestly with all the experience of a happily betrothed man. 'Now that I'm betrothed to Beth I never worry about matchmaking mothers trying to foist their daughters on me. Not that I've ever had the number you've had. No more hounding from my mother about finding a suitable wife. And Beth's a good girl; doesn't have odd fits or expect me to escort her to any of those damned musical evenings.'

Michael was fascinated. 'I never realised there were so many advantages attached to a betrothal.'

'Well, the point is, Michael, if you were already betrothed your family could hardly expect you to offer for Miss Randall.'

'Very true. It would be awkward. But the problem with fiancées is that one is expected to marry them.'

Charles downed several slices of ham, his brow creased in thought. He wiped his mouth on his napkin and looked up. 'You could hire one.'

'Hire one? One what?'

'A fiancée! Remember when Greely hired an actress to be his wife so he could inherit from his old uncle in Manchester or some other ungodly place? Worked too; the old man fell for it and Greely got the money. Dare say he had to pay that actress a bundle.'

Michael grinned. A few of the actresses he knew flashed across his mind.

'That may work very well in Manchester but hardly in London. Where in the world would I find an actress I could hope to pass off in the middle of a London season as my fiancée? Even the best of them couldn't appear respectable enough to suit my father. Besides, my aunt could sniff out an impostor at ten paces!'

'Maybe you could find a foreign actress.'

'Good God, no! My father would be in a rare temper if I announced my engagement to a foreign woman! Don't trouble yourself, I'll figure out a way to avoid this entanglement. I always do.' He polished off his sherry. 'Where are you off to tonight, Charles?'

'To Lady Winthrope's rout. Probably another one of her damned squeezes. Promised to escort my mother and Beth. How about you?'

'I'll put in an appearance.'

'I've heard Elinor Marchant is in town,' said Charles carefully. 'Have you met her yet?'

'Today, while riding in the park. She was determined to regale me with every bit of gossip she could think of, half of it probably unfounded rumour.'

'Hope you don't plan to take up with her again.' Charles shuddered. 'Never saw such a temper in my life. Don't know how you could have put up with it. That last scene—right in the middle of a ball! Heaving vases around!'

A grin lit up Michael's face. 'Only one vase. And it wasn't in the middle of a ball, merely in a private room.'

'One vase, half a dozen vases, what does it matter? You're well rid of her! Never know how you manage to come up with these vixens. Need to show a bit more discrimination in the petticoat line.'

Michael laughed and rose from the table in a lazy movement. 'Put your mind to rest, Charles. I have no interest in renewing a relationship with Lady Marchant. Ready to go? There's a pair of chestnuts up for auction at Tattersall's I've been wanting to see.'

Michael only half-attended to his cousin's conversation as they made their way to the auction yard. Instead, he found himself thinking of Lady Jeffreys. Would she be present at Lady Winthrope's rout? He hoped so, for he had the perfect excuse for speaking to her. After his aunt had departed, Watkins had presented him with a small folded fan, saying he believed it belonged to the young lady. Michael had taken the fan, assuring Watkins he would personally see it was returned to its owner.

Chapter Two

'I was sorry to hear of your brother's troubles. I know how much Meryton means to you,' Edmund Fairchilde said softly. 'Perhaps there is something I could do to help.'

Rosalyn looked up into his cool, hooded eyes, and wished she could escape from him. However, it was impossible in Lady Winthrope's crowded drawing room unless she was to clamber over one of the guests behind her.

'Thank you, there is nothing you can do. But, how did you know? I had thought it was a private game.' She tried to keep the dismay from her voice. She had hoped no one outside of Lord Stamford, James and herself knew about the wager.

A faint smile touched his thin lips. 'I was also there, my lady. I had hoped there was something I could do, but alas, Stamford rarely loses. It makes one wonder…but, his temper, one hates to suggest… At any rate, do not worry, only the three of us were present, and I am very discreet.'

'Thank you.' She managed a smile, not certain she

trusted him at all. He had been a visitor to Meryton, coming down once with a group of her brother's friends. Although he had been charmingly courteous, there was something about his hooded gaze, particularly the way it sometimes rested on her, that made her uneasy.

'But I do wish to offer my help.' He smiled again. 'Before you protest, you must hear my proposal. I am not without resources, and I should hate to see you turned from your family home. Come driving with me tomorrow, and I shall tell you my proposition.'

'That is very kind, but I...I shall be busy tomorrow.'

'Will you? Then the next day.' His eyes rested on her face as if he wanted to calculate the impact of his words. 'I have longed for the opportunity to become better acquainted with you ever since I saw you at Meryton.'

'My dear, there you are!'

Relieved, she turned to see her grandmother, Lady Carlyn, suddenly appear next to her. Lady Carlyn acknowledged Fairchilde with a cool smile. 'If you will excuse us, sir, I must introduce my granddaughter to Lady Carruthers. I fear she is about to leave.' She dragged Rosalyn away, but not before Rosalyn saw Fairchilde's brows snap together in sudden anger.

Lady Carlyn marched Rosalyn from the drawing room to an adjoining room, then stopped. 'My dear, you should not be talking to Edmund Fairchilde. His reputation is, well, not quite what it should be. People will talk.'

'I didn't wish to talk with him. He approached me. He is an acquaintance of James's.'

'Indeed. I must say I am surprised at James, although he has been going about with some rather wild young men. I hope he will settle down soon enough and properly manage Meryton. It has been most careless of him to leave you to do so. Women have no business running estates.'

Rosalyn said nothing. She had not yet informed her grandmother that James had gambled away Meryton. For once she was thankful that her grandmother's mind tended to jump from subject to subject. 'However, we must concentrate on you. What did you think of Neville Hastings?'

'Neville Hastings?' Rosalyn finally recalled a plump, man with thinning hair and creaking corsets. Lady Carlyn had introduced him to her when they first arrived. 'He seemed very nice, I suppose.'

'A bit plump, although a diet of rice and water would help. But twenty thousand pounds a year, that is nothing to sneeze at in a husband.'

'A husband?'

'Why, yes, for you, my love.'

'Grandmama! I don't want a husband!'

'But of course you do. You are only six-and-twenty and still quite pretty. I must own Neville Hastings is not quite what I had in mind. Someone with a bit more dash.'

'I never plan to remarry.'

'Of course, it will be someone you like,' Lady Carlyn continued, paying no heed to Rosalyn as usual. 'I have several eligible men in mind.'

Her sharp grey eyes darted around the packed drawing room, seeking more prey. 'I see Lord Brandon has arrived. He is searching for a wife. A pity he has five children, but I know you are very fond…'

'Please, no! I am rather tired. I would like to rest for a few minutes.'

Lady Carlyn fidgeted with her fan, then snapped it shut. 'Very well. You may stay here. I must admit, you do look a trifle pale. No use having you faint, although Ellen Winthrope would consider that the highest compliment! I must have a few words with Maria Smythe-Howard and then we can leave.'

Rosalyn watched her grandmother make her way through the packed room, a small plump figure dressed in a gown of orange satin completely unsuitable for a woman of more advanced years. The dictates of fashion meant nothing to Lady Carlyn.

Rosalyn shifted uncomfortably. Her feet hurt from standing, her mouth ached from smiling, and her head pounded from the strain of making conversation in the impossible noise. There was no place to sit, as all the furniture had been removed to accommodate the several hundred people Lady Winthrope expected to parade through her rooms.

At least she was free of her grandmother for a few minutes. Lady Carlyn's unflagging energy was exhausting. And this hare-brained notion of finding her a husband…she had enough to distress her without fighting her grandmother's schemes.

Her thoughts turned to James, as they had all day. Ever since their mother's death, four years earlier, he'd become more and more unmanageable. She no longer knew how to reach him. Somehow, she had believed if she tried to preserve Meryton for him, he would return, for he had once loved Meryton as much as she did. Now Meryton was lost and, in her heart, she feared he was lost also.

'Oh!' She gasped as a stout gentlemen stepped back, jostling her with such force that she lost her balance and stumbled sideways against a tall, hard form. Strong hands caught her bare arms, causing an unexpected warmth to course through her.

'I beg your pardon,' she said in confusion.

'There is no need to apologise. I am always delighted when beautiful ladies fall into my arms.'

That familiar, detestable voice caused her heart to stop. Slowly, she lifted her head to meet the Marquis of Stamford's laughing eyes. For the briefest of moments, he seemed not to recognise her, and then, a wicked grin spread across his face.

'Why, Lady Jeffreys, what a delightful surprise to run into you like this. Particularly since you assured me we never moved in the same dissipated circles.'

She jerked away from him. Irritation replaced the unwelcome sensation she'd felt at his touch. 'Please excuse me, my lord.'

'But I have looked forward to seeing you all evening. You cannot mean to leave me now when I have finally found you.'

The hated colour flooded her face at the implication that he actually hoped to see her. Of course, she didn't believe it for a moment. 'I must find my grandmother. I do not have time for idle chatter.'

He laughed. 'Is there any other sort at these tedious affairs? But never mind, I wanted to see you for a particular reason. I have something for you.'

'Something for me?'

'Yes, your fan. I believe you dropped it in my drawing room. I wanted to return it to you.'

'You've been carrying my fan around?'

'In the remote chance I might see you.' He reached under his evening coat, towards his white embroidered waistcoat.

She nearly grabbed his hand. 'No, please, not here.' What would people think if they saw him pull a fan from his pocket and present it to her?

'Shall I call on you, then?'

'No! I mean, why can you not send it to me?'

'But I want to give it to you in person, to make certain you get it, of course. I was hoping we could become better acquainted.'

'I have no desire to become better acquainted with you, my lord.'

'But I would like the opportunity to change your mind.' A lazy half-smile, full of meaning, curled the edges of his mouth as he let his leisurely gaze travel over her person.

Mesmerised, she stared back. It occurred to her that his eyes were really not black at all, but the deepest, richest shade of brown she'd ever seen. And would his thick midnight hair, curling slightly at the nape of his neck, feel as soft and silky to her touch as it looked?

What was she thinking of?

'Never! You'll never change my mind!'

She whirled away, only to find her escape blocked by two ladies standing directly behind them. They gasped and stared, their fans stopped in mid-air. From the looks of pleasurable shock on their faces, she had little doubt they had heard her every word.

Lord Stamford nodded to the ladies, who tittered and turned away. Grasping Rosalyn's arm, he bent his head towards her, and said conversationally, 'It's best not to pick a quarrel with me in public. It will hardly ease your entrée into society.'

Her mouth fell open. Pick a quarrel with him? He was doing his best to provoke her.

'However, any time you wish to quarrel with me in private I would be delighted to accommodate you.'

'If you had an ounce of sensibility you would real-ise that, under the circumstances, I want neither to speak to you nor to see you.'

'I take it you refer to the business with your brother. I cannot see what it has to do with you or…with you and me.'

She was floundering, badly out of her depth. Nothing in her limited experience with the opposite sex had ever prepared her to deal with a man such as Lord Stamford, a man with devastatingly dark ex-pressive eyes, a man as handsome as the devil him-self, a man who was flirting with her in a blatantly sensual fashion that caused her to feel vulnerable and utterly confused.

Desperate, she looked around for escape. With re-lief, she saw Lady Carlyn winding her way towards them. Her relief was short-lived when she noted the look of utter disbelief on her grandmother's face. What if Lord Stamford said something about this morning?

He must have read her mind for he said, 'There is no need to fear, my lady. I promise I will not tell your grandmother how you called on me in such a bold manner without so much as a maid to accompany you.

As far as I am concerned, our first meeting has only now taken place. Of course, I shall not mention your fan. I will find a more private moment to return it to you.'

The wicked spark in his eye did nothing to reassure her, but it was too late to do a thing. Lady Carlyn had already made her way to them.

Lord Stamford's mouth curved in a disarming smile as he bowed over her plump hand. 'Lady Carlyn, I have just had the delightful opportunity of meeting your granddaughter. She is as lovely and charming as her grandmother.'

Lady Carlyn fluttered her lashes at him in a disgustingly flirtatious fashion. 'It's no use trying to turn my head at my age, young man. Rosalyn is much lovelier than I ever was. But how did you come to make her acquaintance? With a proper introduction, I trust?'

His eyes danced. 'Not at all. I was forced to introduce myself after she stumbled into my arms. Quite by accident, of course. But now that I have met her…I hope to secure your permission to call on her.'

A peculiar expression crossed her grandmother's face. 'You may, but I'll have you know I intend to keep a strict watch on her. She may be a widow, but she is not one of your flirts. I will not have you trifling with her.'

He turned his gaze on Rosalyn who felt as if she'd turned to stone. 'I shall behave with the utmost propriety.'

'That I shall have to see to believe.' Lady Carlyn stared at him for a moment. 'Very well, you may call on her.'

Rosalyn had to put a stop to this. 'It is quite doubtful that I would ever be at home to you, my lord.' And how could they discuss her as if she were in leading strings with no mind of her own? She did not know which one to strangle first.

'Nonsense. Of course you will, dear.' Lady Carlyn shot her a quelling glance.

A smile of pure devilment quirked his mouth. 'Unfortunately, I must depart now. I will see you soon, very soon, Lady Jeffreys.' Her name sounded like a caress on his lips.

He made an elaborate leg and strode off. Lady Carlyn watched his dark-haired figure weave its way through the crush.

With a bemused expression, she took Rosalyn's arm. 'My dear, I can scarcely believe this! Lord Stamford wishes to call on you. I cannot image why; he never pays the slightest heed to any respectable woman. Surely he cannot think that…no, of course not. Not with you dressed in that gown!'

'Isn't it fortunate that I wore it, then,' Rosalyn replied with a humourless smile. Her simply cut blue gown had been a source of contention between them, Lady Carlyn declaring it was fit only for a Methodist.

Rosalyn barely noticed as they made their goodbyes to Lady Winthrope, descended the crowded staircase, and waited a good twenty minutes for the carriage to be brought around. Her thoughts were totally occupied with the icy set-downs she planned to give Lord Stamford.

It wasn't until they had settled into the carriage and her grandmother spoke that Rosalyn started out of her reverie.

'My dear, what do you think of Lord Stamford? I hadn't even considered him. But now that I think of it—he would do quite nicely. No woman would ever be bored with him.'

'What are you talking about?'

'Lord Stamford. For a husband.'

'A husband?' Horrified, she stared at Lady Carlyn.

'I don't believe you've been attending at all. His aunt, Lady Spence, told me—in strict confidence, of course—that Eversleigh has been casting about for a wife for him. Why did I not think of this before? There is no reason why you should not be in the running. Now that you are finally in London, I shall call on Margaret and drop a hint in her ear.'

A most alarming headache was beginning in her right temple. 'Grandmama, please, no. I would rather be dead than ever, ever consider him for a husband.'

His most blatant efforts to flirt with her had failed dismally.

Michael received his overcoat and hat from the footman and headed down the steps into the cool spring night. He liked walking at night, despite the risk of footpads.

A smile curled his lips. It was wicked of him to tease Lady Jeffreys so much. Especially in front of Lady Carlyn. But the fire that sprang to her eyes and the all too-ready colour washing over her cheeks was too tempting to resist.

He had no idea why such a respectable widow should interest him. She was pretty but not beautiful. Her dress, even tonight, was unfashionably plain; no rows of lace and flowers adorned its hem, no low-cut bodice designed to reveal its wearer's charms. But it became her.

He usually found such ladies excessively dull. But not Lady Jeffreys. Behind the proper façade she tried to present, he sensed a warm, passionate woman. It would be a challenge for any man to storm those barriers.

Particularly as she detested him and made no pretense otherwise, not even in hopes he might relent and return her brother's estate. He admired her for that. At least she was honest in her dealings with him.

It would probably be too much to hope Miss Randall would harbour the same sentiments. No, from what he gathered of the young lady, she was very biddable and unlikely to disobey her family's wishes. A pity Lady Jeffreys was not his intended bride; he'd never get her to the altar unless she was drugged and bound.

Suddenly, Charles's words flashed through his mind. His head snapped up and he stopped dead in the quiet street, inspiration hitting him like a bolt of lightening. Why not? She was well bred, respectable, pretty, intelligent. And she disliked him thoroughly.

What more could he want in a prospective bride?

Having the proper, disapproving Lady Jeffreys in his power would be most agreeable. He'd wager any sum that by the end of their association, he could break down her resistance to him.

And he knew without doubt he could induce her to agree to his plan.

Chapter Three

Morning sunlight streamed through a crack in the heavy brocade curtains of Rosalyn's bedchamber. She fought to open her eyes, heavy with sleep, wanting nothing more than to snuggle back down into the cosiness of her bed.

It was these late nights. She was not used to staying up past midnight, let alone until two or three in the morning. She had never realized what energy a woman of sixty some years could possess. An evening at home was far too tame for Lady Carlyn; she must be out to a soirée or ball or to a concert every night. And she insisted Rosalyn accompany her.

Rosalyn struggled up as Mrs Harrod, her housekeeper, entered. She carried a tray with a pot of chocolate and a plate of toast.

'Anything else, my lady?' she asked as she set the tray in front of Rosalyn. She was plump and kindly and watched Rosalyn with a motherly eye. 'I thought you might like a tray today seeing how you did not come in until nearly three. Such a long night for you.'

Mrs Harrod bustled about, opened the curtains and

then departed. After pouring herself a cup of the steaming chocolate, Rosalyn sunk back on her pillows, wondering if there was any way she could escape tonight's ball. She had been to more of these affairs since arriving in London ten days ago than in the eight years since her own coming-out.

Her husband, John, had considered *ton* parties a frivolous waste of time, as did most of his scholarly colleagues. After the miserable, tongue-tied shyness of her one and only season, she had been grateful.

Sometimes she had longed for a little more gaiety. It seemed after the first year or so of their marriage, as he became more deeply immersed in completing the massive book he'd spent years working on, that anything which distracted him from his work was a waste of time.

Including her.

Tears pricked her eyes. She brushed them away with an angry hand. It was only that she had lost so many people she loved in the past five years, first John, then her mother a year later. Her father's spirit had been buried along with her mother, his body finally succumbing to a bout of influenza two years later. Now, she was losing James.

She had come to London, hoping to somehow bridge the gap between them. Since their mother's death, he'd walled off his emotions, rarely talking to her as he once had. Her father had been no help; lost in his own sorrow, he'd scarcely noticed James was growing more unmanageable, running around with some of the wildest young men in the neighbourhood. After her father died, he stayed away from Meryton for long periods of time, only once bringing a group of his new friends down for a week.

Rosalyn had been appalled. It took no more than a few hours in their company to discover he kept company with some of the most disreputable rakehells in London. She'd stayed out of their way, afraid to say anything to James for fear he'd shut her out even more. But he'd never asked them again.

She finally forced herself out of bed. Her abigail, Annie, helped her dress in a long-sleeved navy print cambric gown with a ruff around the throat, then dressed her hair in its usual knot.

Rosalyn had just reached the staircase when Mrs Harrod bustled up to her, her plump face shining with curious excitement.

'You have a visitor, my lady. I have shown him to the drawing room.'

'A visitor? Is it James?'

'No, not your brother.' Mrs Harrod clasped her hands. Her voice quivered with anticipation. 'It is the Marquis of Stamford, my lady. He wishes to see you.'

Rosalyn backed away from the staircase, her hand fluttering to her throat. What was he doing here so early? It was hardly the hour for morning callers. Did he think she was at his disposal at any time?

'Lord Stamford? He wishes to see me? Please inform him I am not at home.'

'But, my dear, he is very anxious to see you.'

'No, I certainly do not want to see him. It is much too early.'

Mrs Harrod pursed her lips in disapproval. When she saw Rosalyn did not plan to relent, she nodded and bustled away.

Irritated, Rosalyn turned back to her room. She supposed he'd finally decided to return her fan. A full three days had passed since the rout. Well, he could leave it with Mrs Harrod. She would hide out until he left. She picked up a novel she was reading, but the words jumbled into nonsense.

She jumped at the knock on her door. Mrs Harrod poked her head around the edge, her face devoid of expression.

'His lordship wishes me to inform you he will not leave until you see him. He will wait for your convenience, even if it is past midnight.'

'That is most ridiculous.' But something about his confident, overbearing manner made her think he was perfectly capable of carrying out his threat, effectively holding her prisoner in her room. She could hardly go about her business while he cooled his heels in the drawing room. What if someone called? Her grandmother, for instance. She closed her book and rose.

The strange sensation that her life was about to be altered forever floated over her. But how silly—she had never been prone to such fanciful notions.

With reluctant steps, she entered her drawing room. The morning sun cast a friendly glow about the small yellow room. Her unwanted visitor sat in one of the armchairs near the fireplace, absorbed in a leather-bound volume, his buckskin-clad legs stretched out before him. He didn't notice her presence for a few seconds and then he glanced up, closed the book and laid it aside. He rose to his feet in a lazy movement.

He was dressed much as he had been the first time she saw him, in riding coat and breeches, and top-boots, his cravat tied carelessly about his neck. His elegance looked out of place amidst the fading Oriental carpet and the comfortable but old-fashioned furnishings of the room.

His face was relaxed and his manner confident, as if there was no reason he was not perfectly welcome in her home.

'Lady Jeffreys, I did not expect to see you quite so soon. I was betting on some time in late afternoon.'

This threw her off completely. 'Indeed. I usually don't keep visitors waiting that long.'

'In my case, I was not sure. I am relieved, although my day is at your disposal. I decided to fetch a book from the library to occupy my time.'

'A book?'

'Does that astound you? I occasionally engage my mind in less dissipated pursuits, such as reading. I have even been known to pick up a volume of philosophy or history on occasion. But only when I have tired of sitting around a gaming table, stealing away estates or pursuing improper women.'

'Is there a purpose for your visit, my lord?' she asked with ice in her voice.

'Yes. To return your fan, of course. And to speak with you in private. I would not have called so early, except I did not want you to flee.' He held out her fan. She took it from him, careful to avoid any contact with his hand.

Her voice trembled for some odd reason. 'I see. I can't imagine what you would wish to speak to me about.'

'I wish to discuss your brother's gambling debt. I have a proposition to lay before you that I believe will benefit both of us. If you will sit, I will tell you.'

Even more confused, she quickly seated herself on one of the Queen Anne chairs. He settled back in the other, his eyes fixed on her face. The horrid premonition he was about to offer her another *carte blanche* caused her heart to beat uncomfortably fast. She folded her hands in her lap and waited.

'I do not think you will find my proposal too distasteful. I merely want you to become betrothed to me.'

Her heart stopped for a dizzying moment. 'What did you just say?'

'I would like you to become betrothed to me in exchange for returning your brother's estate to him.'

Her hand went to her throat. 'Betrothed to you! You must be mad! I would never consider such a thing!'

'Do you always answer your offers with such an excess of civility?' he inquired drily. 'Perhaps I didn't phrase it quite right. You don't need to marry me, merely become my fiancée for a short time. I am in need of a temporary fiancée.'

He sounded as if he were discussing the need for a new pair of boots.

'A temporary fiancée? Whatever for? I have never heard of anything so…so ridiculous!' She stood up and backed away from him towards the window, knotting her hands.

He rose and followed her. 'Not at all. My father has informed me it's high time I marry. He's already chosen the bride. I want to put a stop to his plans before I wake up one morning and find I'm expected to show up at the altar before noon. If I produce a fiancée of my own, I can hardly be expected to offer for the young lady he has in mind.'

'I...I should hope not.' He sounded so reasonable, Rosalyn had no doubt he was quite mad. 'But why me? I hardly think I would suit your purposes. We do not deal at all well together.'

A disarming smile settled over his features. 'You mean you wish me to perdition, my dear. There is no need to look so shocked, your face is far too honest. The strong aversion you've shown for my company suits me very well; I've no doubt you will be quite willing to cry off at the appropriate time. The bargain benefits both of us. You want your brother's estate back—it will be done. I avoid a marriage I don't want. And just consider, what could be more natural than for me to return Meryton to your brother as his future brother-in law? It will save a lot of explanation.'

'It is blackmail!'

'Hardly. Come now, Lady Jeffreys, what is so difficult? Is a few months in my company such a sacrifice for your brother? Just think how much you'll enjoy publicly jilting me in the end.'

Apparently the whole thing was nothing but a huge jest to him.

And how dare he be so confident that she would be delighted to play the role of his fiancée?

'A few months! I'd rather spend an eternity in hell than a day in your company.'

Her hand flew to her mouth, horrified at her rude words.

Something wholly unexpected crossed his face, but for such a fleeting moment, she was certain she had imagined it. Only slight amusement remained. 'Indeed? In that case, I shall leave you to plan your move from Meryton.'

He picked up his gloves and moved towards the door, then turned and bowed elaborately in her direction. 'However, I will leave my offer open for a day or so. In case you change your mind. Good day, my lady.'

'My lord, I am…' Before she could frame an apology, he quitted the room.

Mortified, she sank down on the sofa. Never had she said such an unkind thing to anyone. She tried to tell herself he richly deserved it, but she wasn't so certain. For one brief moment, he had looked as if her words had affected him. But no, that was impossible. Not the imperturbable Marquis of Stamford.

She put a hand to her head, which was beginning to ache in a familiar way. She could not possibly take him up on his preposterous suggestion, not even for James.

She stood up and took an agitated turn around the room.

But would a few months in his company really be such a high price to pay for Meryton? It was not as if he demanded she be his mistress. She had heard of men who were unscrupulous enough to ask for a woman's favours to pay off a debt. Not that she thought Lord Stamford was above that if it suited him. Most likely she was not to his taste, thank goodness. The thought of spending a night in his arms filled her with shivery panic.

She bit her lip, trying to think. What would they live on? John had left Rosalyn a small income and this house. The rest of his estate had been entailed to a nephew. Her competence could be stretched to accommodate two people in meagre comfort, but James would never accept that from her.

What would become of him?

She stared into the street with unseeing eyes. After all, how much time would she really be in his company? He was unlikely to spend much time dancing attendance on her. Such a flirt as Lord Stamford would undoubtedly find a woman more to his taste to occupy him.

She had no choice. She only prayed his offer was still open.

Michael entered Lady Burkham's crowded ball room at half past midnight. Almost immediately, Lady Burkham glided forward, and caught his arm. 'Why, Lord Stamford! We had given up all hope that you ever planned to show! I fear there has been more than one lady suffering from pangs of disappointment.'

'I doubt the affliction is permanent.'

Her smile faded a little at his cool tone. 'No, now that you are here. We are about to go down to supper. I hope you will partake of it.'

'Thank you. Your suppers are always superior.'

She smiled again and, after a few more remarks, departed. He watched the guests drift towards the doors, talking and laughing. The boredom he felt at these occasions assailed him. He regretted his impulse to come.

Except he'd felt equally bored at White's.

He finally admitted to himself he came in hopes of

seeing Lady Jeffreys. Why, he had no idea. Until this morning, he had no doubt she would agree to his plan. But he had gravely miscalculated the depth of her dislike for him. Her words had stunned and then angered him. He tried to tell himself it was only because her refusal foiled his plans. He cared little what anyone thought or said of him. Including Lady Jeffreys. But a shaft of hurt he hadn't felt since his youth had shot through him, piercing his careful armour of indifference.

This was ridiculous. He decided he would make his excuses to his hostess and leave. Then he saw her.

She was going down to supper with Lady Carlyn. Dressed in a dark blue gown that emphasised the gentle curve of her breasts, she looked delicately lovely.

He would stay after all.

He finally caught up to her at the supper laid out in buffet style. He waited until she finished putting a lobster patty on her plate before speaking.

'Lady Jeffreys.'

She whirled around and looked up at him as if he'd sprung out of the wall. 'What are you doing here?'

He removed the plate from her hand since the food appeared to be in danger of sliding to the table. 'I was invited.'

'I only meant I had not yet seen you. Did…did you get my note?'

'Note? No, although I have hardly been home. Does this mean you wished to see me?'

'Yes.' Her face turned a delicate pink.

'Perhaps you could continue your conversation elsewhere?' Michael turned to find a stout gentlemen glaring at them.

Rosalyn quickly moved forward, Michael behind her. 'Do you wish some strawberries? They look quite good.'

She looked completely confused. 'Yes, I think so. This is for my grandmother.'

He put some strawberries on the plate. 'You are not eating?'

'I am not hungry.'

'So you hoped to see me? What has caused you to change your mind?' he asked softly.

She looked alarmed. 'Please, not here.'

'No.' He looked down the plate, now containing enough food to feed several elderly ladies. 'Is this enough for your grandmother?'

She eyed the plate doubtfully. 'I hope so.'

'Where is Lady Carlyn?'

He followed Rosalyn. Lady Carlyn sat at one of the long tables, between two older ladies. She beamed when she saw them. 'Lord Stamford! How kind of you to fetch my plate! And you have found my grand-daughter, I see. Perhaps you will join us.'

Lady Carlyn's voice carried. Rosalyn's face coloured as several heads craned their way.

'Actually, I had hoped to have a word with your granddaughter in private.' He smiled at Lady Carlyn.

'Why…why, I suppose so. Yes, but I trust you will be on your best behaviour!'

'Of course.' He took Rosalyn's arm, leading her from the room before Lady Carlyn could make any more pronouncements to the rest of the guests.

He led her to Lord Burkham's study. He closed the door and leaned against it, watching her face.

'What did your note say?'

'I wished to accept your offer,' she replied so softly he almost didn't hear her. She twisted her hands. Her face had all the appearance of one offering to take another's place on the gallows.

'So you decided a few months of misery in my company was worth the price of your brother's estate?'

Guilt washed across her delicate face. 'I didn't exactly mean that. I am sorry I said…'

He held up his hand. 'There is no need to apologise. Your sentiments towards me are quite clear. At least you are honest. Very well, my lady, your brother shall have his estate.'

She cast him a helpless, almost fearful look. 'What do you wish me to do now, my lord? Are we to announce our…our agreement right away?'

His mouth quirked slightly. 'I see no reason to delay the announcement of our…betrothal. As soon as our families are informed, I will put an announcement in the *Morning Post*.'

She looked almost horrified. 'Is that necessary?'

'It is quite necessary, my dear.'

'But what will everyone say? It seems so sudden. We hardly know each other.'

He shrugged. 'What does it matter? I am known for making up my mind quickly. Come, Rosalyn, the sooner this is settled, the sooner your brother will get his estate.'

The frightened look fled. 'I have not given you permission to use my given name, my lord.'

'You have my permission to use mine. You sound like my butler, not a woman who has accepted an offer of marriage.'

'But I have not accepted an offer of marriage. I am merely pretending to be betrothed to you. There is no need to be on such familiar terms when we are alone.'

He raised his brow. 'Pretending? No, you will be betrothed to me. You will be my fiancée and you will address me by my given name, Rosalyn.'

Her eyes flashed with anger. 'You will not dictate to me. I will call you whatever I please, my lord. I understood I was merely to become betrothed to you so you could avoid an arranged marriage. I do not think we need to expand our acquaintance beyond that. We shall do the bare minimum to establish that we are engaged and nothing more. You are free to go your own way.'

So she thought she could avoid him so easily, did she? He settled more firmly against the doorway and folded his arms. 'You're quite wrong,' he drawled. 'I have no intention of going my own way. If this is to succeed, I must play the role of the devoted fiancée. My Aunt Margaret, not to mention my father, has an uncanny ability to sniff out a scheme. In fact, I intend to make it clear I am in love with you. I shall accompany you everywhere and take as many opportunities as possible to be alone with you.'

'That is…is ridiculous. There is no need to go to such lengths.' She seemed at a loss for words, and then recovered herself. 'In fact, it is quite mad and I have no intention of going along with this. We can see each other once or twice a week and no more. I will not have you accompanying me about like some sort of…of lapdog.'

His eyes narrowed. 'Now you are attempting to dictate to me, my lady. I know you wish me to the devil, but we have a bargain. I will return your brother's estate and you will play the role of my fiancée. I expect some enthusiasm on your part for my company. Do you understand?'

She tilted her chin up, meeting his gaze. 'Quite, but I will not pretend to be in love with you. And I want you to understand I have no intention of engaging in idle flirtation with you when we are alone.'

They faced off for a moment like a pair of duellers, eyes locked. He finally shrugged. 'As you wish.'

He moved away from the door. 'I will escort you to the opera tomorrow. You will meet my sister and her husband. I will ask Lady Carlyn to accompany us.'

'Very well, my lord,' she replied.

'You had best begin to practise using my given name.'

'I have no idea what your given name is.'

'It is Michael.'

She said nothing, merely continuing to regard him as if she wished he would go away. He stepped towards her, causing her to put her hand to her necklace, and retreat a step back. He captured her slender hand and lifted it towards his lips, then pure devilment shot through him as he looked down at her. Without warning he pulled her to him, his lips brushing over hers.

She tasted cool and surprisingly sweet. He had a sudden urge to crush her to him. His hands dropped away.

'Until tomorrow, Rosalyn.' He dragged out her name with deliberate, intimate slowness. Her gaze flew to his face. There was no mistaking the apprehension in her eyes.

Chapter Four

Rosalyn stared down at the note, completely dismayed. Lady Carlyn, pleading a sudden headache, would not accompany them to the opera. Since her grandmother developed a headache only to avoid some commitment. Rosalyn suspected Lady Carlyn wanted her to be alone with Lord Stamford. She must have the only grandmother in London who actually encouraged her granddaughter to consort with rakes.

She crumpled the note, resisting the temptation to fling it across her bedchamber. Apprehension made her hand tremble. She had no desire to be alone with Lord Stamford, cooped up in his carriage across from him, forced to make conversation with a man she knew nothing about, a man whose power she was now in.

She was behaving in a ridiculous manner. She rose from her bed and peered distractedly into her looking glass, not really seeing her pale face. He had no power over her. She was hardly alone in the world; she had her family and her own small but adequate income. So there was nothing to fear. She would take part in this absurd charade, Meryton would return to James, and she would return to her safe, well-ordered world.

But nothing, she told herself, could dispel the sense of dread she felt every time she thought of that fleeting kiss. She must make it very clear that she had no intention of engaging in that sort of behaviour with him.

She turned from the mirror in an impatient movement and picked up her gloves and fan. A glance at the small clock on her dressing table showed Lord Stamford was already fifteen minutes late. The least he could do was show up on time.

'My lady?'

Rosalyn started. Mrs Harrod peered around the edge of the door. 'Lord Stamford is here. So very handsome he is. All dressed in black. Like one of those heroes in a novel.'

Even her housekeeper was charmed by the man. Rosalyn picked up her velvet cloak from the bed. But Mrs Harrod stepped in front of her before she could leave. 'There's a bit of hair that's come out, my lady.' With deft fingers, she pulled the offending lock back into place. She stepped back and beamed, her kindly face warm with admiration. 'There, my lady. You look lovely. No wonder his lordship is so smitten.'

Rosalyn flushed, wishing her housekeeper did not have such a romantic imagination.

She slowly descended the staircase, her heart beating much too fast. She entered her drawing room, the lamps casting a cosy intimate glow about the room.

Lord Stamford stood in front of the fireplace, gazing at the landscape over the mantelpiece, hands clasped behind his back. He turned at her soft footsteps.

She caught her breath at his dashing appearance.

His black long-tailed coat, contrasted with the stark white of his ruffled shirt, became his dusky complexion and emphasised the lean, aristocratic planes of his face. A diamond glittered in the folds his white cravat. His hair, wavy from the misty rain, gleamed midnight in the lamplight. The black silk breeches and white stockings revealed a pair of muscular calves.

She tore her gaze away, praying he hadn't noticed her staring. She crossed the room towards him, arranging her features in what she hoped were cool, impersonal lines.

He took her hand and released it. His eyes searched her face. 'I hope I did not keep you waiting too long, Rosalyn.'

'Only a mere fifteen minutes, my lord.'

He grinned. ''Tis some improvement. Usually I am at least twenty minutes late. By the time our association is at an end, you may cure me of my propensity for lateness.'

He removed the cloak from her hands and stepped behind her. She felt the soft velvet slide around her shoulders. And then his hands stilled at the nape of her neck, making her feel as if every nerve had sprung to life.

'It is really your fault, you know,' he said.

'My fault?'

'You are not like most women. They are always at least ten minutes late to add to the stir their appearance will create. That is what I expected.'

'I don't like to waste time.' His touch distracted her so she hardly knew what she said.

He removed his hands and stepped around to observe her. His eyes took in her gown of black crêpe over a black sarcenet slip and the simple diamond necklace and matching ear drops.

'Certainly you didn't tonight.'

A blush crept over her face. Of course, he was a practised flirt who knew exactly how to gaze at a woman, making her feel as if she were especially lovely in his eyes. She dropped her eyes, attempting to get her thoughts in order. 'My grandmother will not accompany us, my lord. She has the headache.'

'She has already informed me.' He continued to watch her with a penetrating look that made her uncomfortable.

'Perhaps we should depart, my lord.' She turned away and picked up her reticule.

'Michael,' he said.

'I beg your pardon?'

'Address me by my given name, Rosalyn.'

'Until we announce our…agreement, I do not think it is necessary to be on such familiar terms.'

'I think it is. My name is not that difficult. I want to hear you say it.'

He moved in front of her. She recognised that particular half-smile and knew they could be here all night if she didn't comply with his request.

'Very well…Michael.' Her voice was barely above a whisper.

He leaned towards her, his fingertips lightly brushing her cheek. 'That is a good beginning. My name sounds very nice on your lips.'

* * *

She could think of nothing to say as she sat across from him on the comfortable cushions of the coach. Even the weather seemed too difficult to discuss. There was nothing but the sound of the horses' hooves on the street and the soft patter of rain on the coach. She hardly knew where to look and mostly stared down at her hands. Finally she glanced up at Lord Stamford, lounging in his corner, and found his unfathomable eyes fixed on her face.

'Must you stare at me in such a way?'

'What way is that?'

'As if you mean to memorise my features. Or as if I am some strange creature! It is most unnerving and quite rude.'

'My apologies, but you have the most expressive features. I find it fascinating to watch your emotions play across your face.'

'I cannot imagine why you would find that so interesting.' She'd always disliked her inability to hide her feelings. It made her feel vulnerable and, at times, awkward. And now with Lord Stamford, she wanted more than anything to present a cool, remote exterior. Instead, he was telling her she had a face that displayed her every emotion.

'Can't you? Perhaps it is because I've known too many women who hide their every thought and feeling under a carefully cultivated veneer.'

'Sometimes I think that would be an advantage.'

'It's not. I prefer honesty.'

She looked away from him, even more disconcerted.

The coach finally halted, and she saw they were near the Opera House. Several carriages waited in line before them. She watched a gentleman followed by an elegantly dressed lady glittering with jewels, and then a younger lady in the dress of a debutante, descend from the coach. The man was dressed much as Lord Stamford in the dark coat and breeches required for admittance to the opera. The young lady stared up at the impressive rectangular building with its façade of columns marching across the row and seemed to bounce in excitement.

It brought to mind her season when she first saw the elegant King's Theatre. She had been so nervous, in her white muslin gown and pearls, as she accompanied Lady Carlyn up the steps and passed through the portico with all the *haute ton* milling about. She could barely speak when she was introduced to some of Lady Carlyn's elegant acquaintances. But she had merely been one among a throng of young girls presented that season and hardly dazzled anyone. No one stared much at her arrival or fixed a quizzing glass on their box. It had been both a relief and a disappointment.

Stamford lightly touched her arm, causing her to jump. 'Rosalyn, we are here. We cannot spend the evening in the carriage.'

She abruptly returned to Stamford's coach and saw the footman had flung open the door. Stamford alighted in one swift, graceful movement and held out his hand to her.

She accepted his assistance, but stumbled a little, so he was forced to steady her. She started away from the unnerving contact and then dropped her reticule at his feet.

He retrieved the bag, handing it to her with his

characteristic half-smile. 'Have you always had the unfortunate habit of dropping your reticule?'

'Only since I've met you.' Thank goodness for the dark, so he couldn't see the dark blush that she knew stained her face and neck.

'That is not the usual effect I have on women.'

She coloured even more, and vowed to avoid any further contact with him. But he lightly caught her arm before they entered the portico, turning her to face him. The half-shadows kept her from clearly seeing his expression.

'Before we go in, there is something I must make clear to you,' he began.

'Yes?'

'I think you fear that I intend to offer you another *carte blanche* as part of our bargain. In light of my conduct at our first meeting, I cannot blame you, but rest assured, I have no intention of doing so. I do not force women to my bed.'

'Of…of course not,' she stammered.

He drew her arm through his as they passed through the doors into the crowded entrance hall.

If she had received little attention during her season, it was made up tenfold tonight. Heads swivelled as they passed. Stamford paid no heed, merely nodding to acquaintances without pausing, his hand resting possessively on her arm as he guided her through the elegantly dressed crowd. Heat flooded her cheeks but she managed to keep her head high.

As they reached the circular staircase, a woman stepped away from a small group and clutched Stamford's arm, forcing him to halt.

'Dear Stamford! How surprising to see you! You

have been so scarce I thought you'd left town. And how remiss of you to not have yet called on me.'

She was tall and well built with a fascinating sultry face. Her low-cut emerald gown revealed a creamy expanse of flesh. Jade-green eyes flickered over Rosalyn, then dismissed her.

'I have been busy,' Stamford replied shortly, his face haughty. He began to move away, but she caught his arm.

'Come riding with me tomorrow, then. I have not seen you for an age.'

'I cannot. Elinor, if you will excuse me.'

'You're always so difficult. At least introduce me to your companion.' Her smile held a touch of malice.

Stamford looked discomfited. 'Lady Jeffreys, may I present Lady Marchant?'

Lady Marchant ran her eyes up and down Rosalyn as if she were summing up an enemy before battle. 'How nice to meet you,' she finally replied, an insincere smile pasted on her lips.

Stamford nearly wrenched Rosalyn away. 'We must go.'

Rosalyn eyed his cool face with fascination. She had never seen him at such disadvantage. With sudden intuition, she knew the voluptuous Lady Marchant was or had been his mistress. How very awkward to be forced to introduce one's mistress to the lady one was to be betrothed to. And how very fortunate Rosalyn was not really his fiancée.

As if sensing her gaze, he turned his head and look down at her with unsmiling eyes. 'Do you find fault with my appearance? Is that why you are staring?'

'Not at all. I was thinking how nice it was to meet

Lady Marchant. She is very lovely. Is she a particular friend of yours?'

His eyes narrowed. She met his suspicious gaze with innocent eyes. 'No,' he replied shortly.

'Do you often ride with her in the park?'

This time he openly glared. 'That is none of your business. That is—' He stopped and clamped his lips in a tight line. 'I assure you I have nothing to do with Lady Marchant. She is an acquaintance, that is all. Does that satisfy your curiosity?'

She averted her head to hide the smile tugging at her lips. How gratifying to know it was possible to provoke Lord Stamford.

The curtain had already lifted on the singers by the time they took their seats. To her surprise, there was no one else in the box.

He must have noted her puzzlement for he leaned towards her, his breath fanning her cheek. 'We will meet my sister and her husband later. I did not wish to entirely overwhelm you.'

He settled back in the box; his eyes fixed on the stage. She stared around the theatre; it looked much as she remembered from her season; the tiers of boxes painted cerulean blue and gold filled to capacity with glittering ladies and handsomely dressed gentlemen, the fops strolling in the pit; the stares, the whispers behind fans as subjects for scandal-broth were spotted.

Only this time many of the glances were directed at their box. She felt as self-conscious as if they were sitting on the stage themselves.

She hoped James wasn't here. She knew she would have to break the news of her agreement—no, betrothal to Stamford, soon. She would rather do it in person than have the news leak to him. She looked around the theatre again and then her gaze fell on Edmund Fairchilde sitting a few boxes away. To her great consternation, he had a quizzing glass fixed on her face. She quickly turned away, only to find Stamford observing her.

'Is there something wrong?'

'No, I…I wished to see if my brother was here.'

'The thought seems to fill you with dismay,' he remarked.

Why could he read her so easily? 'I didn't tell him I was coming with you.'

His mouth quirked. 'I see. That is quite cowardly of you.'

She twisted her hands in her lap. 'I am afraid I am something of a coward.'

'I wouldn't say that. Otherwise, you would not be here with me.'

His words were completely unexpected. She glanced at him, taken aback, hardly knowing what to say. She fixed her eyes on the stage.

Concentrating on the performance proved impossible. She was too aware of the man beside her and of how alone they were, despite the filled boxes. More than once his arm brushed hers, causing her to flinch. She was grateful when the curtain finally fell and the last of the opera dancers flounced off stage for the interval.

'Did you enjoy the performance at all?' Stamford asked.

'Oh…of course. It was very nice,' she murmured, hardly recalling what took place.

'I am not certain you did. You seemed rather distracted.'

'I had forgotten how inquisitive people could be in London.'

'I take it you don't like being the focus of so much curiosity and speculation?'

'No, not at all. Do you?'

His mouth twisted in a sardonic half-smile. 'I am quite used to it, so I pay no heed. Don't trouble yourself about it. They will soon find a more scandalous *on dit* to occupy them.' He held out his hand, assisting her to her feet. 'But for now, my dear lady, I am afraid you must put up with more turned heads. I am going to introduce you to my sister and her husband.'

He led her past the curious stares and whispers down to the saloon, already crowded and noisy with patrons wishing to procure refreshments. They approached a small group standing in one corner.

'Michael!' A stocky fair-haired gentleman turned around and grinned. 'Here so soon? Didn't expect you to show before the last act!'

One of the two ladies standing next to the gentleman laughed. 'That's too kind! I would have said the—' She broke off, her eyes wide with astonishment as she caught sight of Rosalyn.

'I had no idea you were bringing someone,' the lady said, her voice cool. Her haughty gaze brushed over Rosalyn's face. Dark-haired with an olive complexion, her relation to Stamford was unmistakable— she could only be his sister, Lady Hartman.

The other three, the stocky gentleman, the red-haired lady standing next to him and a taller man, observed her with polite curiosity.

Stamford took Rosalyn's hand, pulling her to his side. 'May I present Lady Jeffreys? Lord and Lady Hartman, my cousin Charles Portland, and his fiancée, Elizabeth Markham.' He pulled her even more close and said blandly, 'You must congratulate us. Lady Jeffreys has done me the honour of accepting my hand in marriage.'

The effect could not have been more startling if he had pulled a pistol on them. They froze and stared in stunned silence until Lady Hartman spoke.

'You cannot be serious. Is this one of your jests?'

'I am quite serious. She finally made up her mind to accept my offer yesterday.'

'Good God!' exclaimed Mr Portland faintly. He exchanged a glance with Miss Markham and then turned a fascinated eye on his cousin.

'But does Papa know this? Michael, he—' began Lady Hartman.

'This is hardly the time to discuss the matter,' Stamford replied coolly. His hand closed more tightly about Rosalyn's, who was experiencing the nightmarish sensation of having been plopped down in the middle of a farce without having read the script.

Then Lord Hartman stepped forward and took her hand. Grey eyes twinkled in a pleasant countenance. 'Let me be the first to congratulate you. We are, of course, surprised, although I have no idea why. We always suspected Michael would waste no time once he met the right lady.' His smile was reassuring. 'I had the pleasure of meeting you once a long time ago when I attended a lecture of Sir John's. I was acquainted with him, and you were there. I was sorry to hear of his death; he was a good man and a talented scholar. But I am delighted you have found happiness again.'

'Thank you,' Rosalyn replied, touched by his kind words for John and grateful for his courtesy towards her. She smiled a little shyly. 'I'm sorry I do not recall meeting you, my lord.'

'No matter. I am glad to renew our acquaintance.' He turned to his wife. 'My dear?'

Lady Hartman's bright, inquisitive gaze never wavered from Rosalyn's face. Slender and vivacious with dark hair tumbling about in charming disarray, she resembled a pixie. A smile of pure mischief spread over her countenance. 'What delightful and unexpected news. But you must tell me, wherever did you meet my brother?'

'At…' began Rosalyn.

'At Lady Winthrope's rout,' Stamford replied firmly.

'But that was only two days ago! I see, Michael, you have tumbled into love at last! Who would have thought this would happen! Lady Jeffreys, you must tell me all about yourself. Where are you from?'

'Caro, it is not necessary to interrogate Lady Jeffreys.' His face took on the haughty look Rosalyn was beginning to recognise as irritation.

His sister blithely ignored his black look. 'Oh, but it is.' She turned back to Rosalyn with an innocent smile. 'At least tell me how my brother persuaded you to marry him. I can't imagine how any woman in her right mind would accept his offer. Did he bribe you?'

Mr Portland, who had been silent, emitted a strangled cough.

'My dear, Lady Jeffreys is not used to your rag-mannered ways,' said Lord Hartman.

'Well, did he?' persisted Lady Hartman.

It was all Rosalyn could do to maintain her countenance. 'Not quite,' she managed.

Lady Hartman crowed. 'Now I am even more curious. We must have a coze when my brother is not present.'

'Very pleased for you, Michael. Never thought you could pull it off,' Mr Portland said.

'And I am also very pleased for you,' Miss Markham said.

Mr Portland grasped Rosalyn's hand and grinned. 'Best wishes to you, my lady. Welcome to the family. We're all quite insane, you know. Just keep that in mind and don't let us eat you.'

'Thank you,' said Rosalyn, dazed.

'Charles, what a thing to say!' scolded Miss Markham.

Her fiancé smiled lazily. 'You've often said the same thing; we're all quite mad.'

'Now that you've all managed to properly scare her with such an encouraging welcome, I'd best take her back to our box,' Stamford said coolly.

He first procured Rosalyn a glass of lemonade she did not want, then fixed her with such a fierce stare she felt obligated to force it down her throat. Her temper was beginning to flare over his high-handedness and utter lack of sensibility for all concerned.

Michael was not at all surprised to have Rosalyn round on him once they reached their box. Her hazel eyes flashed fire. She didn't look a bit like the compliant fiancée he'd envisioned. In fact, he'd seen the same expression in his aunt's eyes more than once.

'How could you spring this on them?'

He fixed her with his most bland look. 'What do you mean?'

'You know what I mean. They were so shocked. That was hardly kind of you. You might have at least prepared them in some way.'

'I suppose you wanted me to drop sly hints and be seen in your company an appropriate amount of time before declaring my intentions, is that it?'

She snapped her fan shut. 'What is wrong with that? It would have been the most courteous thing to do.'

He leaned back in his seat and said in his most annoying drawl, 'I assure you, my family would be more surprised if I were to be courteous. This is more what they expect out of me.'

'Indeed. I feel quite sorry for them. And for your future wife if she has to put up with this!'

He was beginning to enjoy himself. 'I will make it worth her while in—other ways.'

He was delighted to see a dark blush stain her cheeks, but she rallied. 'I am certain nothing would be worth it.'

'Now that we're engaged, it would be quite proper of me to demonstrate and let you make up your mind,' he suggested wickedly.

She looked shocked. He must learn to curb his tongue when with her. She was not one of his flirts who would parry his double-edged remarks with an even more suggestive one.

'Besides, I want to squelch any rumours.'

'What rumours?' she asked.

'Rumours about our association.' The puzzlement on her expressive face brought him up short. He found himself unable to tell her there were already bets on the book on how long it would take him to make her his next mistress. She would be appalled.

'I wanted to make certain no one would claim your hand and your affections before we announce our, er…agreement.'

'Since I plan never to remarry there was very little danger that would overset your plans.'

'Why don't you wish to remarry? You are a very lovely woman. I'm surprised you don't have suitors falling over themselves,' he said carelessly.

'I hardly consider that a compliment. Perhaps your only criterion for judging a woman's worth is her beauty or lack of it, but I hope most men don't use that in looking for a wife.'

'You are right, of course, there are more important qualities in a woman than beauty. I do beg your pardon. But tell me, do you consider a man's appearance important?'

'Yes, I generally find the degree of handsome looks a man possesses also determines his degree of conceit.'

He grinned. '*Touché*, my lady. Are you perhaps referring to myself?'

'I didn't exactly say that.'

'No, not exactly. But at least you consider me somewhat handsome. How much conceit do you think I possess?'

She glared at him and turned away.

He eyed his betrothed's profile as she sat concentrating very hard on the performance, ignoring him. Somehow he had entertained the erroneous notion Lady Jeffreys would prove to be quite compliant once he bent her to his will. She appeared so quiet and reserved, which in his experience translated into malleable. He could see now she intended to cross swords with him at every opportunity. A grin creased his face. Suddenly, a betrothal seemed a much more interesting state of affairs than he'd ever imagined.

Chapter Five

Watkins stepped aside as Lady Spence stormed into his master's study. She marched over to the desk where Michael sat writing, a militant expression on her face. Michael put down his pen and looked up, then rose to his feet.

A slight smile crossed his face. 'I somehow thought I would see you today.'

'You might,' she said briskly, seating herself on the other side of the desk. She pulled off her gloves and eyed her nephew coldly. 'I saw Caroline earlier today.'

'Did you?'

'Michael! She said you presented a…a woman to them at the opera last night whom you claimed was your fiancée. I simply cannot believe this! It cannot be true.'

'It is quite true. Only I did not claim she *was* my fiancée, she *is* my fiancée.'

'Impossible!'

'Not at all. Why is everyone so surprised? You have been hounding me to the altar for the past six years. It is my duty to marry eventually.'

A Bargain With Fate

'Don't be dense. You know perfectly well what I mean,' snapped Lady Spence. 'The negotiations for your marriage to Miss Randall have already been started.'

'What sort of negotiations?' Michael inquired, his voice cool. He came around to the side of the desk and lounged against it. 'You're not trying to tell me a marriage has already been arranged without my consent to a woman I've never met? I've told you and my father I would not agree to this scheme. I've no desire to marry a girl fresh from the schoolroom merely because my father and that old martinet Sheringwood have come up with some idiotic notion there needs to be an alliance between the two families. I will chose my own wife.'

Lady Spence snorted. 'You are quite mistaken if you think your father will consent to this. I am almost afraid to ask who this woman might be. Caroline wouldn't tell me; she seemed to find the whole matter highly entertaining. I only pray it is not Elinor Marchant.'

'Put your fears to rest. I don't think you'll find her at all disagreeable. She is Rosalyn, Lady Jeffreys. I believe you are acquainted with her grandmother, Lady Carlyn.'

Lady Spence jerked her head up, her face losing its cool composure. 'Rosalyn Jeffreys? Oh, no! Michael, she could not have possibly consented to marry you. She is much too respectable!'

Stamford sat on one edge of the desk and fingered the letter opener. A sardonic smile crossed his face. 'My family is so highly complimentary. Is it so difficult to believe a respectable lady might possibly wish to marry me? Or am I too far beyond the pale?

I am surprised you wish to throw the innocent Miss Randall into my clutches.'

'It is not that, Michael. I have always thought that if you met the right woman…' She stopped, her eyes full of concern. 'Never mind. But where did you meet her? Lady Carlyn constantly complains she'll never come to London.'

'She is here now. I met her at the Winthropes' rout. I was instantly charmed. Have you made her acquaintance?'

'A long time ago, during her first season. Lady Carlyn sponsored her. She was such a quiet little thing, very pretty with large eyes and dark hair, but so shy—she had nothing to say. Lady Carlyn despaired of ever finding a match for her. But, Michael, unless she has changed, she is hardly in your style! As I remember she is very proper and reserved. I cannot believe you would even notice her.'

'But I did. I discovered those were the qualities I wanted in a wife. After our first meeting, I decided I would ask her for her hand.'

Lady Spence looked at her nephew with exasperation. 'And she accepted. Oh, dear! I have long prayed you would meet a woman that would show you at least a measure of resistance. I rather pity Lady Jeffreys if she has fallen in love with you.' She rose to her feet, clearly agitated. 'Michael, this is a very difficult situation. You have offered marriage to Lady Jeffreys so you cannot with honour back away from it. But there is Miss Randall to consider. Certain promises have been made to her also.'

'But I did not make them. I have never met Miss Randall. I cannot conceive why she would be particularly eager to marry a man she has not met. Has she ever given you any indication she wishes to marry me?'

'No, she has not,' Lady Spence said slowly. She thought for a minute. 'I think she wishes to do her duty, but I've never had any strong feeling that she considered the marriage as settled. I believe she was told the marriage would take place after you had met and decided there was some compatibility. It is not likely that it will be Miss Randall who will feel slighted but rather Lord Sheringwood and Eversleigh. Your father will kick up quite a dust over this, Michael.'

'He'll settle down. He'll be so pleased that I have at last found a suitable bride he'll forget he didn't choose her himself. And I am certain he will consider Lady Jeffreys quite suitable. She is well-bred; her manners are pleasing; she is intelligent. Just imagine how relieved he'll be that I didn't bring home one of my dashing widows.'

'I don't think he'll be that pleased to have his plans overset.' Lady Spence stared at him with a frown. 'You're up to something, aren't you, Michael? How very convenient for you to find a bride in the nick of time. Are you in love with Lady Jeffreys?'

Michael shrugged and said lightly, 'I have been in love a hundred times. But I am very fond of Lady Jeffreys. She is pretty and charming and intelligent, and I will endeavour to be a good husband.'

Lady Spence rolled her eyes upwards. 'God help her. You'll lead her a merry dance. Well, what will you say to your father?'

'I was hoping you would help out in that regard. He'll listen to you,' said Michael. His mouth curved in an engaging smile.

'I shall have to meet Lady Jeffreys again before I attempt to do any such thing. I still can't believe you actually plan to marry someone decent. I would have been less surprised if you had announced you wanted to marry Lady Marchant or one of the other ill-bred creatures you've associated with. Sometimes I have felt you deliberately go out of your way to find the most annoying and vulgar sorts merely to irritate your father and the rest of the family as well.'

Michael grinned. 'Caroline has frequently accused me of the very same thing.'

'You're a rogue, Michael.' She sighed. 'And far too charming for your own good. I will call on Lady Jeffreys and decide if I wish to plead your cause.'

'Don't scare her too much. Caroline did a pretty good job of it last night, and Charles informed her she was marrying into a family of lunatics.'

Lady Spence pulled on her gloves and tied the ribbons of her bonnet. 'She is. There is no need to hide the truth from her. Perhaps she will come to her senses in time. However, I promise not to intimidate her.'

'Thank you.'

Michael accompanied her to her waiting carriage and handed her in.

Lady Spence started towards home and then changed her mind. She tapped the roof of her carriage with her parasol and instructed the coachman to drive to Grosvenor Street. She would call on Lady Carlyn. The whole affair was highly suspicious. She had fully expected Michael to find a way to defeat his father's plan, for he was as stubborn and high-handed as the Duke in getting his own way. He had successfully blocked the Duke's move this time, but who would win the game was still up in the air.

Rosalyn had barely removed her pelisse when Mrs Harrod bustled into her bedchamber to inform her that Lady Spence had come to call. 'She is such an elegant woman, my lady. Such an honour to have her come, for she moves in the highest circles. You shall want to change your dress.'

Rosalyn looked down. Mud had spattered across the bottom of her cream gown. In the past few days she had begun walking in Green Park with Annie, her abigail, wanting to escape from the confusion her life had suddenly become. The park with its dairymaids and cows reminded her a little of the country.

Usually, her walks were peaceful. But not today. She had been pestered by a fop in a revoltingly green frock coat over a butter-coloured waistcoat who persisted in speaking to her in a bold manner. Her most icy demeanour hadn't fazed him. He flustered her so much she stepped in a mud puddle, soaking her kid half-boots and splashing mud on her gown.

And now Lady Spence, Lord Stamford's formidable aunt, the aunt with the uncanny perception, sat below. She vaguely recalled meeting Lady Spence years ago, but could remember little about her. She pushed back her hair, trying to think. She wished she could send Lady Spence away and crawl under the covers pleading a headache, but she knew that would hardly do. She sighed. 'Yes, I shall change. Please inform Lady Spence I will be with her shortly.'

Rosalyn finally entered the drawing room, her hands clammy. She saw an elegant, aristocratic lady with a fine-boned face and observant blue eyes, immaculately dressed in a dark green spencer over a dress of pomona green. Her cool appearance as well as the speculative look in her eyes would have been quite intimidating, except for the warmth of her clasp as she took Rosalyn's hand and the kindness that lit her face.

'Thank you for receiving me on such short notice, Lady Jeffreys, but I had to come. I saw my nephew this morning and he told me the delightful and most unexpected news. Congratulations, my dear. We are so very pleased that Michael will be wed at last.'

Rosalyn was momentarily stunned. 'Thank you,' she said, feeling the colour mount her cheeks. 'Won't you please be seated, my lady?'

Lady Spence sat down on the small sofa near the fireplace. She patted the spot beside her. 'Come and sit by me, my dear. I want to hear all about this. I could get very little out of my nephew, which is so like him.'

With some trepidation, Rosalyn sat down beside Lady Spence, catching a whiff of her delicate perfume. She waited.

Lady Spence turned to her. 'So you met Michael at the Winthropes' rout? He said he was instantly charmed by you.'

'Did he?' Rosalyn asked faintly.

'Yes, he was determined to marry you after the first meeting. I never thought he could be so romantic.'

She didn't seem to notice the dismay Rosalyn could not quite keep from her face. She continued blithely on. 'I imagine he quite overwhelmed you. He is that way when he wants something. Your grandmother said you did not particularly care for Michael at the outset.'

'You have seen my grandmother?'

'Yes, before I came here. She will come to call on you later today to congratulate you. She had not been certain last night that you would accept him.'

The world was beginning to spin. 'Last night? I do not understand.'

Lady Spence's smile was bland. 'Did Michael not tell you he called on your grandmother yesterday to assure her his intentions were honourable?'

'No, he…he never said a thing.'

'That is not surprising. So Michael overcame your resistance. Tell me, Lady Jeffreys, what do you think of my nephew now?'

'I beg your pardon?'

Lady Spence's lips curved in a slight smile. 'Lord Stamford, my nephew. What do you think of him?'

Rosalyn was momentarily confused. What did she think of Lord Stamford? What she thought would hardly be polite to say to his aunt. She decided on a neutral tact. 'He is very amiable,' she replied cautiously.

This time it was Lady Spence who looked startled. 'Amiable?' she repeated. She looked at Rosalyn with frank interest.

Rosalyn realized she had blundered. She should have come up with a more enthusiastic answer.

To her relief, Lady Spence suddenly smiled. 'Forgive me for sounding so surprised, but I don't believe I have ever heard Michael described as amiable. Certainly by many other terms, including exasperating and overbearing, if you talk to his sisters, but never merely amiable! Do you find him at all charming?'

'He can be when it pleases him,' Rosalyn replied truthfully.

Lady Spence didn't seem displeased with her answer. 'That is very good. He is the sort of man that one should never be too charmed by. Are you in love with him?'

Rosalyn's mouth fell open. Certainly his family asked the most amazing questions. 'I…what?'

Lady Spence looked amused. 'I can see you are not. Thank goodness, I was quite worried about that. If you were in love with him, I would caution you against marrying him.'

Rosalyn could only stare. She felt as if she'd wandered into a family of Bedlamites.

Lady Spence apparently did notice her dazed look. 'Eversleigh will be quite pleased with you once he accepts Michael has defied his wishes. He doesn't like to be crossed, but no matter. He'll come around. You probably know he was trying to arrange a match for my nephew. Michael was quite against it. How fortunate the match didn't take place before he met you. I think you will be quite good for Michael.'

'I…I hope so,' Rosalyn said uncertainly. The shrewdness in Lady Spence's eyes rendered her uneasy. She had the odd feeling Lord Stamford's aunt knew something was amiss, but for reasons of her own, chose not to say anything. She only hoped she would never meet the Duke. She fumbled about in her mind for something else to say.

'We will need to discuss the wedding.'

'Wedding?'

'It should take place as soon as possible. Your

grandmother and I thought perhaps in six weeks, at the end of June. That should give us enough time to make the necessary arrangements.'

'In six weeks?' Rosalyn exclaimed in panic. She had never dreamed anyone would actually wish to discuss a date for the non-existent wedding. 'That seems so…so soon.'

Lady Spence raised delicate brows. 'So soon? We have been waiting for my nephew's wedding date for the past decade. And Michael was in such a hurry to persuade you to marry him, that I don't think he'll wish to wait very long. In fact, I am certain he will not.'

'I…' Rosalyn was at a loss for words. She racked her brain for some plausible reason they could not marry so quickly. And if her grandmother was involved… Rosalyn shuddered inwardly. They'd be at the altar before they could turn around.

'I had really hoped for an autumn wedding,' she found herself saying. 'I love the autumn, the leaves are so pretty and it is my favourite time of the year. And Lord…Michael and I would like to become better acquainted.'

'I see.' Lady Spence regarded her curiously. 'I quite understand. An autumn wedding will be ideal if that is what you wish.'

'Oh, yes!'

'We will give a small dinner for you next week to celebrate your betrothal,' Lady Spence said.

'Surely a dinner is not necessary.'

'Of course it is. We must celebrate your engagement and formally introduce you to society as the next Marchioness of Stamford.'

'But, I don't think…'

Lady Spence rose. 'My dear, I am certain this is all quite overwhelming for you. Now, I will leave so you may rest. You will attend the Fawnworths' ball tonight, I understand. I shall look forward to seeing you there.'

She embraced Rosalyn and then left, leaving Rosalyn staring after her in a daze.

Mrs Harrod's voice jerked her out of her reflections. 'My lady, you've another visitor.'

'I shall announce myself.' Lady Carlyn pushed past Mrs Harrod into the room. 'Oh, my love! I knew how it would be! There was something in his manner... We haven't a moment to waste! This time you will have a proper wedding!'

Rosalyn sunk back on the sofa. This charade of a betrothal was going to be much more complicated than she'd ever imagined.

Rosalyn stood in one corner of Lady Fawnworth's ballroom, which had been decorated as a Greek temple with vines running up false pillars, statues of nymphs and goddesses tucked in corners. The lively strains of a country dance filled the room as the dancers galloped through the steps.

Lady Carlyn chattered with an acquaintance, occasionally flinging a delighted smile in Rosalyn's direction. Rosalyn suspected she could scarcely contain the news of Rosalyn's betrothal. She had declared it was certain to be the coup of the Season.

Rosalyn was already experiencing regrets. Not only must she deal with Lord Stamford but now with her grandmother. She sighed and shifted positions. At least one problem had not yet arrived.

Her eyes strayed towards the doorway as the music

ended. She stiffened, all of her senses springing to
life. Lord Stamford entered the ballroom with his
usual air of nonchalant elegance. As he strolled into
the room, she noticed several feminine heads turning
in his direction. He paid little attention, his eyes roving over the room. Undoubtedly looking for her.
Rosalyn fled.

She found an unoccupied spot behind a pillar, near
one wall of the ballroom. Rational thought returned.
Whatever was she doing? She had to face him some
time this evening. It was only that she'd had a sudden
vision of her grandmother making some embarrassing
remark designed to hint to anyone within hearing that
a special announcement was to be expected soon.

'Hiding, my sweet?'

She gasped and spun around. Lord Stamford stood
next to her, a slight half-smile lifting his lips.

'Oh! I did not hear you!'

'Is there a particular reason you are standing behind
this pillar? Your grandmother said you suddenly disappeared. If I wasn't so certain of your delight in
seeing me, I would almost think you were avoiding
me.'

He leaned one shoulder against the wall and
crossed his arms. The movement emphasised the muscles beneath his black evening coat. Perhaps she
should have chosen a spot where she wouldn't feel
so cornered. 'I always find balls so stifling. I suddenly
needed some fresh air.'

'You would do better if you stood near a window.
Come, I want to dance with you.' He held out his
hand.

She stared at his hand as if it were a hot coal.
'Thank you, but I really don't care to dance tonight.'

'And why is that?'

'I am rather tired, that is all.' His brows shot up. She stumbled on, 'That is, I haven't danced much, and I...I will probably step on your feet.'

'I doubt that.' He moved away from the wall towards her, causing her to back up a few steps. 'My dear Rosalyn, perhaps I did not make this clear to you. I expect you to behave like a proper fiancée in public. Not only will you dance with me, I expect you to make it clear you find the experience enjoyable.'

His dictatorial tone set her back up. 'And how am I suppose to do that?'

'You will smile at me, and attempt some sort of conversation. I do not want you to give my family any reason to suspect why you accepted my offer.'

'So you wish me to lead them to believe I accepted you for your wealth and title?'

He gave her a startled glance and then suddenly grinned. 'So you do have claws, my dear.' His voice dropped to an intimate level. 'I was rather hoping you would lead them to believe you fell head over ears for me the first time we met. That is the impression I hope to create.'

Rosalyn felt colour rise up her face. 'I really wish you would not. It will only make everything more complicated.'

'Why?'

'Won't it be more difficult to explain why we do not suit in the end if you are pretending to be in...that is, hold a fondness for me?'

He snorted. 'Hold a fondness for you? You do have an interesting way of putting things. Don't you mean if I am in love with you?'

'I really don't know what I mean! Perhaps we should dance.' She looked around to find several people staring at them, including a dandy who had levelled his quizzing glass on her face.

'An excellent idea.' He took her arm, leading her around the side of the pillar. The musicians were striking up the notes of a waltz.

'Oh, dear,' Rosalyn said faintly. Not a waltz. The dance had only gained formal acceptance last year and she had never danced it in public.

'Now what is wrong?' Lord Stamford asked, as he led her to the ballroom floor.

'I can't waltz with you. Not here.'

'Do you wish to waltz with me in private then? I must admit that might be more interesting.'

'That is not what I meant! I have never danced the waltz in a ballroom before. In front of people!'

His mouth quirked as he looked down at her. 'I have no doubt you'll manage quite well.' He placed one hand lightly above her waist and drew her into position, then began to move in time to the music.

He was a graceful dancer and, after treading on his foot once, Rosalyn managed to follow him.

'Relax,' he murmured. 'You're doing very well. And look up at me.'

She obeyed. He smiled down at her, a warm smile that made her catch her breath. His hand suddenly seemed to burn through the light silk of her dress. She glanced away, trying to remind herself he was only pretending. The thought stiffened her spine. She looked back up at him to find his eyes fixed on her face.

'That is better,' he said softly. 'I prefer to see your

face, not the top of your head. Although it is very charming.'

'Indeed.'

'Yes, although I suspect you do not believe me.'

'Are all your conversations so ridiculous?'

'I am afraid so. But I am willing to reform if you so desire.'

'I really have no desire to reform you in any way.'

'But isn't that the task of a fiancée?'

'I should hope not. In your case, I think it would be quite impossible. I would never attempt it.'

'I believe I might enjoy being reformed at your hands,' he said lazily.

'Perhaps, then, you could start by ceasing to flirt with me.'

'You are undoubtedly correct. I am not certain I could reform if that is your condition. I must admit I enjoy it too much.'

'Have you ever attempted a serious conversation?'

He grinned. 'On occasion. Do you have a topic in mind? Plato's *Republic,* perhaps, or the political ideology of Edmund Burke?'

'Those topics are a bit too serious for a ball. You could start with more mundane subjects…the weather, or perhaps a remark or two on the company.'

'Are those what most men you dance with discuss? They must either be complete fools or blind. I can think of much more interesting things to say when I'm holding a lovely woman in my arms. Did you know your hair is touched with flame under the candle light?'

She looked away, flushing. Why couldn't she turn his compliments away with a cool smile or witty repartee? Instead she behaved like a young miss out of the school room.

He said nothing more and the waltz finally came to an end. He guided her towards the edge of the room, then looked down at her.

'There you are!'

Lady Hartman bounded up next to them. She bestowed a delighted smile upon Rosalyn. 'I had to come and properly congratulate you. I was so astonished last night—you must think I was terribly rude.'

'I quite understand. It must have been a horrible shock.'

Caroline laughed, and her dark eyes so like her brother's sparkled with pleasure. 'Oh, not a horrible shock! A wonderful shock once Giles—my husband, that is—explained who you were.' She glanced at Stamford. 'Perhaps you could go and fetch some glasses of lemonade? I wish to talk to Lady Jeffreys without you hovering about.'

'I trust you are not planning to malign my character.'

Caroline sent him a teasing smile. 'Oh, not at all. I shall just tell her about all the horrid things you did such as putting mice into our beds and...'

His brows snapped together. 'Has Giles ever considered locking you up?'

'Oh, all the time. Do go away! I promise I won't say anything...at least now.'

He gave her a warning glance and stalked off. Rosalyn watched in fascination. Caroline turned to her with an impish grin. 'He can be quite impossible—in fact, he is most of the time. But if one only knows the right things, he is remarkably easy to provoke. I shall give you a few hints.'

'I really don't wish to provoke him.'

Caroline patted her arm. 'Oh, but you will. Particularly when he is behaving in his most top-lofty fashion. Come and sit by me for a bit. I know of a little alcove.'

Rosalyn followed her, genuinely liking Caroline. Despite her outspoken manner, she possessed a warm heart. Rosalyn had never considered she might actually like his family.

Caroline nodded at acquaintances. They stopped once, and Caroline introduced Rosalyn to a small group of ladies who could not quite hide their curiosity under polite smiles.

They turned away, Rosalyn nearly stepping into a lady behind them. The apology died on her lips when she encountered Lady Marchant's icy stare. Stunned by the anger she saw, Rosalyn looked away.

They finally made their way to a small niche in a room connected to the ballroom. They seated themselves on the sofa.

'How surprised everyone will be when your betrothal is announced,' Caroline said. 'I can scarcely wait! I do wish you would marry right away, but Aunt Margaret says you wish to wait until the autumn. I must admit it will be good for Michael to cool his heels a bit. He is used to women falling over themselves to do his bidding. If I were you, I would make him wait until winter. He should be quite compliant by then. Don't you think a Christmas wedding would be nice?'

Rosalyn choked with a laughter she had not felt for an age. 'I am not sure half a century would be enough time,' she said shakily, trying to imagine a compliant Lord Stamford. 'He does not seem very biddable.'

Caroline merely laughed. 'Oh, you'll manage him very well.'

Caroline began to talk of their family. By the time Lord Stamford arrived with two glasses of lemonade, Rosalyn felt as if she was beginning to know them very well. There was a younger brother, Philip, who had been at the Congress in Vienna with Castlereagh, and had been in Europe forever, but was soon to arrive home. Their younger sister, Julianna, was to be presented next year. She found out their mother had died when Michael was scarcely twenty, and his father had been very much in love with her.

Lord Stamford handed Rosalyn a glass. 'I hope Caro has not talked your ear off.'

'Oh, no. She has told me all about your family.'

'I see.' His expression was unreadable. 'Perhaps you won't mind if I steal Rosalyn away. Giles is looking for you, at any rate.'

'Oh, is he? I dare say he wishes to dance with me. We are most unfashionable in that regard.' Caroline squeezed Rosalyn's hand. 'I will leave you to my brother, then. Will you be home the day after next? I should love to call on you.' She flitted off, leaving her lemonade on the window seat.

'I hope Caroline did not overwhelm you overmuch.'

'She didn't a bit. I liked her very much,' Rosalyn said warmly.

He looked at her for a moment. 'I am glad.' But she really could not tell if he was pleased or not. He touched her arm. 'Will you stand up with me again?'

'It is not necessary for you to dance attendance on me all evening. Surely we have spent enough time together to satisfy everyone.' She stared at her lemonade, feeling rather awkward.

'Trying to rid yourself of me again?' He sounded rather angry.

She looked up at him, surprised. 'No, I just thought you might wish to do something else.'

'What I wish to do is dance with you again.'

'Oh.' She twisted her hands together. 'Thank you, then.'

He took her arm and led her through the room which had become increasingly crowded. As they reached the doorway, a woman stepped back into Rosalyn, knocking her arm.

Her lemonade spilled down the front of her bodice. 'Oh!'

'I beg your pardon.' Lady Marchant's lovely face showed feigned surprise. 'Why, Lady Jeffreys, is it? How very clumsy of me! I am terribly sorry!' She suddenly seemed to notice Lord Stamford. 'Why, my lord! What a surprise to see you here! I thought you detested balls!'

By now several people had turned to stare at them. Rosalyn was mortified. Her glass had been nearly full and she could feel the liquid seeping through her shift. 'Tis no matter.' She glanced up at Stamford. His face was expressionless, but she could sense his anger. 'Please, perhaps we could find my grandmother.' She wanted nothing more than to escape before there was some sort of scene.

'Of course.' He escorted her from the room and into the ball room, then released her as soon as he found a vacant space near the wall. The dancers were executing the steps of a quadrille. 'Damn! Rosalyn, I beg your pardon,' he said stiffly.

'There is no need. You did not knock into me,' she said in a feeble attempt to reassure him as he looked completely at sea.

'No, but I've no doubt she purposely did it.' He scowled. 'I am afraid it is rather noticeable. Do you wish to find a more private room and see if it could be dried?' he asked doubtfully.

She sighed. 'I think it is hopeless. I rather think I should like to go home.'

'Of course. I will escort you.'

She looked at him swiftly. 'That isn't necessary.'

'It is the least I can do. Don't fight me on this.'

She waited while he collected her cloak. To her consternation, Lady Carlyn declined to accompany them, merely sending a message that she would call on Rosalyn tomorrow. Lord Stamford said little, however; his thoughts seemed to be elsewhere. And when he escorted her to her door, he only bowed over her hand, then seemed to think of something. 'I will call on you tomorrow. I will also see that you have a replacement for your ruined gown.'

'What?'

But he had already departed.

Chapter Six

Rosalyn finally gave up and pushed the letter aside. She had spent the morning struggling to explain to her dearest friend, Lucy, the Countess of Darmont, why she had entered into such a hasty betrothal. Particularly since Lucy had always teased her about her cautious nature.

She rubbed her temples. She'd slept little after last night's ball, making it all the more difficult to concentrate. Perhaps if she walked in the park she'd feel more alert.

'My lady?' She looked up from her desk to see Mrs Harrod standing in the door of the library. 'You have a visitor. Your brother.'

'James?'

'I'll show myself in.' He pushed past Mrs Harrod, who took one look at his livid face and beat a hasty retreat.

Rosalyn stood. 'James? What is wrong?'

'What is wrong? Are you out of your mind?' he shouted.

'I beg your pardon?' For the first time she could

remember in years, he had an expression on his handsome face besides a closed, sulky indifference.

He took a deep breath, his fists clenched at his sides. 'Stamford. He called on me to announce he intended to marry you.'

'Oh, dear.'

'I can't say you seem surprised. My God, I had no idea you'd ever met the man! Then I hear some blasted rumour you were at the opera with him and now he's wanting to marry you!'

Rosalyn knotted her hands together. 'I had meant to tell you myself.'

'You're telling me this is true? He has asked you to marry him?'

'Yes, it is true.'

'And you're planning to accept him?' His dark hazel eyes were filled with disbelief. 'Are you in love with him?'

'I am very…very fond of him.'

'Fond? I don't believe you! He's not the sort of man you would ever consider, not after John. Stamford is a rake! A libertine! Some of the stories I've heard. And he has our estate.' He stared at her as if hit by a sudden thought.

'He said he would return Meryton. Something about it being a family matter.' His eyes were full of accusation. 'You're doing it to save Meryton.'

'I…I am not.'

'You are. Blast it, Rosalyn! How can you interfere like this! I told you I would take care of it! You are not going to marry him!'

'You cannot dictate to me, James. I will marry him,' she said quietly.

'You've lost all reason. Has he seduced you? If he has I vow I will kill him.' His voice held a distinct threat she had never heard before.

'No, of course he has not.' She stepped towards her brother, holding out her hand imploringly. 'James, please listen to me.'

He refused her hand. 'The man has cast some sort of spell over you. I only pray you'll come to your senses in time. I, for one, have no intention of accepting your marriage.'

He turned and stalked towards the door. He wrenched it open and then paused and looked back at her. 'I will never take Meryton back with Stamford as my brother-in-law!' He closed the door softly, a sound more ominous than if he'd actually slammed it.

She sank back down on the chair behind her desk, willing herself not to cry. She had never dreamed he would guess why she became betrothed to Lord Stamford. And she had never expected such anger. Indifference, scorn, perhaps, but not this. For years she'd watched him shut away his emotions and now anger had erupted from him like the sea crashing through a wall.

The familiar wave of helplessness she experienced when it came to Lord Stamford washed over her. She had planned to break the news to James herself. Instead, Lord Stamford, in his usual high-handed manner, had taken care of that.

Tears welled up in her eyes, and spilled over. Never had she felt so completely defeated in her entire life.

The day was perfectly beautiful; the park glittered with that particular dewy freshness that came with the sun after a night of rain. A herd of cows grazed peacefully at one end of the park. Three urchins and a shaggy black and white dog were occupied with a stick and hoop. A couple, clearly in love from the fond gazes they threw each other, strolled down one of the paths.

These bucolic delights were lost on Michael. He reined his gelding, Faro, to a stop, his eyes searching for his affianced. When he finally spotted her purchasing a nosegay of violets and cowslips from a small girl, he swore. What the devil was she doing in Green Park without her maid?

He'd come to call on her, only to have her housekeeper inform him Rosalyn seemed a trifle overset and left for a walk in the park. He had no idea what had upset her, but he was determined to find out.

He waited until Rosalyn had started back down the path, a petite figure in a pelisse of dark violet and a high poke bonnet, before he urged his horse into a trot. He halted beside her.

'What in the devil are you doing?' he inquired sardonically.

She gave a little jump and stared up at him. He could have been Satan himself from the look of consternation that crossed her face.

'Doing? I...I am talking a walk.'

He swung down from his gelding and caught the reins. 'It is quite improper of you to be strolling around in the park without your maid. Do you have no sense of propriety? This is hardly the country where such conduct might be acceptable, but the middle of London.'

'I know perfectly well what I am about, my lord. You need not concern yourself with my behaviour. My abigail had a headache today so of course I would not ask her to accompany me.'

'You could ask a footman.'

'My footman has other business to attend to.'

An exasperated snort escaped him. 'Then, in that case, I suggest you forgo your walk.'

'If you have interrupted my walk merely to lecture me on propriety, then I suggest you leave. You are wasting your time, my lord,' she replied with stiff dignity. She turned her back on him and moved away, her head high.

Her prim accents and attempts to keep him at arm's length filled him with the most wicked desire to flirt with her unmercifully.

He caught up to her. 'That was not my chief reason for calling on you. I wanted to discuss our betrothal, my love,' he replied softly, pulling her arm through his, drawing her closer to his side.

He was gratified to see the action noticeably confused her, causing the pink in her cheeks to intensify.

'I am not your love, my lord. I pray you will release my arm.'

'Only if you will address me by my given name.'

'This is most ridiculous, my l—Michael,' she replied.

'My Michael?' he drawled, raising a satirical brow. 'That is certainly some improvement over "my lord." Does this mean you hold me in some affection after all, my dear Rosalyn?'

She yanked her arm out of his, stopped on the path and turned to face him. He was delighted to see her eyes flash and her cool composure melt. Her fist closed about the small bouquet of flowers, causing them to wilt.

'That is not what I meant, as you very well know!'

'Really? I am disappointed. What did you mean?' he inquired.

'Can we please stay with the matter at hand?' she snapped.

'You seem rather out of sorts for a lady about to receive an offer,' he remarked blandly.

'I am not about to receive an offer! Why must you always be so odious!'

To his astonishment, her lip quivered and tears welled up in her large eyes. She quickly turned her head.

The lone tear trailing down her cheek, which she wiped away hastily, had an instant sobering effect on Michael. Feminine tears usually inspired little emotion in him besides exasperation, but he felt an overwhelming sense of guilt that he had gone too far.

'My dear girl, I did not wish to make you cry,' he said.

'I...I am not crying.' She sniffed and another tear rolled down her cheek.

'Yes, you are,' he insisted softly. 'Look at me.'

She shook her head, refusing to face him. 'I...I never cry.'

He gently touched her averted cheek. 'Of course not. But I can see you are overset. Can you not tell me what is wrong? I am sorry if I have teased you too much. My sisters have often flung that accusation at me.'

'There is nothing wrong. I would like to return home, if you please.'

She brushed ineffectively at the tears that were now freely falling. He fumbled in his pocket for a handkerchief and handed it to her. Taking her arm in a firm grasp, he led her under the spreading branches of an oak, his horse following obediently behind. He dropped the reins and caught both her hands in his. Her nosegay fell to the ground.

'What has you so blue-devilled, Rosalyn?'

She finally raised her head. Her eyes searched his face. She drew in a deep breath. 'It is James. He called on me, and he was so angry. He said he did not want Meryton. I...I had wanted to tell him about our...our betrothal myself.'

'Is that it? I did not mean to cause you more distress by going to your brother. I thought to save you some trouble by telling him myself that my intentions were honourable. I thought, too, you would want to know I intended on keeping my side of the bargain.'

She sniffed again and dabbed at her eyes with the handkerchief. 'I...I see. But...but he doesn't want Meryton if I...I am betrothed to you.'

He touched her cheek. 'But you want it.'

'Y...yes.'

'Do not distress yourself too much, he will come around. I will see to it.'

'Thank you, then,' she said quietly and gave him a shy smile. For the first time in their brief acquaintance, he nearly found himself at a loss for words. He was suddenly aware of the clean light scent she wore, a mixture of lavender and roses, and of how very soft and pleasing her small gloved hand felt in his.

An unexpected bolt of desire shot through him. He dropped her hand as if it burned him and then could have cursed himself for the startled expression on her face.

'I believe I should escort you home,' Michael said, running a distracted hand through his hair. He avoided touching her as she fell into step beside him. Faro trailed along behind.

He cleared his throat. 'I had something else I wish to tell you, which is the other reason I wanted to settle the matter with your brother. I will be going to Eversleigh for a day or two to see my father. He has summoned me. I believe he wants a first-hand account of our, er...relationship.'

'Oh, dear.' She shot him a quick look. 'Do you think he will be angry?'

'No.' His father's brief note had been surprisingly cordial, although it was a summons none the less.

'I hope not.' She continued to watch him with that faintly puzzled look as if she didn't know what to make of him. Michael hardly knew what to make of himself—he felt as unhinged as if he were actually about to ask for her hand.

'Well, shall I go down on my knee and declare my sentiments? I have not done this before.'

'Whatever for?'

'I have not made you a proper offer.'

'It is not necessary since we are not really to be married. You should wait until you meet the lady you wish to marry. It would also be best if you waited until you are in a drawing room before going down on your knees. In the midst of a public park with a horse at one's heels is not the most convenient place to make such an offer.' To his surprise, her eyes shone with gentle laughter.

He grinned back at her. 'And probably not the most romantic, either.'

They reached the steps in front of her townhouse. Michael paused and looked down at her. 'By the way, there is something else you should know. I told your brother he was not to gamble again until his debts were paid off.'

Her hand closed around the locket she wore. 'But why? Is that necessary?'

He frowned. 'Yes. Does that distress you? It should not. He must learn that it's foolish to gamble what he does not have. Particularly when he possesses such little skill.'

A flash of anger showed in her eyes. 'So it is acceptable to gamble when one is wealthy and skilled, then? Is that the philosophy you follow, my lord?'

The censure in her tone rankled him. 'Of course, my lady. I am extremely fortunate to lay claim to both.'

'I see. So what happens if he does gamble again?'

'I will take possession of the estate.'

She stared at him with disbelief. 'But you are changing the terms of our bargain! You said nothing of that before!'

He smiled coolly. 'Not at all. What good will it do to return the estate to him if he either stakes it again or is forced to sell it to pay off his debts? Is that what you want to happen?'

'No. You are right,' she said softly.

Her admission should have given him a small victory. Instead, he felt angry. 'I will see you in a day or two, my dear.' He looked down into her flushed face and was filled with the unwelcome desire to pull her to him and kiss her hard. With a muffled curse, he turned and strode away.

Rosalyn gazed at the closed door, completely bewildered by his behaviour. She had obviously angered him, but surely not so much that it would make him look as if he wanted to strangle her.

Even more confusing was his kindness before that. The rueful apology in his eyes when she'd expected mockery had thrown her off completely.

Still puzzling over his behaviour, she slowly made her way to her drawing room and sank down on her sofa.

She put a hand to her head, which was beginning to ache. For the first time since she had braved his drawing room, she saw him as something other than an enemy. She had glimpsed another side to him, a side that was kind and understanding. A side that was much more frightening than that of the charming rake she knew.

Two days later, Rosalyn stood in her bedchamber staring with more than a little dismay at the hat boxes and packages strewn across her bed. Any idea she'd had of spending the two days away from Lord Stamford in quiet solitude had been dashed the instant her grandmother had shown up in her drawing room shortly on Stamford's heels. With grim determination on her face, Lady Carlyn had announced that no granddaughter of hers would be marrying a Marquis looking like a governess.

So Rosalyn had spent the last two days in a whirl

of visits to milliners and dressmakers. Not to mention shopping for gloves, fans, slippers, and stockings. She was exhausted. And she dreaded to see the bills. James would not be the only one in debt, she reflected wryly.

James. She idly picked up a bonnet trimmed with sea-green ribbons, a frown creasing her brow. She hadn't heard from him since the day he'd come to call and had been so angry about her betrothal. She had visited his rooms, but he had not been in. After waiting for over a half an hour, she'd finally given up and left a message.

Her grandmother had brushed aside her worries. 'My dear, he has probably gone off with one of his friends. Young men are like that.' They had been sitting in her grandmother's Chinese drawing room taking tea.

'But he was quite angry with me when I told him about my betrothal. He…he thinks Lord Stamford is a rake.'

'Of course, he is a bit wild, but that makes him much more interesting. I was fond of John, and I never wanted to say a thing, but he was, well, a bit dull. Particularly for such a young girl as yourself.'

'I loved John,' Rosalyn had said stiffly. 'I never found him dull.'

Lady Carlyn had patted her hand. 'I know, dear. But it was a respectful sort of love. With Lord Stamford it will be quite different.'

'I hardly think so.' Rosalyn was hurt and insulted that her grandmother would make such an unfavourable comparison between John and Lord Stamford.

Her grandmother had smiled in a knowing manner.

'You won't be able to escape it, my dear. I have seen how he looks at you. Which brings me to another point. I have no idea why you have this harebrained notion about delaying the wedding.'

'I don't want to be married so soon. We hardly know each other.'

'At least you might consider Lord Stamford's wishes in the matter. I cannot imagine he wishes to wait until autumn. It is quite foolish of you to make a man of his passionate temperament cool his heels too long!'

'A man of his passionate temperament? Whatever do you mean?'

A loud, exasperated sigh escaped Lady Carlyn. 'Must I spell it out for you, dear? You are a widow, you should know that men have certain needs, however inconvenient they may be for a woman. I do not think he wants to wait that long, not with the way he watches you.' She stared at Rosalyn with speculative eyes. 'Unless, of course, you already have…'

'Grandmama! I would never do such a thing!'

'There is no need to look so shocked! You are not exactly an innocent young girl, and it would hardly raise an eyebrow as long as you were discreet. I have heard from several sources that he is most pleasing to women in that regard! You are certainly the object of much envy.'

'I cannot believe anyone would ever speculate on such a topic. This is most dreadful!' exclaimed Rosalyn, truly shocked and completely mortified.

'Of course they do, dear. Most of society does not share the same scruples as you.'

Even now, the memory of that conversation made

her blush. Unbidden, a vision of lying in his arms, his dark face hovering over hers, that teasing half-smile on his face, as he lowered his lips to hers...

Her knees went weak. She jerked her thoughts away from such a disturbing image. Of course, she had no interest in him in that way. He was the most handsome man she had ever encountered but also the most aggravating and arrogant and...

'My lady, you have a visitor,' Mrs Harrod said, interrupting her thoughts.

Rosalyn started and put the bonnet back in its box. 'Who is it?'

'Mr Fairchilde.' Her housekeeper's voice was stiff. 'Are you at home?'

'I...yes. I will be there shortly.' She had no real desire to see him, but perhaps he'd know James's whereabouts.

Mrs Harrod bustled off with a disapproving snort. Rosalyn removed her pelisse and bonnet, which she realized she was still wearing, and, after straightening her locks, reluctantly made her way to her drawing room.

He sat on her striped sofa, long legs stretched before him. He rose at her entrance, his size shrinking the room. He was dressed in buckskin breeches and a light blue coat which made the steely grey of his eyes more noticeable.

His smile was cool and appraising. 'Lady Jeffreys, how good of you to see me. I called once before, but you were not at home.'

She gave him her hand, resisting the urge to snatch it away and smiled diffidently. 'I have been out with my grandmother. Please, sit down.' She seated herself on the nearest chair and folded her hands in her lap wondering nervously what he wanted.

'Have you seen James?' she asked, trying to think of something to say.

He shrugged. 'Not for several days. That is not why I called.'

He sat back down, his eyes fixed on her face. 'I will not dissemble. I was surprised to see you at the opera the other night with Lord Stamford.' His voice was light, but there was an underlying edge in it that made her uneasy.

'We are acquainted.'

'But how did he ever persuade you to accompany him? I will own I was quite envious of his position, having you at his side. But are you certain it was wise? His reputation is not the most sterling. In fact, his taste for lovely widows is quite well known. I should hate to think of you falling under his spell.'

'I assure you there is no need to worry about that,' she said stiffly.

'Good. He would be a most unfaithful lover.' His gaze drifted over her in a way that made her nervous.

'I...I have no idea what you are talking about.'

'Don't you? He has your brother's estate, and you are quite lovely. Perhaps he hasn't made you an offer yet, but I've no doubt of his intentions.'

She rose, trying to keep her voice calm. She longed to throw her betrothal in his face, but it was not yet public knowledge. 'You have no idea of his intentions. And I certainly would never think of becoming his mistress, if that is what you are saying. I pray you will leave, sir.'

His gaze was unfathomable. 'I have something to

discuss with you. Your brother's debt. I am quite willing to loan him the money for repayment. At a reasonable interest. I might even be persuaded to forgive him the small loan I have already made him.'

'What is his debt? I have a little money of my own.' She had no idea James owed him money. She was beginning to feel slightly sick.

'I was not talking about money. There are other things you could do to make the terms even more reasonable.'

'Really.'

'Yes, my lovely Rosalyn. Come to Vauxhall with me tomorrow, and we can discuss the terms.'

'Vauxhall? I have never cared for Vauxhall.'

'Then come and dine with me.'

'Dine with you? No, I cannot.'

'If you want your brother's estate back, then you will.' He also rose, and looked down at her, a hardness in his gaze that made her afraid.

Suddenly, she knew what he wanted. How could she be so stupid? She backed away from him. 'You are mistaken if you think I will agree to that.'

'There is no need for these games, my dear. I know why you accompanied Stamford to the opera. It is as good as agreeing to his terms, even if he hasn't yet offered them in so many words. But I can offer you much more pleasure than Stamford ever will.'

She glanced towards the door. At least she was in her own home. If she screamed, Mrs Harrod would come running. 'No! He has offered me nothing like that.'

His hand shot out, and for a moment, she thought he meant to grab her. Then he dropped his hand and smiled coolly. 'Hasn't he? Then I am certain that is what is on his mind. Not that I blame him. I have wanted you, desired you, since that first time I saw you at Meryton.'

Fear and revulsion coursed through her. 'Please, say no more. I want you to leave.'

'As you wish, my dear lady. I am persuaded that once you think about it you will reconsider. Your brother is in my debt, and I do intend to be repaid.'

She backed out of the drawing room then, almost tripping over Mrs Harrod, who stood at the door with a militant look on her face, broom in hand. Rosalyn had no doubt her loyal housekeeper meant to use it on Fairchilde if necessary. Rosalyn fled up the stairs, to the sanctuary of her bedchamber. She closed the door, and leaned against it, taking deep breaths to calm herself. Her concerns had always been for James and Meryton. Now she felt more than a little frightened for herself.

Chapter Seven

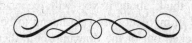

Three days later, Michael entered Rosalyn's small study. Occupied in arranging a vase of flowers, she did not notice him until he was nearly behind her. She jumped, dropping a stalk of delphinium. 'My lord…Michael, I did not expect you back so soon.'

He retrieved the flower and handed it to her with a smile. She looked different today. Instead of the pale blues and greys she usually wore, her dress was white muslin patterned with swirls of flowers. Her hair was pulled back and arranged in soft tendrils around her face. She looked soft and fresh and utterly charming. He experienced the sudden urge to touch her soft cheek. His voice came out more abrupt than he'd intended.

'I just returned last night.'

'Oh.' She moved around the table and tucked the delphinium in the vase, then looked at him. 'But Caroline said Eversleigh Hall is nearly a day's journey away.'

'That is true. After I saw my father, I found little point in remaining.' He had tried to convince himself he merely wanted to return so his father wouldn't suspect something was wrong, but now the truth hit him. He had wanted to see her.

'You must be exhausted. Was he very angry?'

'No, not at all.' He smiled briefly. 'He has given his consent to our marriage.'

'Our marriage?'

'I mean our betrothal. Amazingly, he had no objections.' Which had puzzled Michael greatly. He had expected arguments, but instead his father had seemed quite pleased. Michael had nearly reeled with shock.

A faint suspicion entered his mind that something was afoot, but he could hardly bring that up with his father.

'Didn't he? I am glad it was not too difficult for you.'

'No.' He moved away from her, not looking forward to telling her the next item of news. 'There is just one complication, however—he wishes me to bring you to Eversleigh.'

'Eversleigh? Oh, no! I...I really do not want to meet your father.' Then she flushed. 'That is, I am certain he is very nice...but, I...'

His mouth quirked. 'There is no need to explain. More than one man has been known to tremble at the prospect. But don't worry, I'll try to fob him off as long as possible.'

'Thank you.'

'I will put the announcement in the *Morning Post*. I believe our betrothal dinner is tomorrow?'

'Yes.' She looked uncomfortable. 'I wish your aunt had not decided to hold a dinner. I feel so dishonest!'

'I fear it is part of a betrothal. Caro informs me we were fortunate it was not a ball.'

She sighed. 'Could we have not had a secret engagement?'

His lips twitched. 'That would have spoiled the purpose for contracting the engagement in the first place.'

He pulled a small jeweller's box from his waistcoat pocket and stepped to her side. 'I have something for you. My father wanted me to give it to you.'

He held the box out. Her eyes flew up to his face as she hesitantly took it.

She removed the lid. Inside the box lay an elaborate ring of diamonds and rubies in an ornate, old-fashioned setting. She stared at it, a stunned expression on her face.

'It's a ring, my dear.'

'I...I know. Michael, I cannot accept this.'

'Why not? It is customary to give one's fiancée a ring. It would be considered extremely remiss of me to not do so.'

When she said nothing he added, 'I know it is rather hideous. I would have preferred to give you something less ostentatious as you have such delicate hands, but I'm afraid this is a family heirloom. It is a tradition for brides to wear it. My father commanded me to give it to you.'

'No...no, it is not that. I mean it is not hideous. I am certain it is too valuable for me to wear.'

Michael laughed. 'If you were Caroline, I might worry about your losing it. But I am sure it is quite safe with you.' He held out his hand. 'Give me your hand, Rosalyn. I'll place it on your finger.'

'I must remove my wedding ring first,' she said with a slight tremor in her voice. Her dark hair hid her face from his sight as she slowly slid the plain gold band from her left hand. She looked at it for a moment before placing it on her other hand. He thought she looked rather sad. For the first time since he'd struck the bargain with her, he felt a twinge of remorse over forcing her into it.

He took her hand and slipped the heavy ring gently on her finger. Her soft hand trembled in his clasp.

She looked up at him. 'I will take care of it. I shall, of course, return it to you when this is over.'

'I have no doubts on that score.'

She clasped her hands together in that way she had when she was distressed.

'Is something wrong, Rosalyn? Are you worried about the dinner or my father?'

She shook her head, and then swallowed. 'It is James.'

He frowned, feeling impatient at her brother's name. 'James? Has he gambled away the estate again?'

'No, of course not. He has disappeared without any word. I have no idea where he is.'

'I see. I doubt if he's met with foul play, if that is what worries you.' Michael thought it most likely the young fool had gone off with some friends for a few days.

She looked even more anxious. 'I…I hope not. But he's never done anything like this before. I know I am probably very foolish, but I worry that something has happened. He was so angry with me. Perhaps I drove him to leave.'

Michael made an impatient sound. 'That is ridiculous. He's one-and-twenty years of age, certainly—'

'He is twenty.'

'As if that makes any difference.' He frowned at her. 'He's old enough to make his own decisions. You're not responsible for him.'

'But I am. When my mother was dying, she asked that I look after James and Papa.'

Michael had no idea whether he wanted to shake her or kiss her. 'I am certain she only meant until your brother was grown.' He stepped towards her. 'The devil! Rosalyn, there is no need for this.'

She backed away from him and sniffed. 'I pray you will go. I am sorry to have troubled you.'

'No.' He ran a hand through his hair. 'Very well. I will make some inquiries and see where he's gone.'

'I don't wish you to do that. I…I have been making some inquiries myself.'

'Without much success, I take it,' he said sardonically. 'I probably have a better idea where he might have gone than you do.'

'It is not necessary for you to involve yourself in our…our lives,' she said with stiff dignity.

He raised a brow. 'Whether you like it or not, I am very much involved, my dear.' This time when he came towards her, she had no place to retreat since she was backed up against the wall. He touched her cheek. 'Don't look so worried. Your brother will be fine.'

She raised startled eyes to his face, looking like a doe that was about to flee. Her breathing grew shallow. 'Th…thank you,' she whispered.

'Not at all. Rosalyn…' he said hoarsely. He bent towards her, knowing he had to kiss her.

'Oh, my lady, I beg your pardon!'

Michael's head jerked up at the sound of the house-keeper's voice. Rosalyn's hand flew to her throat. 'Wh…what is it?' she said.

Mrs Harrod, her face slightly red, came into the room. She was followed by the footman carrying a huge bouquet of flowers. 'These arrived for you, my lady. Where do you want them?'

Rosalyn stared at them as if she had never seen a flower before. Then she seemed to come to life. 'In the drawing room, I suppose. Who sent them?'

'I do not know. Here is a card.'

Michael watched as she took it, and waited until Mrs Harrod had departed with the flowers, before speaking. He folded his arms. 'Another admirer, my dear?'

'Oh, no. I don't have any admirers,' Rosalyn said distractedly. She opened the card, and read it. He watched as her face turned pale.

'Who are they from?' he inquired.

She looked up, a rather sick look on her face. 'No…no one. That is, just someone I…I knew. It is nothing.'

He held out his hand. 'Give me the card.'

'No!' She whipped it behind her. 'Please, Michael.'

Now what? She looked so distressed, he didn't want to press her. However, he had every intention of finding out who would send her flowers that would make her look so upset. And then he'd put a bullet through the man.

The intensity of the thought shocked him. He'd

never felt the least urge to fight a duel over any woman in his life. In fact, he'd never been the least bit inclined to put himself out for any woman, except for perhaps his sisters. And now this petite widow, with the large hazel eyes, was embroiling him in her concerns.

No. He was embroiling himself.

This time it was Michael who backed away, putting distance between them. 'I will take my leave of you, Rosalyn.' His voice was unnaturally stiff for one of the *ton*'s most notorious flirts.

'Very well.' She gave him a confused little smile.

She followed him to the door of her study. He turned and looked down at her. 'I will let you know what I find out about James.'

'Thank you. You are very kind.'

'Hardly.' Pulling his eyes away from her mouth, he turned abruptly on his heel and left.

A few inquiries at Fallingham's was all Michael needed to discover James had gone to the races at Newmarket with several of the wildest young bucks in London. Michael only hoped James decided to forgo any wagers, but he thought it highly unlikely.

Michael was about to leave the establishment, when a soft voice spoke from behind him. 'I fear you got the worse of the bargain when you took on the estate of James Whitcomb.'

Michael turned and met the hooded gaze of Edmund Fairchilde. His hackles rose. There was something about the man's tall, broad-shouldered figure and craggy face that never failed to arouse his worst instincts. Perhaps it was because Fairchilde reminded him of a watchful predator on the prowl for an unsuspecting victim.

'I hardly think so.'

'Obviously you have not seen the place, then. It is small and in dire need of all sorts of improvements despite Lady Jeffreys's efforts to maintain it. I doubt if it is worth the vowels it was to cover.'

'Perhaps not, but I fail to see why it is any of your concern.'

'But it is. I am quite willing to offer you the sum of young Whitcomb's vowels, plus something in the nature of interest for the mortgage.'

'Why?' Michael demanded bluntly.

Fairchilde smiled gently. 'I will not dissemble. I have little interest in either Meryton or Whitcomb. But there is something else. In fact, I believe we share a common interest.'

It took only seconds for Fairchilde's meaning to penetrate and then shock jolted through Michael. 'You are referring to Lady Jeffreys?' His voice was cold.

'Yes.' Fairchilde still smiled, but his gaze was hard. 'I have had an interest in the lady for some time. I must own I was rather displeased to see her with you at the opera.'

'Were you?'

'Yes. I do not like competition. Particularly when my opponent holds such an unfair advantage.'

'So you are hoping to buy the advantage yourself?' Michael could barely keep the sneer from his voice.

'Of course. I cannot see what it matters to you. She is hardly the sort of woman you favour. You have left her unattended for several days, and I have it from a…er, reliable source that you have not yet purchased the lady's favours.'

'That is because I have no intention of purchasing them.' Michael's gaze was deadly. 'The lady in question is betrothed to me.'

He had the satisfaction of watching displeasure flit through Fairchilde's eyes. Then a quizzical half-smile curled his lips. 'How very interesting. I beg your pardon, my lord.' He executed a neat bow and walked off, leaving Michael staring after him.

Michael quit the establishment, paying little heed to his surroundings. He settled into his carriage, his mind in a whirl. Fairchilde was interested in Rosalyn? The notion of the man touching her made him ill. He had heard rumours of Fairchilde's sexual habits and they involved perversions that could turn the stomach of the most jaded of men.

And he was ruthless. He was not above using force if he wanted a woman. With sudden clarity, he knew exactly who had sent Rosalyn her unwanted bouquet.

Rosalyn's stomach churned with nervousness as she and Lady Carlyn followed Lady Spence's butler up the elegant staircase to the drawing room the next evening.

'My dear, there's no need to look as if you're about to mount the gallows,' Lady Carlyn whispered loudly as they approached the tall double doors.

Rosalyn clutched her fan tightly, trying to keep her hand from trembling. 'I am just a little nervous. I don't like being the centre of attention.'

'There's nothing to it. Just smile and don't spill soup on your gown.'

Lady Carlyn took her arm, almost dragging her into the drawing room. Rosalyn stopped, wondering if it were too late to run. A small dinner party? There must be at least thirty people in the drawing room. A quick look around the room revealed Michael was not one of those present. She found herself wishing for his support.

Lady Spence broke away from a lady with whom she had been conversing to greet Rosalyn and Lady Carlyn. She embraced Lady Carlyn, then turned to Rosalyn. 'How lovely you look, my dear,' she said warmly as she noted Rosalyn's dark pink silk. 'What a pretty colour on you.'

Taking Rosalyn's arm, she said, 'I want you to meet our other guests. I don't know where your fiancé is. He hasn't shown up yet which is so very typical. I hope you can influence him to put in an appearance on time.'

Lady Carlyn bustled away to talk to an elderly lady in puce, leaving Rosalyn to fend for herself.

Lady Spence introduced her to the other guests; a bewildering number of relations whose names Rosalyn could only hope she would recall, and several old friends of the family.

They finally stopped in front of a dark-haired young man with features that seemed familiar. He stood with Michael's cousin, Charles, and Charles's fiancée, Miss Markham. They both smiled at her in welcome.

Lady Spence brought her forward. 'Rosalyn, may I present Lord Philip Elliot, Michael's brother? Philip, may I present Lady Jeffreys? Philip has only arrived in town today. I believe you know he has been travelling on the continent.'

Lord Philip's warm grey eyes surveyed her face with lively curiosity for a moment and then he said, 'My pleasure, Lady Jeffreys. You cannot conceive my surprise when I arrived today to find my brother is to be married at last.'

'No more than the rest of us,' Charles said with a grin.

Philip laughed. 'I understand you met him only a few weeks ago. He tends to make up his mind quickly when he knows what he wants. I am afraid you hadn't a chance, Lady Jeffreys.'

Elizabeth smiled up at her fiancé. 'Then there are some men who need a bit more prodding.'

Charles looked unabashed. 'Oh, I knew what I wanted. Just didn't know if you'd agree.'

'At any rate, welcome to the family,' said Philip. He smiled at her. Although he was not as handsome as his brother, she saw he possessed the same easy charm. He held out his hand.

She no sooner had taken it, smiling at him in return, when Lord Stamford's voice spoke behind her, causing her to jump. 'I see you have met my fiancée, Philip.'

Philip released her hand. 'Yes. She is lovely. Under the circumstances, I am surprised you were not on time for once.'

Rosalyn glanced up at Lord Stamford and he smiled at her, a warm intimate look. She was momentarily thrown into confusion until she remembered it was part of the role he played. She tentatively smiled back at him. He took her hand and slowly raised it to his lips. An odd tingle shot through her body at the soft pressure.

'I meant to be, but one of my horses strained a hock. Otherwise, nothing would have kept me from your side,' he said, gazing into her eyes.

'I see.' Rosalyn was embarrassed that he should speak to her like this in front of the others. She prayed the butler would announce dinner. Whatever was taking so long?

Lord Stamford appeared about to say something when there was a sudden lull in the conversation. Everyone's head seemed to swivel in the same direction. Rosalyn, too, turned to look.

Entering the drawing room was the most beautiful girl she had ever seen in her life. From the top of her golden curls to the tips of the dainty white slippers peeking from beneath her simple white gown, the young lady who glided into the room was perfection. Large violet blue eyes shone from a face with a complexion that could truly be described as porcelain. Her slender figure with its graceful curves was only enhanced by the simple gown.

She appeared perfectly unaware of the effect she had on the assembled company as she greeted her hostess with a soft pretty smile. The other two ladies, an older woman in a lavender gown and a younger lady dressed in cream and lace, were hardly noticed in the beauty's wake.

'Who is she?' asked Lord Philip who appeared as dazed as any man in the room.

'Miss Helena Randall,' Charles replied.

Miss Randall? The lady to whom Stamford was to have been betrothed? Rosalyn's mind was in a whirl.

She had tried to imagine Miss Randall and had envisioned a pretty, but naïve, young girl from the schoolroom with the giggling manners so many girls in their first season displayed. She had never thought Miss Randall would be a composed beauty who walked like a young goddess. If Stamford had known…he surely would not have suggested this sham. She stole a quick glance at her fiancé, expecting him to be gazing at Miss Randall as besotted as anyone.

Instead, to her utter confusion, his unsmiling eyes were fixed on her.

Chapter Eight

Rosalyn smiled at Lord Philip who was seated to her right at dinner. 'Will you be in England long?'

'Permanently, I hope.'

'Your family will be glad of that.'

He slanted her a half-smile reminding her of Michael's. 'Perhaps. Well, at least at first,' he amended.

She picked up her wine, thinking she liked Michael's brother very much. They had talked a little of his travels and of her husband's writing. He had read several of John's essays.

Taking a sip of wine, she stole a glance down the table at Michael. His unsmiling gaze met hers, the same one he'd fixed on her during most of the dinner. In fact, he almost was glowering at her. She flushed and dropped her eyes. Was she doing something wrong? Or did he find fault with her appearance?

Seated between Philip and Charles Portland, she had found the dinner less of an ordeal than she had expected. Both were easy conversationalists. To her surprise, she actually enjoyed herself. But it was quite apparent Michael did not feel the same.

A short time later Lady Spence stood, signalling for the ladies to depart, leaving the men to their port and conversation. She led them upstairs to the drawing room. Rosalyn sat down on a brocade settee next to Caroline and across from Miss Randall.

With her impish grin, Caroline immediately began to tease Miss Randall. 'Dear Helena, I'm afraid you've added another heart to your collection. Poor Percy Milhurst has fallen at your feet! What shall you do with all your admirers?'

Miss Randall looked alarmed. 'Oh, dear. I…I did nothing to encourage him. And he said such odd things, I could not understand half his conversation.'

'What sort of odd things? I hope he said nothing improper, Helena!'

'Oh, no! Of course not! He kept talking about my hair and eyes and comparing them to spun gold and lakes. And he offered to dedicate a poem to me. It was very tedious. His conversation is not at all sensible.'

Caroline bit back a laugh. 'No, it never has been. But how many young men have you met with sensible conversation? I imagine their wits must leave their heads when they see you.'

Miss Randall blushed and looked uncomfortable, and Rosalyn suddenly felt sorry for her. It was obvious she had no desire to be the reigning beauty of the Season with a horde of young men constantly at her side.

Miss Randall turned to Rosalyn and smiled shyly.

'I have not yet congratulated you on your engagement. I hope you will be very happy.'

'Thank you.' Rosalyn smiled back at her.

'Will you live at Eversleigh after your wedding? It is one of the most beautiful homes I have ever seen. The gardens are so lovely,' Miss Randall continued.

Rosalyn was startled. 'I really do not know. We have not discussed it.'

'I imagine you will. Unless Michael wishes to keep you to himself for a while,' Caroline said, casting Rosalyn a mischievous glance. 'He has a very small estate in Cornwall that would be most romantic.'

Rosalyn could feel a blush rise to her cheeks, which was completely ridiculous. One should only blush if one was in love with the man in question. Hastily she asked Miss Randall if she was fond of gardens.

'Oh, yes.' Miss Randall looked rather wistful. 'I miss my rose garden at home.'

Caroline excused herself, saying she must speak with her aunt. Miss Randall stayed with Rosalyn, telling her about her garden and home, and asking Rosalyn about London. Rosalyn could not comprehend why Michael would object to marriage with such a lovely girl. Perhaps now that he saw Miss Randall he would change his mind. For some reason, the thought brought her little joy.

She looked up to find Michael standing next to them. Engrossed in conversation, she had not heard the men enter the drawing room. He greeted Rosalyn and then turned to Miss Randall. 'I hope London is to your liking, Miss Randall.' His voice was polite.

'Oh, yes. Everyone has been very kind.' She smiled but Rosalyn could see nothing in her manner suggesting she regretted the loss of Lord Stamford as a potential husband. She rose in a graceful movement. 'I must speak to my cousin, if you will kindly excuse me.'

Rosalyn looked away, not certain what to say. 'Miss Randall is very lovely and quite charming.'

'I am delighted,' he said coolly. 'You seemed to be enjoying yourself at dinner.'

'Oh, yes. I very much like your brother. He has so many interesting stories about the places he has travelled.'

'Does he?' His voice was so terse, she stared at him in surprise.

'Is something wrong?'

'No,' he snapped. He looked at her for another disconcerting moment, and then frowned. 'I've located James.'

'Have you? Where is he?'

'He is at the races at Newmarket. He went with Lord Coleridge and several others.'

'Lord Coleridge?' Rosalyn's spirits which had been momentarily lifted, fell. Rodney Coleridge was a dandy and a wastrel and hardly the sort of young man she wanted James to be with. But what had she expected? 'I see. Thank you for your trouble.'

'It was no trouble.' He continued to look at her as if he were displeased.

'Michael, is there something wrong?'

'Lord Stamford, I must have a word with you.'

Startled, they both turned to see Lady Carlyn next to them, lips pursed. She tapped Michael's arm with her fan. 'I am quite disappointed. I would have thought by now that you would have persuaded her to be more reasonable.'

Oh, no. Did her grandmother have to bring this up now? Rosalyn wanted to drop through the floor.

'Lady Carlyn, I am at a loss,' Michael said with a little bow in her direction.

'Your wedding. I cannot possibly believe you wish to wait until autumn. Not when you've been in such a hurry to bring her to heel.'

'Grandmother, please,' said Rosalyn frantically.

'Well, it is impossible to do a thing with you. I thought perhaps Stamford could talk some sense into you. She never knows what is best for herself, particularly in these matters.'

Michael glanced at Rosalyn's face, which was by now hot with embarrassment. He looked bemused. 'If you'll excuse us, I would like to have a word alone with Rosalyn.'

'Of course,' replied Lady Carlyn, flashing Rosalyn a triumphant smile.

He led Rosalyn to a small study near the drawing room and closed the door, then turned to face her. 'What the devil is that all about?'

She avoided his eyes. 'It is nothing to signify. She cannot fathom why we don't wish to marry right away. I cannot persuade her we would rather wait until autumn.'

He looked completely astonished.

She smiled slightly. 'Don't worry, my lord. I plan to cry off at the appropriate time. I have no intention of marrying you in the autumn or any other time.'

'I have no fears on that score, my dear. I am quite

aware of your thoughts on the subject.' His voice was so cool, she flushed.

Then a rueful smile lifted his lips. 'I supposed it never occurred to me we would actually be asked to consider a wedding date.'

She sighed. 'Nor did I. Not until Lady Spence brought it up. She and my grandmother thought a wedding in six weeks would be most appropriate.'

He stared at her. 'Six weeks! Good lord! What did you say to that?'

'I was so taken aback I hardly knew what to say. I told Lady Spence I would prefer autumn as it is my very favourite season. The leaves are so pretty, you know,' she said with a wry smile.

'Of course. Did she accept that?' he asked. His mouth twitched.

'She had no objections. But Grandmama does not like it. She thinks we should be married immediately. She is horribly tenacious once she gets an idea in her mind. One is almost compelled to do as she wishes just to be left alone.'

'Riding you pretty hard, is she?'

'Yes.'

'Don't trouble yourself about it any further. I will handle your grandmother.'

'No, I cannot let you do that.'

'Why not?'

'It is just…' She floundered, not knowing quite how to explain how she felt. 'I don't want to hide behind you.'

'Hide behind me? What in the devil are you talking about?'

'I am not completely helpless. I have been man-

aging Meryton. And before that, I managed my husband's household. I am perfectly capable of controlling my grandmother. I don't want you to interfere in
everything I do.'

'I'm not trying to interfere. I am trying to make
this situation easier for you.'

'There is no need to do so.'

'I am responsible for you.'

Her mouth fell open. 'Responsible for me?
Whatever gives you that idea?'

'You are betrothed to me. Therefore, you are my
responsibility.'

'I am not betrothed to you! I am pretending to be
betrothed to you.'

He scowled and folded his arms across his chest.
'I will not argue that point with you again. You are
my fiancée until we sever our agreement. I will do as
I see fit in these matters, particularly those that concern our betrothal.'

'You mean you intend to high-handedly interfere
in my life.'

'If that is how you want to see it, yes, I intend to
do so.'

'Well, really! I have nothing more to say to you.'
She marched towards him, intending to stalk out of
the study with as much dignity as possible.

He caught her wrist before she could pass him,
pulling her around to face him. 'But I have more I
wish to say to you.'

She glared at him. 'Is this how you intend to treat
your fiancée? Forcing her to listen to you by imprisoning her?'

He stared down at her, anger and frustration clearly

showing in his face. Suddenly a cool smile lifted his lips. 'You are right, there are more effective ways.'

Before she could even think, he yanked her hard against him, his mouth imprisoning hers. Stunned, she offered little resistance until his mouth softened on hers, sending shivers down her spine. Her mouth parted and his tongue lightly touched hers. She pushed against his chest, panicked by her own reaction.

He released her, staggering a little, his expression unreadable.

She backed away, her hand groping for the door-knob. Without a word, she wrenched the door open and fled.

Michael thrust the paper aside. Impossible to concentrate on the damned thing. The only item that caught his interest was the announcement of his betrothal. The sight of his name coupled with Rosalyn's was unnerving. He read it over at least five times.

Of course, it meant nothing. It was, after all, a false betrothal as Rosalyn kept reminding him.

And after last night, he would do best to remember that. He nearly groaned. Whatever had possessed him to kiss her again? He could still recall the taste of her sweet mouth, and the feel of her soft curves pressed against him. The memory had kept him awake a good portion of the night.

And then there had been the blasted dinner last night. He'd never been jealous of his brother before, but he was as he watched her smile and talk to Philip with an easiness she'd never displayed with him. It had occurred to Michael that Philip was exactly the sort of man she would prefer. And when she'd innocently told him how much she did like Philip, it was all Michael could do to keep himself from forbidding her to so much as glance at his brother.

Undoubtedly, it had been too long since he'd been with a woman. Some latent sense of honour kept him from taking another woman to his bed as long as he was betrothed to Rosalyn. And after last night, he was finally forced to admit, only one woman aroused more than a passing interest in him—his reluctant fiancée.

He shook himself. Involving himself with Rosalyn in any other way than business was pure folly. From now on, he'd keep his distance.

He threw the paper down and stood up, then started at the sight of Elinor Marchant in the doorway, her demeanour cold. His butler stood behind her, his face frozen in icy disapproval.

'Elinor, what a surprise,' Michael said coolly. 'And to what do I owe the pleasure of this visit?'

'Dear Michael! I have not seen you for an age!' she exclaimed, holding out her hand. The cold look disappeared, to be replaced by a charming smile. She was elegantly dressed in a pomona green gown topped by a matching pelisse trimmed in white braid. The green of the gown brought out the lovely jade green of her eyes. The low cut of her dress, almost breaching propriety, showed a tantalising glimpse of her full breasts. Michael had once found her semi-scandalous mode of dress exciting, but now he found himself comparing it to Rosalyn's prim gowns. He found he much preferred his betrothed's more restrained style of dress.

'An age? That is something of an exaggeration,

since I saw you only the other night when you so conveniently backed into Lady Jeffreys.'

Elinor opened her eyes very wide. 'An accident as you surely know. Tis so crowded at these affairs.' She laughed, a low throaty laugh, and moved to touch his arm. 'You know that is not the same. I mean we have not—really seen each other.' It was impossible to mistake her meaning.

'No. I believe you made it clear last winter that you wished to sever our relationship,' said Michael bluntly.

'You mean our little quarrel? It was only a lover's tiff. I never thought you would take it seriously,' said Elinor with a little pout.

'If a lady says she never wants to see me again and wishes me to perdition, I, of course, do not question her meaning,' said Michael. He had been relieved when Elinor quarrelled with him. The stormy relationship with the dashing widow had begun to pall on him, and her departure to the north after violent words during a ball had saved him the trouble of giving her her *congé*. 'But rehashing this is meaningless—what exactly is the purpose of your visit?'

'Why, I read the most amusing thing today. I had to come to verify it for myself.'

'And what is that?'

'The announcement of your betrothal to that quiet little creature, Lady Jeffreys. I could not believe my eyes! Tell me it is not true.'

'Very true. I sent the announcement myself.'

'But how very odd! Marrying one of your flirts? Really, Stamford, whatever possessed you to do such a thing!'

Her tone was light, but the tight lines about her mouth betrayed her inner fury.

'For all it is your business, I find nothing odd in the fact I have decided to marry,' said Michael coldly. 'And Lady Jeffreys is hardly one of my flirts.'

'Really? I thought you never had any intention of marrying. And then to marry such a dull creature. She is so old! She must be at least thirty. I would have been less surprised if you had announced your engagement to a schoolroom chit. Whatever can you find to say to her? She has no conversation.'

Most of the time he reacted to Elinor's goading by pretending to misunderstand, thus turning the tables on her, but hearing her insult Lady Jeffreys filled him with cold, dangerous anger. 'I'm not sure you know what conversation is, my dear. I can't recall we had that many.'

Two spots of red appeared on her cheeks. 'Is that why you've decided to marry her? You can't get anything but conversation any other way! What a sly little thing she is. I am surprised you would be caught so easily by such wiles. Although I could almost feel sorry for her; marriage to you will be unbearable when you tire of her!'

Michael stepped towards her and Elinor involuntarily took a step back. Fear flickered in her face. 'If you were a man, I'd call you out for that remark,' he said softly, coldly. 'As it is, I suggest you leave. You may show yourself out. I will not trouble Watkins with you. And by the way, I trust there will be no more accidents to Lady Jeffreys's person.' He turned his back to her in dismissal and picked up the paper.

When he heard the door open, he looked up in time

to catch the look of hatred which distorted her lovely features as she glanced back at him. She then turned on her heel and left, slamming the door behind her.

Michael stared at the closed door with an uneasy feeling. He knew Elinor's temper and capacity for revenge. The maliciousness beneath her lovely façade was one among several other undesirable qualities that made him glad to be rid of her. But what could she possibly do? He did not think she planned to murder Rosalyn or him for that matter. He dismissed Elinor from his mind.

Lady Marchant burst into her cousin's breakfast room, causing Edmund Fairchilde to grimace. He put down the cup of coffee he was about to put to his lips and raised a lazy brow. 'My dear Elinor, whatever brings you here? And in such a temper so early in the day! I cannot recall what I have done to offend you.'

'Nothing, Edmund. I must speak to you. I want your help!'

'My help? How intriguing. But do sit down, I cannot finish my breakfast with you pacing like that!' He motioned her to sit across from him. Elinor seated herself and pulled off her gloves in short angry strokes.

'Now, what has put you in such a towering rage?' he inquired.

'Stamford is to marry that creature!' exclaimed Elinor without preamble. 'How could this happen? I thought you wanted her!'

'I still do. But what is the problem? I thought you were finished with his lordship.' When she said nothing, he regarded her speculatively for a moment. 'Did you actually hope to be the next Duchess of Ever-sleigh?'

'Why not? Was it so impossible?'

'It was a long shot, my dear, even if you had played your cards right. But I'm afraid your last scene at the Oxford ball ruined your hand. Damning your lover to hell and throwing vases in public is not good *ton*, my dear.'

Elinor glared. 'And I suppose the proper Rosalyn Jeffreys would never do such a thing.'

'It is unlikely.'

'Well, I don't intend she shall ever be the next Duchess, either!'

'I hope you still don't have hopes in that direction, Elinor. I'm afraid Stamford is a hopeless cause. If you plan to regale me with tales of your loss, I shall ask you to leave as I find the topic quite boring.'

'I quite detest Stamford,' she replied coldly. 'I wouldn't take him back for all the gold in the world! No, it is revenge.'

'Ah, revenge,' said Edmund. He pushed his coffee cup aside. 'Now you begin to interest me. What do you have in mind?'

'I should like Stamford to find out his intended is not as virtuous as he thinks. That under that proper exterior beats a heart as faithless as any.' She leaned forward in her chair. 'I want you to break up their betrothal.'

'I hoped you would come up with something a bit more original. I quite intend to do so.'

'Well, how could you let it get this far?'

'My dear, Stamford holds the trump card. He has the estate. His lovely fiancée would do anything to retrieve that worthless piece of property for her brother.'

'So she is marrying him for the estate?'

'Possibly.'

'Can't you get it back?'

'I have already offered Stamford the price. He refused.'

Elinor scowled. 'I can't believe he wants her enough to marry her. He is a fool.'

'He may be many things, but he's not a fool. No, he has his reasons. However, they don't concern me.' He smiled in a way that made Elinor suddenly glad she was not his intended victim. 'I fully intend to bed Lady Jeffreys. Resistance only makes the game more interesting. And I will quite enjoy thwarting Stamford.'

'I have no idea what any man could see in such a mousy thing. And she is so prim,' said Elinor with a sniff.

'Sometimes the most prim ladies are the most challenging of all. They can be quite passionate beneath the proper exteriors. It merely takes the right man to bring it out.'

'Don't be vulgar, Edmund!'

'And what are your plans for thwarting this marriage, m'dear? Or are you leaving it entirely up to me?'

'I shall think of something.'

Edmund's mouth curled. 'I've no doubt you will. You know, of course, he will call me out. And I always get my man.'

Elinor shrugged. 'He never misses either. I dare say

you shall be quite evenly matched and it will prove
to be quite amusing.'

She was quite calm now; plans for intrigue and
revenge always had a soothing effect on Lady Elinor
Marchant. She took a dainty bite out of a piece of
buttered toast.

'You are a wicked woman, Elinor,' remarked
Edmund.

'Me? I am not wicked. I merely do not like being
insulted. I am quite nice when people are pleasant to
me.'

He laughed, pushing his chair back from the table.
'I do not wish to be rude but I must go, m'dear. I
have an appointment. Enjoy yourself.' He left Elinor
sitting at the breakfast table, her chin propped in her
hand, a secretive pleased smile on her lovely face as
she plotted away.

Chapter Nine

Rosalyn shoved the pile of bills away and sighed. She feared she would go broke by the end of this betrothal. An engagement to a Marquis was turning out to be an expensive proposition. Perhaps she should present Michael with the bills and demand compensation. Except she had the lowering feeling he would probably pay them as part of the responsibility he seemed to assume for her.

A frown creased her brow. A week had passed since the dinner party. An uncomfortable week in which she and Michael seemed to be at odds with each other. After that kiss, any fears she might have entertained that he planned to pursue more intimacies with her had been put to rest by his stiff behaviour. He was perfectly attentive in company, but he acted as if she had the plague the few times they were actually alone together.

Which was what she'd wanted all along, she tried to tell herself. Guilt rushed through her every time she thought of how she had melted against him as if she welcomed his embrace. Despite the disappointments in her marriage, she had loved John. Never had she dreamed another man's kiss could temporarily make her forget him. Worse, the kisses of a man such as Lord Stamford, a hardened rake, the antithesis of all that John had been. Unfortunately, she had a difficult time remembering that.

'Rosalyn?'

She looked up. As if her thoughts had conjured him, Michael stood in the doorway. In his hands he carried a parcel. Flustered, she rose, pushing a tendril of hair aside. 'I didn't expect you today.'

He advanced into the room. 'I had no idea if you would be home.'

'I have a mound of bills to pay as you can see. I thought I should do that.'

He came to stand in front of her desk. 'Are you managing?'

'Oh, yes.' She was embarrassed as she remembered her earlier thought. Certainly she did not want him offering her money. 'I have just been putting them off. Paying bills is very tedious. Is there something you wish?'

'I have brought you a replacement for your ruined gown.'

Her eyes flew to his face. 'There was no need for that. I cannot accept it.'

He set the parcel on the desk. 'You must. I had it made especially for you with Caroline's advice. Open it.'

'But it is not proper.'

'How can you be certain? You've not yet seen it. It is a very proper gown.'

'No, I mean it is an improper gift. I cannot accept such a thing from you.'

He lifted a brow. 'Must you always argue, my dear? I wished to replace the gown that was ruined. I told you I would do so.'

'The gown was hardly new.'

'Rosalyn. Are you going to open it or not?' He sounded as if he was fast running out of patience.

He was in one of those exasperating moods where argument was futile. With unsteady hands, she undid the string and lifted the lid. Her breath caught at the sight of the lace-trimmed, pale pink satin bodice with its delicately puffed sleeves. With gentle hands, she lifted it from the box. The skirt consisted of a lacy overdress over a white satin slip. She stroked the silky material, thinking it was the most beautiful gown she had ever seen.

She looked up to find Michael watching her. 'Do you like it?'

'It is beautiful.' She laid it back in the box. 'But I cannot accept it.'

He made an impatient movement. 'If you don't wear it, then no one will. Caroline claims she cannot wear that shade of pink. And it is not suitable for my younger sister.'

'I see.' She looked back down at the gown. John had never had a gown made up especially for her. It seemed to speak of an intimacy between Michael and herself which did not exist. But Caroline had helped him. Usually men did not solicit their sisters' help in choosing gowns for a mistress, did they? Why must he always confuse her so? Nothing he did seemed to fit in the mould of proper behaviour.

'Now, what is it? Will you accept it?'

'Yes, thank you.'

'Will you wear it?'

'Well, yes.'

'Then I will expect to see you wearing it tonight.'

'Tonight?'

He raised a brow. 'Why not? You are planning to attend Miss Randall's coming-out ball, are you not? You and she seemed to have become fast friends.'

'Of course I will be there. But I had planned to wear a...a different gown.'

'You don't like it.' His voice was flat, almost as if he were disappointed.

'Oh, but I do! I don't think I have ever seen a lovelier gown.'

'Then you object to it because it is from me.'

She sighed. 'No, not precisely. It is such a personal gift. I know you wish to replace my other gown, but I cannot help but feel very peculiar about it. If I was married to you, it would be different. I would be much more comfortable if you had brought me a bouquet of flowers, or perhaps some sweetmeats. A dress seems the sort of thing you would give to a...a...'

'Lady of easy virtue?'

'Well, yes.' She coloured.

His lips twitched. 'I beg your pardon. I see we have been speaking at cross-purposes. I was merely looking at it as part of a business arrangement, and you have been worrying about the propriety of accepting a gown from a man you are not permanently attached to.'

Her mouth opened in amazement. 'What do you

think I have been trying to tell you? I told you it was not a proper gift!'

He looked slightly abashed. 'I wasn't thinking of it as a gift.'

'I quite understand that now.'

'Will you wear it tonight?'

She looked up at him with a faint smile. 'Yes, if only so you won't glower at me the entire evening.'

'Do I glower at you?'

'When you want your own way. Sometimes you fold your arms and raise your brow in a particularly haughty fashion.'

'I had no idea I was so intimidating.'

'I dare say you cannot help it. I imagine it comes from your being the son of a Duke and used to having others jump to do whatever you wish.'

'A most devastating reading of my character. However, I cannot see that you jump at all to do my bidding.'

'I try not to, but in the end you generally prevail.'

He appeared genuinely surprised. 'Do I?'

'Yes, my lord, you do.' She was torn between laughter and exasperation. Sometimes, when he forgot to be so aristocratic, he actually was quite human.

Her breath caught as he suddenly levelled a devastatingly attractive grin at her. 'I can see I must do something to right matters. Would it help if I put myself at your bidding? I am completely at your command.'

'I…I fear I wouldn't know what to do with you.'

'I could think of a few things,' he suggested with a wicked smile.

'Really, my lord!' Colour rose up into her cheeks.

This betrothal would be so much easier if he wasn't such a flirt and always attempting to make her blush.

'What is wrong?' he asked innocently. 'I was merely thinking of doing an errand or two, or perhaps delivering some messages. Or I could carry parcels for you.'

She shook her head, wanting to laugh. 'You are quite ridiculous! I don't think you would want everyone to think I considered you a…a sort of footman. It would ruin your reputation.'

'I wasn't aware I still possessed much of one. However, it would be worth losing what little I have in order to see you smile at me like that.'

'Oh.' The smile faded from her face, as awareness flared between them. She looked away from his suddenly intent gaze, confused by the emotions he was arousing in her.

'I will be off, then.' His now cool voice made her look up. He picked up his gloves and with a slight nod, strode away without another word.

By the time Rosalyn arrived with Lady Carlyn, the ball was in progress. They had been late due to a misplaced necklace Lady Carlyn was determined to wear, followed by a spot on her cloak which necessitated looking for another wrap. Nearly an hour had passed by the time they were underway. Rosalyn would have been happier to stay at home, but she did not want to miss Helena's ball.

After they were announced, Lady Carlyn declared her intention of joining some friends in the card room. Rosalyn drifted towards the edge of the ball room to stand near a group of matronly chaperones in turbans and headdresses. She wore the gown Michael had brought. The fit was perfect and, as she had viewed herself in the looking-glass, she was forced to admit she had never had a gown more becoming. The soft pink colour set off her dark hair and made her pale ivory complexion glow.

Much to her relief, Lady Carlyn hadn't asked where she had purchased the gown, merely saying she had never seen her look so charming. Rosalyn wondered if Michael would think the same, then mentally shook herself for caring what he thought.

Where was he anyway? She searched the crowded ball room and finally spotted him leading Helena on to the floor for a quadrille. His dark head bent towards hers as he spoke, and she responded with one of her lovely, unaffected smiles. The music began. Helena danced as gracefully as she did everything, moving through the steps with Michael as if they were made for each other. And they looked charming together, Rosalyn thought with an odd pang.

She turned away, sudden fatigue washing over her. Perhaps she would join her grandmother in the card room. She started to make her way there, only to be stopped by an acquaintance of Caroline's, and then by a friend of her grandmother's. She finally escaped only to nearly slam into Lady Marchant who was leaving the card room.

'I have never properly congratulated you on your engagement,' Lady Marchant said. She ran her eyes over Rosalyn as if hoping to find some fault with her appearance.

'Oh?' Rosalyn gave her a polite smile and attempted to move past her.

Lady Marchant also moved, neatly blocking her escape. 'How did you ever manage such a coup as to persuade Stamford into marriage? He has been extremely adept at evading the matrimonial trap all these years. Everyone is quite amazed that you managed to pull it off. And in such a short time.'

Rosalyn looked into the lady's coldly smiling face. So many people had said the exact same thing to her since her engagement, she was suddenly out of patience. As if she had trapped Michael into this betrothal, particularly when circumstances were so much the opposite. She was tired of smiling politely at the notion that it was such a miracle she had managed to bring him to heel.

'That is not precisely how it happened, Lady Marchant. I did not persuade Michael to marry me, he persuaded me to marry him. I really had no intention of ever remarrying, but Michael can be very persistent when he wants something.'

A flash of anger quickly came and went in Lady Marchant's eyes.

'Really? That is more in Stamford's style. He always enjoys the hunt, but I should warn you that once he catches his prey he becomes bored. Until that point he can be very charming. I'm not certain he would make the most comfortable of husbands, but perhaps you know what you are about.'

'I quite understand Michael.'

'Do you? Then perhaps you aren't quite as naïve as you appear. As long as you are willing to overlook his indiscretions I am certain he will allow you yours.'

Rosalyn stared at her, outraged. 'I have no intention of being unfaithful to my husband.'

Lady Marchant's smile held disbelief. 'Then you will undoubtedly spend many a night alone.' She gave a little laugh. 'My dear, I did not intend to distress you, merely warn you. Of course, when a woman is lying in his arms he is skilled at making her believe she is the only one. I know.'

'But then, he is marrying me.' Rosalyn was pleased to see her shaft hit home. Lady Marchant's smile vanished. 'If you will excuse me.'

Rosalyn turned on her heel, but not before she saw the malice in the lady's green eyes. She entered the card room, searching for her grandmother. Her small triumph faded when she realized she had undoubtedly made an enemy. She suddenly felt bone-tired.

Lady Carlyn, engrossed in her game, paid scant heed to Rosalyn's presence, except to ask if she cared to join them. Rosalyn, whose skills extended only as far as jackstraws, declined. She finally grew tired of watching and drifted away, wishing she could call the carriage and leave.

She wandered back to the ball room. She did not see Michael anywhere in the crowded room.

Someone touched her arm. 'Lady Jeffreys.'

She swung around to find Lord Philip behind her, elegantly dressed in a dark blue evening coat and black pantaloons. He smiled. 'My brother has been looking for you all evening. Has he found you yet?'

'No, I have not yet spoken to him. I've been in the card room.'

He laughed. 'I believe he was under the impression that was one place you would not be found.'

'Most of the time he would be right.'

'If you wish to find him, he is out on the terrace. Now that he has dutifully danced with Miss Randall, I don't think he'll dance with anyone else until he finds you. Not that I blame him,' he added, his eyes sweeping over her with admiration.

She suddenly felt happy. 'Perhaps I will go to the terrace, then.' She smiled at him, and after promising him a dance, made her way through the guests to the doors leading to the terrace.

A cool breeze brushed her cheeks as she stepped through the French doors. Lanterns spaced along the low wall terrace wall cast a dim light. She stood for a moment, letting her eyes adjust to the dark. A few couples strolled in the small garden below and a group of men stood in one corner of the terrace, their laughter carried on the night air.

She drifted in the opposite direction, not certain where she would find Michael. Perhaps looking for him was a stupid idea. Then, as she approached a large urn filled with flowers, she heard his voice. She stopped when she saw two figures in front of her, only partially hidden by the urn.

'Damn it, did you have a reason for accosting me or not? I'm in no mood for these games,' Michael was saying.

'Dear Stamford, I hated to see you here by yourself, brooding in such a poetic fashion. It is quite unlike you. But then you have hardly been yourself.' Lady Marchant's velvety tones were unmistakable.

'This is nonsense.'

'I dare say it is due to your charming fiancée.' She

moved towards him. 'She certainly keeps you on a tight rein. I'm surprised you've not yet bolted.'

Even in the dark, Rosalyn felt her face go hot. She had no desire to hear Michael discuss her with his ex-mistress or, for all she knew, his present mistress.

She started to move away, but she must have made a slight sound. Elinor glanced over Michael's shoulder. Her eyes narrowed for an instant and then she draped her arms deliberately around his neck. 'My love, I knew you'd come! Tell me you miss me as much as I miss you!' she exclaimed in a voice rather loud for true intimacy.

Rosalyn froze. Mesmerised, she watched Michael struggle to remove her hands from his neck. 'What the devil! Elinor, let go of me!'

'No! No! Not until you kiss me, my darling!'

'Are you mad?' Elinor attempted to drag his head down. Michael tried to shove her away. Elinor clung to him like a cat with its claws caught. Rosalyn gasped as he staggered backwards into the urn. He cursed. Elinor abruptly let go.

Then he saw her. 'Rosalyn?' He looked as if he'd just swallowed a vial of poison.

'I…I beg your pardon. I see you are occupied.' Her face hot with embarrassment that he had seen her, she turned and hurried away.

Inside the ball room doors she stopped, hit with the insane desire to laugh. Had Michael been engaged in a tête-à-tête with Elinor Marchant, or had she actually been attacking him? Perhaps she should have stayed and defended his virtue.

'My dear, I have been looking for you all evening.'

She spun around. Edmund Fairchilde stood at her side, a lazy smile on his lips.

'Indeed.'

'I had hoped to speak to you, perhaps steal a dance with you.'

'I can't imagine why you would think I would consent to do either after the last time we met.' She started to edge away, only to find his hand closing around her wrist.

'I understand you are looking for your brother.'

'He is at Newmarket. Please release me.'

'He was at Newmarket. He is no longer there.'

She stiffened. 'How would you know?'

He let her go. 'I am very interested in your brother's whereabouts. He owes me money, you see. I always see to it my debtors pay. Come and dance with me and we can discuss this matter.'

A little smile played about his mouth, making her think of a predator about to close in for the kill. She looked around, but no one paid them the least attention. For once, she wished Michael would suddenly appear.

As if reading her mind, Fairchilde laughed. 'I fear your fiancé is otherwise occupied. Which is one reason I wanted to talk with you now. He is a trifle possessive, is he not?'

'How much does my brother owe you?'

'Dance with me and I will tell you.'

'I don't care to dance.'

'If you want to hear about your brother, you will.' There was no mistaking the veiled threat in his voice.

With a sickening feeling, she allowed him to lead her to the ball room floor with the other dancers. Too late, she realised the dance was a waltz. 'I…I don't waltz very well. Perhaps another dance?'

'I don't believe that, not when you do everything else with so much grace.'

He pulled her on to the floor, his arm circling her waist. His breath smelled unpleasantly of brandy and tobacco. She held herself stiffly away from him, but his fingers only tightened.

He looked down at her. 'You look particularly lovely tonight. The gown brings out the colour in your cheeks.' His gaze drifted down lower, and she had the sudden urge to tug her bodice up to her chin.

She said nothing.

'It is noble of you to sacrifice yourself for Meryton. But are you certain it is worth it? I fear tying yourself permanently to Stamford will bring you nothing but unhappiness.'

'I wish to speak of my brother. How much does he owe you?'

'Two thousand pounds. But do not trouble yourself, I have no doubt his debt will be paid.'

Two thousand pounds? That was half of her income. And how much did James owe elsewhere? She looked up into Fairchilde's hooded gaze and shivered. 'Do you know where my brother has gone?'

'I don't wish to discuss your brother now. I would rather admire you.'

She tripped, stepping on his foot. His eyes hardened, and his fingers tightened at her waist.

'You are holding me too close for propriety, sir!'

'Am I? I fear having you in my arms makes me forget myself.' He did not loosen his grip.

Feeling trapped, she looked around trying to reassure herself that nothing could possibly happen in the middle of a ballroom. And then she saw Michael.

He stood near the French doors, his eyes searching the room. They fell on her. Even from across the room, she could see him stiffen. Then he pushed past a group of ladies.

She had no doubt he was coming towards them.

She glanced away, her stomach twisting in knots.

'Did I tell you how lovely you look tonight?' Fairchilde whispered.

'I…I don't feel well. I need to sit. Please!'

Fairchilde raised a disbelieving brow. The next moment a hand closed on his shoulder, yanking him back. He nearly stepped into a whirling couple, causing the lady to let out a shriek.

'I suggest you keep your hands off my fiancée,' Michael snarled. He looked as if he was about to do murder. Although the music continued, most of the dancers near them had by now halted, their fascinated gazes on the two men.

Fairchilde raised a lazy brow. 'I was merely dancing with her. Surely you cannot object to that?'

Michael stepped forward and took Rosalyn's arm in a viselike grip. 'I do object. If you come near her again, I will call you out.' His voice rang out in the ballroom which had suddenly gone completely quiet.

'This is…is most ridiculous. Michael, please.' Out of the corner of her eye, she could see her grandmother's mouth open in a horrified circle. Next to her stood Lady Jersey. For the first time in her life, Rosalyn wished she could swoon dead away.

'Lady Jeffreys is right. Do you plan to call out every man she dances with or is it only me? She did agree to stand up with me. I did not force her.' Fairchilde's eyes glinted.

Michael glanced down at Rosalyn, his mouth tight. 'I wish to speak with you in private,' he said.

His dictatorial tone, combined with the humiliation of having the entire ballroom watching, set her back up. How dare he take her to task in front of everyone?

She raised her chin. 'But I don't wish to speak to you, my lord. Please release me, you are hurting my arm.'

Colour tinged his cheekbones, but he instantly dropped her arm. She marched away from him past the crowd of fascinated guests.

She barely registered Lady Marchant standing nearby, her eyes glittering with malicious pleasure. The musicians chose that moment to strike up the next dance, causing the assembled group to disperse. Heedless of the others, Rosalyn dashed towards the tall double doors leading out of the ballroom.

Her grandmother caught up with her when she reached the hallway outside the ballroom. 'Whatever possessed you to dance with Fairchilde? Oh, dear! How could you! This is most dreadful! I never thought to see you involved in such a scene!'

To be blamed for the whole thing was the last straw! She lifted her chin and stared straight at Lady Carlyn. 'I would like to go home. Now!'

Lady Carlyn's mouth fell open, and then she closed it abruptly. For once in her life, she made no argument.

Chapter Ten

Rosalyn set her plate of toast and marmalade aside. Eating seemed pointless, particularly when the food refused to move down her throat. After last night, she doubted if she'd ever survive this nightmarish Season. She'd either collapse from lack of sleep or lack of food.

What ever had possessed Michael? Nearly brawling with Fairchilde and threatening a duel. Then speaking to her as if she were at fault in front of the entire *ton*.

Every time she thought of his high-handed behaviour, she cringed. How dare he? Especially after that scene with Lady Marchant, whatever that had been about! For all she knew, he had been having a rendezvous with the lady, not that it meant a thing if he was. If she had any courage, she would send his ring back with a curt note telling him their bargain was off. Except, he might think she cared what he did, which, of course, she did not.

Well, she had more important worries than the arrogant Lord Stamford.

Such as what to do about James. She pushed her

chair back and crossed to the window, staring out at the street. Despite the sun shining through the window, she felt cold. If he was not at Newmarket, then where was he? Had he fled from his debts? She could not believe he would do such a dishonourable thing.

Two thousand pounds. Meryton made enough to cover the mortgage and the wages of her servants, but there was not much left over. Somehow, Fairchilde must be paid. The memory of his touch made her flesh crawl. She was protected now with her betrothal, but what would happen when it ended? And what if he threatened James?

She leaned her head against the wooden shutter. Asking her grandmother for the money was out of the question. Lady Carlyn usually borrowed heavily on her income. Not to mention the awkward questions and unwarranted advice. She'd never let her grandmother know the extent of the debt her father had left. Lady Carlyn had never forgiven Lord Frederick Whitcomb for stealing her daughter away from his older brother, the Marquis of Wrotham, as she saw it. No matter that they had been blissfully happy.

Perhaps her solicitor could be persuaded to make her an advance on her income. Her glance fell to her wedding ring.

She still had her jewels.

'My lady! Look what has just arrived for you!'

Rosalyn looked up. Mrs Harrod stood in the doorway, peering around a huge bouquet of pink roses she held. She beamed. 'So lovely, they are!'

She waddled into the room, the heavy scent of roses filling the room. 'And here is a card and a small box!'

Rosalyn looked at them with trepidation, praying it was not another bouquet from Fairchilde. She took the card and opened it.

'Please accept my sincerest apologies.' It was signed in Michael's dark, sprawling hand.

'And this, my lady? Shall you want to see what's inside?' Mrs Harrod thrust the box at Rosalyn, her face eager.

Rosalyn gave the card back to the housekeeper. With trembling fingers, she lifted the lid of the box. Inside lay a gold brooch in the shape of a rose, its delicate petals glistening in the sunlight streaming through the window.

'How lovely!' Mrs Harrod exclaimed, peering around the bouquet she still held.

'Yes, it is,' Rosalyn said slowly. It was beautiful, the sort of jewellery she had always preferred, simple and elegant. And she loved roses. She hardly knew what to think, and then reminded herself it was only a gesture to keep a temporary fiancé in line. He undoubtedly had sent hundreds of gifts to women in his lifetime.

'Shall I put some roses in here? And perhaps some in the drawing room?'

'Yes, of course. That would be lovely.'

Mrs Harrod bustled away to find a vase. Rosalyn stared at the brooch, touching the delicate petals with one finger. How ironic that, just as she had decided to sell her jewels, Michael should send her such a gift.

She laid the brooch back in its box. She would return it to him, of course. As for now, she'd best go before she lost her courage.

* * *

Three hours later, Rosalyn returned. As she entered the house, Mrs Harrod informed her Lady Spence had just arrived and was in the drawing room, taking tea.

'She said she would wait a bit for your return,' Mrs Harrod said, taking Rosalyn's pelisse and bonnet.

'Oh, dear.' How could she possibly face Michael's aunt after last night?

But when she entered the drawing room, Lady Spence rose to greet her with all her usual warmth. She held out her hands. 'My dear girl, I had to see how you were faring after last night. I hope you are not too overset.'

Rosalyn took her hands. 'I am so sorry.'

'But why? It was hardly your fault that Michael decided to quarrel with Fairchilde in public. I dare say you had no idea they quite detest each other.' She sat back down, drawing Rosalyn down beside her.

'No. Oh, dear. I really did not wish to dance with Fairchilde but…' her voice trailed off. She could not tell Lady Spence why she had felt obligated to dance with the man.

'Of course not.' She patted Rosalyn's hand. Her eyes held a twinkle. 'It is probably quite dreadful of me, but I must own I was rather pleased to see Michael become so angry.'

'Were you?'

'Oh, yes. He is always so horribly indifferent to everything, I have sometimes wondered if anything ever affects him. How splendid to see him stalk forward and threaten to call Fairchilde out! Particularly in the middle of a ball room! Certainly there was nothing indifferent about that!'

'No,' Rosalyn said weakly. The resemblance between Lady Spence and her niece was suddenly quite apparent.

'And you handled him very well. I was quite pleased to see you did not let him force you to go with him. Walking away from him was just the thing to do. I have always feared he would decide to marry some meek, worshipful creature who would obey his every word.'

'I…I see.'

'I hope you will not be too hard on him for last night. I think he fears you may not wish to speak to him after the way he spoke to you in such a high-handed manner.'

'You have seen him?'

'Today. I suggested he call on you, but he wasn't sure if you would receive him.' She leaned forward and smiled at Rosalyn reassuringly. 'He really does care for you, my dear. He is rather like his father in that he tends to become most overbearing with those he cares for most.'

Rosalyn felt a deep blush cover her face. Of course, he did not, but why must he carry the charade this far? Interfering in her life, threatening duels and convincing his family he cared about her.

She didn't want that! Any more than she wanted to care about him. She moistened her lips, trying to think of something to say since Lady Spence was looking at her expectantly.

'Of course I will speak to him,' she finally said.

Lady Spence smiled. 'I had no doubt. You are a sweet girl. Michael is very fortunate.' She leaned forward and kissed Rosalyn's cheek, then stood. 'Now you must rest. You look rather pale. Poor child, I fear this has all been most tiresome for you.' She tied the strings of her bonnet, then looked at Rosalyn. 'Oh, yes, will you be attending Almack's tonight?'

Rosalyn also rose, her mind a blank. Almack's? She had quite forgotten she was to go with her grandmother. 'I believe so.'

'Very good. Then you will see Michael there. By the way, Caroline is planning a little houseparty for next weekend. Three days, I believe. It shall be a perfect time for you and Michael to be away from London, particularly in light of last night.' After giving Rosalyn a quick hug, Lady Spence departed.

Rosalyn sank back down on the sofa and rubbed her head. A houseparty? As usual after dealing with a member of Michael's warm, but overpowering family, she felt completely lost.

The thought of a night at Almack's made her groan. She supposed she must go, if only to prove to society she and Michael had not seriously quarrelled. On the other hand, she was feeling quite out of sorts with society's dictates. She really wanted to do nothing more than curl up at home and read one of the Gothic novels she'd borrowed from the circulating library.

Other ladies had headaches. Rosalyn had never stooped to using a feigned one in her life, but there was always time to start. Why not tonight?

She was tired of the pretence, tired of trying to keep her life in control. Tired of worrying about James. She wanted to escape.

With great resolution, she marched to her desk in the library and pulled out a piece of stationary. Nothing was going to drag her from her house tonight.

* * *

Michael entered Almack's, a place he never set foot in except under extreme duress.

The only reason he had come was to see Rosalyn. His aunt had assured him of her presence. But after scanning the ball room, then making his way through the other rooms, he saw no sign of her. He returned to the ball room. A young lady in a white muslin gown trimmed with yards of muslin and lace cast him a flirtatious smile. He scowled, and she fled.

'Poor Michael!' He looked down to see Caroline smiling up at him, mischief dancing in her eyes. 'I never thought to see you so lovestruck. Pacing the floor, waiting for your beloved. Why, just now, Lady Jersey was remarking on how tame you've become, with the exception of last night, of course. She said that could only be put down to how far gone you are.'

He raised a brow. 'I am hardly lovestruck, my dear.'

'And cross! That is another sign. Men are always cross when they're in love.'

No scathing remark leapt to his mind, unless he wanted to deny he was in love with Rosalyn. But since he'd fully intended to create the impression he was, he'd only be cutting his own throat. How in the devil had he gotten himself in this muddle?

Caroline glanced towards the door. 'Lady Carlyn has just arrived. But I don't see Rosalyn with her. I do hope nothing is wrong, Aunt Margaret was quite certain she would be here tonight.'

He nearly bolted from Caroline and made his way across the room to where Lady Carlyn stood with his aunt. Was she ill or merely avoiding him?

Lady Carlyn eyed his approach with a disapproving

expression. 'I suppose you wish to know where Rosalyn is. She is at home with a headache. A headache! She has never had one in her life! I dare say it is all because of that business last night.'

'She looked quite pale when I saw her earlier,' Lady Spence said. 'I have no doubt she is not particularly well. Although I had hoped she would be here, as I fear her absence will be noted.' She gave Michael a cool glance. 'I take it you did not deliver your apology in person.'

'I sent her flowers and a note,' he said stiffly. He had no idea why he felt it necessary to defend his actions.

'I suppose that was a start,' Lady Carlyn said. 'Although I think she must be quite overset. She was not receiving any visitors when I called. Her housekeeper informed me she was resting. I have never known her to rest during the day! I remember when I visited her when John was alive. She had the most severe cold. She insisted on seeing to the household management even though it was obvious she was quite ill.'

'Confound it,' Michael said. He scowled. 'Very well, I will call on her now and apologise. Does that please you?'

'Michael! Really!' Lady Spence exclaimed. 'This is hardly the time!'

'I only hope she will receive you,' Lady Carlyn added.

'She will.' He gave them a baleful glance and stalked out.

Rosalyn stared down at the pages of her novel, *Bungay Castle*. Unfortunately, the trials of the heroine failed to distract her from her own troubles, which seemed just as complicated as poor Roseline's, only not quite as improbable. With a sigh, Rosalyn closed the volume.

She glanced up at the clock ticking on the mantel. The hour was nearly eleven. Perhaps she should go to bed, but because of her long afternoon nap, she no longer felt tired.

The rap on the door startled her. Who would be calling at this hour? She rose, setting her book aside, and pulled her shawl more firmly about her shoulders. She was dressed in an old cream gown and had not bothered dressing her hair, only tying it back from her face with a ribbon.

She heard Mrs Harrod's voice outside the drawing-room door, then a very familiar masculine voice. She froze. Whatever was Michael doing here? She had an absurd desire to hide, but unless she dived behind the sofa, she hadn't a prayer. The door opened. He came into the room. One look at his dark, forbidding face made her wish she had hid.

She stood. 'My lord! What you doing here?'

He scowled at her, the low light of the lamp making him look even more saturnine in his evening clothes. 'I could ask you the same. After waiting for you at Almack's, I was informed by your grandmother that you were so overset by last night's ball you had taken to your bed.'

'Why ever would she say that? I was resting when she called but that was merely because I slept rather poorly last night, and then I did not...' Her voice trailed away at his raised brow. No doubt he was angry because she was not keeping up the pretence of dutiful fiancée very well. 'I am sorry. I should have gone to Almack's, but I was terribly tired and the thought of another assembly with everyone staring, then trying to smile and talk as if nothing mattered, was too daunting. I thought I would stay home and read.'

He moved into the room. 'And you did not see fit to inform me? After last night it was imperative that we be seen together.'

'Perhaps, but I am not accountable to you for my every move. And I was not the one who chose to create such a…a ridiculous scene. If you are here to rip me up about that, then I would like you to leave.'

'I have no intention of ripping you up.' He took a step towards her and stopped. 'Damn! You are right. I came here to apologise to you, and instead I behave badly. It was only…' He paused and frowned at her. 'Will you accept my apology for causing you such distress last night?' he asked stiffly.

'Yes, of course.' She twisted her hands together. 'But I don't understand why you were so angry. I know you do not like Fairchilde, but the dance meant nothing. I have never liked him, but I did not know how to refuse him.'

'I don't want him near you. He's dangerous.'

She stared at him, taken aback by the harshness in his voice and face. She pushed a strand of hair away from her face, taking an involuntary step back, suddenly afraid of him, afraid of Fairchilde, and of something she didn't understand—something primitive and completely out of her depth.

He said roughly, 'There's no need to look at me in

that fashion. I did not mean to frighten you. But I must know, what did he want from you?'

'Nothing.' He looked as if he could do murder. She dreaded what would happen if she told him Fairchilde had asked her to be his mistress.

'Are you certain?'

She turned away from him. 'Of course. But this is the most insane thing! Such melodrama is hardly necessary. I could perhaps understand if I was really your fiancée, but even then, such behaviour would not be called for. I am not certain what you think Fairchilde will do.'

'He is completely unscrupulous when it comes to women and to getting what he wants. He will stoop as low as he wishes without regard for anyone.' He took her by the shoulders and turned her to face him, looking into her eyes. 'He indicated once that he had an interest in you. I had thought our announcement would be enough protection. But if it is not, I will not hesitate to call him out. I will protect what is mine.'

'This is ridiculous, my lord. I will not have you fighting a duel because of me. And I am not yours, may I remind you!'

'Yes, you are,' he insisted, his features set in stubborn lines. 'As long as you are engaged to me.'

His dark, handsome face, hovering so close above hers, was rendering her dizzy. Her gaze fell to his firm lips, and for an insane moment she remembered his kiss. What would she do if he kissed her again? She heard his quick intake of breath and knew he was as affected as she. She was jerked out of his grasp, attempting to regain her senses.

'If you call him out, I will break off our agreement.

I will not have you putting yourself at such risk, nor do I want such a scandal on my behalf.'

His eyes locked with hers for a moment, then a slight smile lifted the corners of his mouth. 'I am accounted a deadly shot, my dear. But it is gratifying to know you are concerned for my neck. I was under the impression you often wish me dead.'

'Wish you dead? How ridiculous. I find you extremely provoking, but that does not mean I want you dead.' And especially not now, with him standing there, that half-smile on his face that made her heart beat much faster than it should.

'I am relieved to hear that,' he said softly.

She cast about in her mind for a safer topic. 'Thank you for the roses and the brooch. It is so very beautiful, but it was not necessary for you to go to so much trouble. I assure you, I was not planning to break our agreement over last night.'

'Is that the only reason you thought I sent it? To placate you?' He sounded almost offended.

'No, I...I really did not know what to think.'

'I wanted you to have it. I was waiting for the right time to present it to you. It is a mere trifle, but when I saw it I thought of you. I thought you might like it.'

'Oh. I do. It is very kind of you.' That had not been a particularly safe topic. She was becoming more confused by the minute. Not even John had given her such a beautiful ornament merely because it made him think of her.

'Not at all. I am happy it pleases you.' His gaze studied her face in a way that made her aware that they were quite alone.

Her mind was blank, she could think of nothing to say.

Even more disconcerting, she was completely aware of him, the broad shoulders beneath his dark black coat, the thickness of his hair, his strong masculine features.

'Is something else wrong?' he asked.

'No! I am just rather tired. It is very late.' Why must he stand there watching her with that peculiar look as if he wished to read her soul?

'Is that a hint for me to leave?'

'I suppose you must have other things to do.'

'Such as what?'

'Don't you usually go to a club or…or something?' What else did men do? Visit their mistresses? She could hardly ask him that.

A sardonic smile lifted his lips. 'Since I've met you, my dear, I've spent most evenings attending some damnable function or another. In fact, Caroline informed me tonight that Lady Jersey declares me quite tame.'

'That is hardly my fault. I haven't asked you to attend all of those da—functions! In fact, I would be quite grateful if you would go back to doing whatever it was you did before you met me. Perhaps I could have a bit of peace and some sleep.'

'I believe we've had this conversation before, my dear.' He folded his arms, a sure sign, along with the drawl in his voice, he was going to become even more difficult. 'Spending my evenings at White's will hardly convince my family I hold you in affection.'

She felt unexpectedly hurt that he considered her nothing more than an inconvenience. 'I am beginning to question why this charade is even necessary,' she told him coldly. 'Miss Randall is a most superior young lady in every respect. And you certainly seemed to get along very well with her last night. I have no idea what possible objections you could have towards marrying her.'

If anything, the expression on his face grew even darker. He stalked towards her, causing her to back up against the sofa.

'So you think I should marry Miss Randall, do you?' he snarled. 'I suppose you cherish some hope I'll release you from this arrangement early and you'll be rid of my presence.' His hands came down on each side of her, imprisoning her against the back of the sofa. His dark eyes impaled her. Blood rushed to her head, and she prayed she wouldn't faint. 'I have no interest in Miss Randall. I have no intention of releasing you from our engagement. Furthermore, you will spend as much time in my presence as I deem necessary in order to carry out this betrothal.'

His gaze fell to her lips, his eyes darkening. He brushed a strand away from her face, and she knew he was about to kiss her. She shoved him with all her might. Caught off guard, he staggered backwards.

She beat a hasty retreat behind the sofa, then glared at him. 'Not if you intend to browbeat me in such a revoltingly high-handed fashion, my lord. I pray you will go, or I…I will call my housekeeper. She is very dangerous with a broom!'

He stared at her as if she'd taken leave of her senses. For a moment, she thought he intended to strangle her, but instead he snatched up his gloves and beaver hat.

'A threat to inspire fear in any man's heart,' he drawled. 'You will ride with me tomorrow in the park.'

'I have other things to do.'

'You will be here and ready.'

He turned on his heel and stalked out. She stared at the door, her heart racing furiously. She couldn't remember being so livid in her whole life. Her entire body seethed with anger. She felt like throwing something at the door.

She sank down on the sofa, trying to calm herself. What was wrong with her? What did she care what he thought of her? Why should it matter whether he viewed her as a means to an end or not? He was nothing more than that to her.

As her anger dissipated, she wanted to cry. The carefully constructed wall she'd built around her emotions seemed to be collapsing around her. And the destruction was all due to him.

Chapter Eleven

Michael reined Faro to a walk. He'd hoped a hard ride through Hyde Park would clear his head after last night. Unfortunately, letting his horse run at a full gallop only increased his headache.

No doubt because of his excesses at Fallingham's after leaving Rosalyn last night. He swore. Faro's ears twitched. Somehow she'd managed to pierce through the cool indifference he'd displayed to the world. He couldn't remember the last time he'd felt angry enough with a woman to lose his temper, much less threaten one to do his bidding. Reluctantly, he acknowledged it was because with most women he was quite aware of having the upper hand in the relationship.

But not with Rosalyn. She made it quite clear last night she wanted nothing to do with him, that she only suffered his company because of their bargain. He'd felt that peculiar hurt again when she told him to leave and then he'd blown up at her.

The damnable thing was he wanted her to like him. Several drops of rain fell on his bare head. The grey overcast sky reflected his sour mood. He best get home before he was caught in a downpour.

Watkins opened the door to him. Michael strode past him, only to stop as his butler cleared his throat.

He turned. 'Yes?'

'I have a message for you. I think it might be of a somewhat urgent nature.'

Michael took the note from Watkin's hand. It bore the mark of one of London's jewellers, Compton's, an establishment he occasionally frequented. He had no idea why they would contact him; his bills were always sent to his agent. He perused the contents, then crumbled the note. 'Damn!'

'My lord?'

'Never mind.' He turned and dashed up the staircase to change. Whether Rosalyn liked it or not, she was going to see him now.

But she was not at home. Mrs Harrod, a fount of information where he was concerned, told him she intended to do a bit of shopping and perhaps stop at Hookham's. 'And I will say, my lord, that she appeared a bit overwrought. Great big circles under her eyes as if she hardly slept, poor lamb. I hate to say much, but it's my belief her brother is in a spot of trouble.'

Michael thanked her and decided to head for Compton's in Bond Street. He emerged a half-hour later, after instructing Compton where to send his purchases, more determined than ever to track down Rosalyn. His next stop was at Hookham's library.

She was there, dressed in a grey pelisse, standing

in front of a shelf, thumbing through a book. She did not notice him until he spoke from behind her.

'You're devilish difficult to find, my dear.'

She jumped, the book tumbling from her hands. Her eyes widened in surprise, then a cool expression settled on her features. 'What are you doing here, my lord?'

'I wanted to speak to you.'

'Indeed. I am certain it can wait until later. I am busy now.' She turned back to the shelves in dismissal.

'What I have to say cannot wait until later.'

She gave him an icy glance. 'As far as I am concerned, it can. I am not at your beck and call every hour of the day or night, no matter what you may think.'

He touched her arm. She flinched. 'I don't think you are at all,' he said quietly. 'Will you at least look at me?'

'I am certain I will be forced to do that later.'

'Rosalyn. Look at me.'

She pulled another book from the shelf and determinedly flipped through the pages.

'Then I will be forced to follow you around until you do.'

She finally turned. The expression of martyred resignation on her face was not encouraging. 'What is it you wish, my lord?'

'I wish to talk to you.'

'And I wish to borrow some books. You will have to wait.'

'Very well.' His glance fell to the one at her feet. He bent and retrieved it. 'Is this one you want?' Then he saw the title. He snorted. '*The Libertine?* Is this the sort of thing you read?'

'Give it to me, my lord.' She held out her hand, her face turning pink.

'No.' He thumbed through the volume, a passage catching his eye. '"…a deadly chill crept through her blood, a universal weakness trembled through her frame, her mouth became parched, now her cheek turned of an ashy paleness…"' He looked up and grinned. 'Fascinating prose.'

'Please!'

For some reason, the discovery the prim Lady Jeffreys read Gothic novels delighted him. Even more rewarding was watching her cool composure crumble. His ill humour evaporated. He raised a brow. 'And here I thought you read only elevating literature. History, Hannah More's tracts and the like. This is a most enlightening side to your character.'

'Stop it! What if someone hears you?' she said in a fierce whisper. She looked mortified as she glanced around the library.

No one was near them, but he moved closer to her just the same. 'They'll just think I'm reading you love poetry.' He lowered his voice.

She walks in beauty like the night,
Of starry climes…

'Don't! Michael!'

'Ah! You've finally remembered my name!'

'Why are you being so difficult?'

'For the sole purpose of watching you blush.' He

grinned, pleased at the results. She looked utterly discomposed. 'Do you want this book?'

'No! I have changed my mind. I don't want any books.'

'Perhaps another day,' he said kindly. He took her arm. 'Come with me. I have something for you.' After setting the book back on the shelf, he propelled her out of the library.

In front of the library, she stopped and looked up at him. He saw she looked pale and tired. 'What is it you want?' she asked.

'I need to talk to you, Rosalyn,' he said quietly. 'We can't do it here on the street in this rain. I am taking you home.'

'Home?'

'My home.' He looked around. 'Where is your footman?'

She flushed. 'He has the toothache.'

'And I suppose your abigail is occupied elsewhere.' He took her arm again and led her down the street. 'You seem to be woefully lacking in servants.'

'I really don't need very many.'

He glanced down at her. 'You should at least have enough to make your life comfortable.'

'My life is very comfortable,' she said stiffly. 'At any rate, I cannot afford to keep on a retinue of servants to meet my every whim.'

Unlike himself. His father was one of the wealthiest men in England. He'd never had to worry about the lack of money for servants or anything else he'd desired. He had no idea what it would be like to worry about money.

But one thing did puzzle him. They arrived at his

carriage and he helped her in. After instructing the coachman, he settled in across from her. 'Why are you not staying with your grandmother, Rosalyn?'

She looked out the window for a moment and then turned to look at him. 'Because then my life would not be my own. I want to live by myself and come and go as I please. I don't want to be beholden to anyone.'

Her words surprised him. Not only were they coming from a woman, which was extraordinary enough in his experience, but that they so much reflected his own philosophy. He had spent most of the last ten years avoiding any sort of entanglement that might endanger his independence. His position shielded him from ever becoming financially beholden to any man. But what he had avoided was the other kind, the more dangerous sort, the kind that might mean he could no longer call his life his own. An entanglement that would mean his life was intricately tied to another's.

He looked at the woman across from him. Whether he wanted it or not, her life had become intertwined with his. And he had no idea how to stop it. Worse yet, he wasn't certain he wanted to.

Rosalyn had no idea why she was sitting in Michael's carriage, allowing him to take her to his house without protest. She must be more tired than she realised. Perhaps if he hadn't been so…so nice, she would have worked up the energy to argue with him.

Nice? It was hardly a word she would associate with the arrogant Lord Stamford, but that was what he had been. His unusually quiet manner had broken down her resistance.

Her gaze fell on him. Not that he hadn't been his usual commanding self. No one would ever think him anything but arrogant with the strong, stubborn line of his jaw and the proud tilt of his head.

The carriage halted in front of his mansion. She shivered a little, recalling the only other time she'd been here. If she had known then how bound up in her life the Marquis of Stamford would become, would she have ever come? She had no answer.

The footman had flung open the doors. Michael helped her out, and then took her arm. He hurried her through the rain and up the steps. His butler opened the door.

'Lady Jeffreys will be staying for luncheon,' Michael said.

'Very well, my lord.' He turned to Rosalyn. His stiff face creased in what appeared to be a rare smile. 'May I offer my profound congratulations, Lady Jeffreys, and tell you on behalf of the rest of the staff how pleased we are that you are to be wed to Lord Stamford.'

'Thank you. That is very kind,' Rosalyn replied, taken aback by the sincerity in his eyes. She would have thought, after the first disastrous visit, that he would have quite disapproved of her.

'Come.' Michael allowed her to proceed him up the winding staircase, past numerous portraits of ancestors in wigs, swords, and jewels, to the first floor. Instead of showing her to the drawing room, he took her into the library. She looked around at the dark-panelled room with its shelves of books, instantly liking the warmth of the room. A fire burned in the grate.

'You may wish to remove your bonnet and pelisse,' Michael said. When she hesitated, he added, 'I did not bring you here to rip it up again, if that is what worries you.'

'No, it is just…perhaps I should go home.'

'After we eat. I missed breakfast so I will confess I'm quite ravenous. And I would prefer to eat with company.' A slight smile lifted his mouth. 'I hope you don't plan to suggest I eat at my club.'

She blushed. 'I am sorry. I really did not mean to insult you last night.'

'Have you ever noticed we spend an inordinate amount of time apologising to each other?' he asked.

He was definitely in a most peculiar mood. Neither angry, nor teasing, he seemed to actually want to talk to her.

'I suppose it is because we argue so much. I have no idea why.'

'Neither do I.' He watched her while she removed her bonnet and pelisse with shaky fingers and then indicated a wing chair near the fire. 'Come and sit.'

She hesitantly sat down, wondering what he wanted. He took the chair across from her. The warmth of the fire combined with the steady beat of the rain made her feel warm and drowsy. She forced herself to say, 'What is it you wished to speak with me about?'

'This.' He pulled a small box from his waistcoat pocket and rose. He held the box to her. She took it, after glancing up into his now-expressionless face. 'Open it.'

She did, and then her heart stopped. 'Where did you get it?' she whispered.

'The same place where you sold it as well as your other pieces. Compton's.'

She stared down at her beloved locket. 'But…how did you know?'

'Compton sent a note around informing me you had sold some jewellery.'

She looked up at him with a frown. 'He had no business doing so.'

'He correctly thought I should know. Why did you find it necessary to sell your jewellery?'

'I…I have some debts to pay.'

'Whose debts? Yours or your brother's?'

She looked down at her lap. 'I will pay you as soon as I can.'

He made an impatient sound. 'Rosalyn, the money means little to me. Tell me why. Has James been gambling again?'

She took a deep breath. 'It…it is for an old debt. The creditor wishes to be paid. He is making threats.'

'And who is this creditor?' His gaze was suddenly alert. 'Is it Fairchilde?'

She stared at him. 'Yes.'

'Rosalyn, how well do you know him?'

'He came to Meryton once. I only met him again when I came to London.'

'Rosalyn, why did you stand up with him?' he asked, his voice quiet.

She rose, knotting her hands together. 'He said James was not at Newmarket and if I wanted to know where he was, I would stand up with him. He…he said he always sees to it his debtors pay.'

'Is that all he said?'

'Isn't that enough? I have no idea where James is! I don't know what he owes anyone! And I am worried he…he means to harm James!' Her voice broke.

'Rosalyn, he won't harm James.'

'How can you know that? He…he is despicable.'

'Because I won't let him.' He spoke with such calm assurance she believe him. He frowned. 'Why didn't you come to me instead of selling your jewellery?'

'I didn't think it was—'

'My concern.' He took two steps away from her, then turned. 'When will you get it through your head that you are my concern? I am responsible for you until this damn betrothal is over.'

'But I don't want you to be responsible for me. I…I can manage.'

'You are not managing very well, my dear. How much is his debt?'

'Two thousand pounds. Michael, really, there is no need to worry. As soon as I give the money to Fairchilde it will be over.'

'You're not paying Fairchilde, I am.'

'Michael, this isn't necessary.'

'Yes,' he said ruthlessly. 'You're not going near him. And you will tell me if Fairchilde approaches you again for any reason.'

The vehemence in his voice left her speechless.

Two footmen entered the room, one carrying a heavy silver platter. Michael stared at them for a moment as if he had no idea who had invaded the room. He snapped into motion, directing the servant to set the tray on the massive library table. The footmen then set a smaller table in front of the fire, arranging the two wing chairs on either side.

Michael turned to Rosalyn. 'Shall we eat?'

Without looking at him, she took her place.

After the footmen efficiently set out appetising plates of assorted cheeses, cold meats, pickles, bread, fresh peas, and tarts, Michael dismissed both servants. They departed on silent feet, leaving Rosalyn wondering what to say next.

She stole a glance at Michael. He appeared to be contemplating his wine, a shock of dark hair falling over his brow. She swallowed, the cosy atmosphere suddenly too intimate.

He finally looked up at her, his face serious. 'There is one more thing. About Lady Marchant. Despite what you may think, I was not meeting her that night. She was...' A dull red colour rose up his neck.

'Attacking you?'

'In a manner of speaking, I suppose.' If anything he looked even more disconcerted. He looked back down at his wine glass as if desperate to down the contents, then lifted his eyes to hers. 'She is not my mistress.'

'I see.'

'Well?'

'I was sorry I did not stay and offer my assistance.'

He appeared startled. 'Were you?'

'Yes, but you were managing quite well,' she told him reassuringly. 'I imagine it must happen quite often.'

'No,' he said curtly, then scowled.

She could see he was embarrassed. 'I am sorry. I wished to tease you a little.'

A rueful look crept into his eye. He finally gave her a slight grin. 'The whole evening was a damnable mess.'

'Yes.' His hesitant smile and the lock of hair falling over his forehead made him almost appear vulnerable. She quickly looked away, before she gave in to the urge to smooth the hair from his brow.

'I hope you eat something,' he said. 'My cook will be on pins and needles wondering if the future Marchioness approves of his cooking. He's rather temperamental. I should hate to have him threaten to leave if your plate comes back untouched.'

'I had no idea a future Marchioness had so many responsibilities.'

He grinned at her, his face relaxing. 'Unending, I'm afraid.'

She sighed. 'I fear I'm ill suited to the role. I will most likely do something to disgrace you.' She thought of the accomplished Miss Randall, the epitome of grace and poise, who would make a most admirable Marchioness.

'You are doing splendidly.'

The warmth in his eyes brought a blush to her face. Completely disconcerted, she picked up her fork. 'I...I had better eat, then. I should hate to be responsible for your losing your cook.'

She ate a few bites of chicken and then looked up to find Michael's eyes fastened on her face. 'You may tell me it is none of my business, if you'd like. Why haven't you remarried?'

She started, spilling a drop of her wine. She was silent and then said after a moment, 'I have not thought much about it. I suppose I don't really care to marry again. I still miss John.'

'So you were fortunate to have a love match?'

'Yes,' she said a little sadly, for it had been despite everything. 'I was very much in love with my husband. I had read some of his work; my father very much admired him, but I had never met John until Father invited him for dinner one night. He was visiting a neighbour of ours. He came every day after that and after a fortnight we were engaged.'

'I see. So you do not think you will fall in love again?'

'No. I really don't want to fall in love again.'

He looked at her quizzically. 'Why not? Most people do.'

'It is much too painful to love someone and have them leave you. I will not go through that again. No, I shall never fall in love with anyone,' she said firmly.

He still watched her in a way that made her feel vulnerable. She said lightly, 'Now it is my turn to ask a question. Why are you so reluctant to marry? Surely you will need to some day.'

'So I have been informed.'

'You have not answered my question.'

'Very well. I'll tell you. I have yet to find a woman I want to marry.'

'But is it so difficult? I am certain you have had many ready to fall at your feet.'

'Yes. But I don't necessarily want someone at my feet.' He smiled slightly. 'I don't have any particular set of qualities. I suppose I have always hoped I would meet someone the way you met Sir John and know I wanted to marry her.'

She eyed him with surprise. She never would have guessed he was a romantic. 'You want to fall in love,' she said gently.

'I suppose you think that is quite ridiculous?'

'No, it is not. But even love does not ensure happiness. Sometimes two people can love each other and still live as strangers.'

'Is that what happened in your marriage?'

The penetrating look in his eyes scared her. She had never talked about the reality of her marriage with anyone.

She started to deny it, but found she could not lie to him. 'His work was his true passion, and I cannot blame him for that. I knew when I first met John that it meant everything to him. I had never known anyone with such dedication. That was one of the things I admired most about him. But I thought there would be more time for us. I expected too much from him and it made us both miserable. I was not the wife he needed.'

'Perhaps you expected too much from a man such as Sir John, but you can hardly be faulted. I attended one of his lectures once. He was brilliant. But I could see, even in that short time, how single-minded he was in his purpose. It would be difficult for such a man to give much of himself to anyone. Perhaps he was not the husband you needed.'

His words stung. She had told herself that John had been the only man for her, from the first night she saw him, so handsome and fair and cool, sitting across from her at her parents' dining table. She had fallen in love with him then; he resembled her girlish dreams of a romantic knight. All her mother's cautions against marrying a man so much older had gone over her head. And even in their four years of marriage, as she felt her dreams fade away, she had persisted in her belief that any unhappiness she experienced was from her own foolish desires. It had never occurred to her, until now, that she had may have been wrong.

Tears welled up in her eyes. She set her wine glass down and looked away.

'Rosalyn, I am sorry.' His voice was rough.

She stood up, only to find him in front of her.

His arms came around her, pulling her to his chest. She could not help the tears that coursed down her cheeks on to his coat. His comforting hand stroked her hair. She struggled to gain control of her emotions before she made a complete cake of herself. But it was difficult to pull away from the safe haven of his embrace. No one had held her in such security for years.

But her need for comfort was rapidly overpowered by her awareness of him. His scent was clean and masculine. The strong beat of his heart sounded in her ear. The feel of his hard, muscled body against hers was causing a warm languid sensation in the pit of her being. She pulled abruptly away from him.

'You must think I am a veritable watering-pot,' she said. 'I…I hate to cry. It is just with…James…I am so worried…and Fairchilde…and…' She swiped futilely at her eyes.

He lifted her chin and wiped her eyes with a handkerchief he produced from his pocket. 'Don't worry so much. I'll find James for you. And you'll both be safe from Fairchilde, I promise you.'

'Oh, Michael…' Tears sprang to her eyes again.

'Don't cry,' he said roughly.

'No.' She pulled away, dabbing at her eyes with the handkerchief he pressed into her hands. 'I am fine.'

Trying to clear her head, Rosalyn glance up at the clock on the mantelpiece.

'Oh, no! I had no idea of the time!'

'Is there a problem? You don't turn into a pumpkin or some such thing, do you?'

'That was only the coach,' she said distractedly. She stood up. 'I have been with you over two hours.'

'I see. You are limited as to the amount of time you can spend in my company. An hour at the most?' He watched her with a careful expression.

'It is not that. I do not think it is very proper of me, and we are here alone. Not that you…' She stumbled to a halt, not certain what to say.

His face relaxed. 'Very well. Although our betrothal and your widowhood allows us to stretch the bounds of propriety.' He set his wineglass on the table near the fire. 'I'll call for the carriage and escort you home.'

'That is not necessary.' She wasn't certain if she wanted to be shut up with him in a carriage, even for only a short distance. Her emotions were too close to the surface, too connected to him.

'I want to do it.'

He helped her on with her pelisse and then picked up the box with her locket. 'By the way, I'll return the rest of your jewellery to you.'

She made a helpless gesture. 'Thank you. I…I will pay you. I still have the money. Of course, I must give it to you for Fairchilde.' But then she would still owe him. Perhaps she could get another advance on her allowance.

'I don't want your money,' he said coolly.

'But…'

He shot her a quelling look. 'The subject is beginning to bore me, my dear.'

They rode to her home in silence. The rain had not abated, if anything it was worse. He hurried her up the steps. Mrs Harrod opened the door, and Michael followed Rosalyn into the hallway.

She looked at him uncertainly. 'I don't suppose we are going to ride in the park today?'

His mouth quirked. 'I'm not so much of a taskmaster I'd force you ride in a flood. Will you be at Lady Lavenham's tonight?'

'Yes. With my grandmother.'

'If we are seen there engaged in amicable conversation, all rumours of a quarrel should be put to rest. However, I hope if you change your mind, you'll let me know before I show up. I have no desire to listen to her daughters mutilate various pieces of music for a lost cause.'

'Michael! What a dreadful thing to say!'

He grinned, unabashed. 'But true. You'll see for yourself.' He took her hand, raising it to his lips. 'Until tonight, Rosalyn.'

A shock ran through her at the light pressure. She managed to smile. 'Thank you for the luncheon, and for everything else.'

'Of course.' He stared down at her, looking rather hesitant. 'Caroline is having a houseparty over the weekend. She said she will send you an invitation. Will you come?'

'I...I had planned to. I received the invitation today.'

He gave her a brief smile. 'Good.' He departed.

Rosalyn went to her bedchamber, and sat down on her bed. She lifted the locket from its box, staring down at the beloved, familiar piece. Instead of thinking of her mother every time she saw it, she would now think of him.

Chapter Twelve

Rosalyn peered out the window as the coach rounded the final bend of the lane that led to Longburne Hall. She fought back the bout of nervousness assailing her at the first glimpse of Lord Hartman's primary seat. Certainly it was a lovely house. Built of mellow red brick, it sat in the midst of a large park as if growing there. Clumps of trees surrounded the park. The green, rolling hills in the distance made her think of the peaceful countryside around Meryton.

She settled back in the coach. For once in this betrothal she wished her grandmother was close by. But no, Lady Carlyn had declined the invitation, saying she was certain Rosalyn would do well to have a little time alone with Michael's family. 'After all, they will be your family, dear. I won't always be around to guide you.' Apparently she decided Rosalyn was unlikely to bolt surrounded by his family.

Perhaps she could avoid spending too much time alone with him. After that day in his home, where she had made a fool of herself by crying all over his coat, and forcing him to act as her knight-errant, she had tried to conduct herself with as much dignity as possible. Unfortunately, his very nearness made her shaky as if she was coming down with some illness. But perhaps he would spend most of his time shooting and riding and staying up all night playing cards as men usually did at house parties.

'How pretty it is,' Helena Randall said, breaking into her thoughts. Helena, Rosalyn, and Caroline had shared a coach on the three-hour trip from town. 'I do look forward to leaving London for a few days. 'Twas very kind of you to invite me.'

'I thought you might like a respite from all your suitors. However, I fear I could not exclude all of them,' Caroline said with a wan smile. She had grown increasingly pale as the journey progressed and spoken less and less. Rosalyn worried she had been taken ill, but Caroline insisted she was fine.

Helena sighed. 'I must admit I never knew a London Season could be so tedious. I sometimes think I will say something quite…quite rude if I hear one more compliment on my violet blue eyes! I wish for once to have a sensible conversation!'

The coach entered the carriage sweep, hooves clattering on the paving stones. Liveried footmen sprung out of nowhere to fling the doors open, then helped the three ladies descend to the walk in front of the house. Rosalyn paused and stared up at the house. Four shallow steps led to a terrace in front of the long windows.

Rosalyn followed the others up the steps, feeling hot and sticky in her carriage dress, and waited by one of the columns flanking the entrance as the other carriages arrived. One carried Lady Spence, Elizabeth Markham and her mother, and Miss Randall's nearly deaf great-aunt. The other chaise carried Caroline's sister-in-law, her husband and an enormous number of trunks and bandboxes.

The other men had decided to ride and now stood by their heated mounts. The riders fared no better: beads of perspiration covered their foreheads, and the fair Lord Brighton's face had turned an alarming red. Charles was mopping his brow with a handkerchief. Only Michael appeared comfortable. Some time during the trip he had removed his riding coat. Rosalyn watched him retrieve it from Lady Spence and shrugged himself into it. He handed his big bay over to a groom and headed for the house.

Rosalyn turned, and hurried through the portico, wanting to avoid him. Ever since that afternoon with him, his very nearness made her edgy.

Caroline appeared next to her. 'Rosalyn, are you well? You looked rather odd for a moment.'

'I feel very well. It was nothing at all.' She looked at Caroline's pale face. 'But I fear you are the one who is ill. You were so quiet on the journey. Are you certain nothing is wrong?'

Caroline gave a little laugh. 'Oh, no. It is just...' She took Rosalyn's arm. 'I am certain I will be better now that we are here.'

'Perhaps you should rest for a bit.'

'You are sweet to worry. It is nothing at all.'

'Rosalyn is right. You should go to your chamber,' Lady Spence interrupted. 'I will take care of your guests.'

Caroline turned to Rosalyn. 'Will you come with me?'

'Of course.'

They stepped around Caroline's sister-in law, Lady Cummings, who was engaged in a heated discussion with the housekeeper.

She followed Caroline up the curved staircase, with its elaborate wrought-iron railing, to the first floor and then down a long corridor. Caroline halted in front of one of the doors. 'I must show you your room.'

'I think we should go to your room first.'

'I am feeling much better. Come and see.'

Rosalyn stepped inside the room. 'How lovely!' The panelled walls were a soft shade of apricot. A light breeze fluttered the muslin curtains and through them, she caught a glimpse of blue sky and green hills.

'I instantly thought of this room for you. It reminds me of you. It will be yours until you marry, and then I imagine Michael will want you next to him.'

Rosalyn could not control the blush that stained her face. Whatever ailed her? One would think she were a young virginal miss who coloured at the mere mention of the marriage bed, not a widow. Besides, she was not even planning to marry Michael.

Unfortunately, Caroline never missed a thing, particularly when it came to romance. She hugged Rosalyn and laughed. 'You are still so shy when it comes to my brother! It is delightful and one of the reasons I like you so well! How refreshing for all of us after all the women who have thrown themselves at him.'

She plopped down on the damask bedcover and patted the place beside her. Rosalyn sat.

The sparkle had returned to Caroline's eyes. 'And I never thought to see him in love! It has quite changed him. He actually seems quite human now! I sometime tease him about being in love and he turns red.'

'Oh, dear,' Rosalyn said

'Oh, no! It is true.' She gave Rosalyn another smile. 'And I have something else I wanted to tell you. Only Aunt Margaret knows and Giles.' A slight blush stained her cheeks. 'I…I am increasing.'

'Oh, Caroline! How wonderful!' This time, Rosalyn hugged her and then released her, catching Caroline's hands. 'No wonder you looked so awful in the coach. That must have been dreadful with all the jostling!'

'Well, yes. At least I didn't cast up my accounts.'

Rosalyn laughed. 'Very true. But I do think you should rest.'

Caroline rose from the bed. 'And so should you. After that, we will have luncheon. You would think I wouldn't want to eat, but sometimes I feel so ravenous!' She gave Rosalyn a fond smile. 'I will send my maid to help you undress.'

After Caroline departed, Rosalyn sat back on the bed. Oh, why must his family be so delighted with her? And they were so kind, so pleased she was to be part of their family. Rosalyn had always wanted a sister to confide in and love, and she could think of no one she would rather have than Caroline.

Why couldn't Michael remain the cynical, uncaring lord, pursuing other women and neglecting his fiancée? Then it would appear she had a valid reason for jilting him. They would undoubtedly think her the most callous woman alive when she broke off the engagement, particularly if he still maintained this pretence of caring for her.

She never considered it might not be a pretence at all.

The soft voice of the maid roused Rosalyn from a drugged sleep.

'My lady? Lady Hartman wishes me to inform you that luncheon is being served on the lawn. Perhaps this dress would be suitable?'

It took a minute for Rosalyn's groggy mind to register the gown of cream muslin sprinkled with small dark green flowers the maid held up for her inspection.

'That will be fine.' Rosalyn sat up, trying to clear her head. 'How long have I been asleep?'

'Not more than three-quarters of an hour, my lady.'

It felt like much longer, but the sun had not moved from when she first shut her eyes. She heaved herself up from the bed, dressed only in her shift and petticoat.

The little abigail, who could not have been more than eighteen, made short work of tying the ribbons of her gown, expertly brushing tangled locks, and pulling Rosalyn's hair into a high knot at the back of her head. She stepped back, pronounced Rosalyn lovely and then departed in a great hurry.

Rosalyn located her gloves and a flat straw hat she was particularly fond of. Her belongings had been unpacked and hung neatly in the mahogany wardrobe.

She found it rather unnerving to think she could sleep so soundly while someone unpacked her belongings without arousing her.

She stepped out into the hallway and made her way down the staircase. A footman sprang forward as she reached the grand entry hall. She followed him through the large drawing room and out the French doors to the terrace. Laughter and talk drifted up from below. The rolling expanse of lawn stretched out before them, gently rising to a knoll where Rosalyn caught a glimpse of a summer house in the shape of a classical temple among the trees. A small lake lay beyond that.

She crossed the lawn to join the others underneath the trees. Servants were still bringing out food. Long tables groaned with mounds of chicken, fresh peas, baskets of fresh fruit, strawberries with fresh cream, luscious peach tarts.

Several people she did not recognise had joined the group from London. Rosalyn spotted Michael standing with Charles and Giles. He must have been watching for her as he immediately excused himself from the group.

'Caroline says you have been resting. Are you not well?' Michael said, as he reached her side.

'There really is nothing wrong. Only a little tired, that is all.' Her pulse fluttered at the concern in his voice.

'Perhaps you should still be resting.'

She laughed a little shakily as she glanced up into his face. 'It is hardly that serious. There is nothing wrong with me.'

'I am glad. I worried the heat affected you. Those

coaches can be like riding in an oven. What would you like to eat? I shall fetch you a plate.'

'A plate? I don't know. Anything, I suppose.'

He smiled down at her, his face relaxed and teasing. 'Then you're at my mercy, my lady. You may find us a place to sit.'

Small tables and chairs had been set up under the trees. Blankets were scattered about the grass for those who wanted to sit on the ground. Rosalyn chose one of the blankets spread under a towering oak and carefully seated herself on it, arranging her skirts properly over her knees.

Glancing up, she saw Helena stood nearby with a rather uncertain expression on her face. 'Would you care to sit with us, Helena?' Rosalyn asked.

'Thank you.' Helena sank gracefully down beside her. Her simple dress of white muslin emphasised her serene beauty. She smiled at Rosalyn.

'Miss Randall!' Lord Brighton, a thin young man with a carefully cultivated air of Byronic tragedy, hovered over them. He carried two plates of food. 'Are you certain you should be sitting on the ground? I should hate to have you catch a chill. Young ladies with their delicate constitutions cannot be too careful. It would be especially tragic if the fairest flower of the season should lose its bloom.'

'I never catch chills,' Helena replied in a voice that was decidedly peevish for such a soft-spoken young lady. Then an arrested expression appeared in her eyes. 'Oliver?'

A young man in a bottle-green coat and buckskin breeches turned at her voice. 'Helena, what are you doing here?'

'I have been invited by Lady Hartman for a few days.' Rosalyn was amazed to see a blush rise in her cheeks. 'How did you come to be here?'

'I'm putting up with Richard Blenkham. His estate runs next to this. What luck to see you here! Your sister asked me to look you up when I arrived in London.'

By now Lord Brighton was openly glaring at the interloper. Oliver glanced in his direction and an amused expression crept into his eyes. 'Mind if I join you?'

'That would be very nice,' Helena said. Her eyes lit up with pleasure.

He settled down on her other side. She smiled shyly at Rosalyn. 'Lady Jeffreys, may I present Mr Oliver Redding. He is a neighbour of my grandfather's.'

'I am pleased to meet you,' Rosalyn said. She liked his open, intelligent face. He looked quite sensible.

Lord Brighton was less cordial at the introduction, scarcely bothering to open his mouth. Oliver seemed unconcerned at his rudeness.

Lord Philip joined them, followed by Beth and Charles. The small space on the blanket shrank even more when Michael arrived. He dropped down beside Rosalyn, and she jumped when his leg brushed hers.

'It's just me,' Michael said. He set a plate before her.

'I fear I was daydreaming.'

'How complimentary you are. I was hoping you were eagerly awaiting my arrival, and instead I find you daydreaming away amidst a crowd.' He looked around at the half-dozen people seated on the blanket.

'I see a new suitor has joined the hopeful. Who is he?'

'Michael! Keep your voice down. He is a Mr Redding, a friend of Helena's. His estate runs next to her grandfather's.'

'He's certainly putting Brighton's nose out of joint. Perhaps that will have dampened his tendency to quote poetry. Otherwise, I might be forced to forgo my food.'

Rosalyn stifled a giggle. Lord Brighton's poems were truly dreadful. He subjected them to a reading once, and it had been all Rosalyn could do to keep her countenance.

Michael grinned at her and then lowered his voice. He lightly touched her bare arm, sending shivers down to her fingertips. 'Actually, I had hoped we could dine alone. It has been a long time since we have had a tête-à-tête.'

Heat rose in her face. She kept her eyes fixed on her plate. 'Michael, please, not here!'

'Why not? It's perfectly natural for a man to want to spend a little time alone with his betrothed, don't you think?'

'I don't know. I suppose so,' she replied, uncommonly agitated. He sat so close she could feel his warm breath on her cheek. His muscular thighs were pressed against her legs. It was impossible to move away from him on the crowded blanket. She reached for her cup of lemonade and nearly knocked it over.

Michael grabbed the cup and righted it. 'Are you well, Rosalyn?'

'Oh, of course.' She brushed the hair back from her face giving him a vague smile.

'Is the food not to your liking? You are not eating much. I should hate to have you grow weak from hunger,' he said, his voice overly solicitous.

'I find it quite impossible to eat when someone is staring at me in that way.'

'I am merely concerned for your well-being. You should eat a bite of the chicken, it is quite tender.'

She glared at him. He grinned back and popped a forkful of the meat into his mouth.

Why must he bedevil her in front of everyone? At least no one paid any heed since the rest of the men, except Charles and Giles, were occupied with Helena. She stabbed at a strawberry and missed. It leaped off her plate and landed on Michael's lap.

He plucked it up and stared at the fruit before placing it reverently on his plate. 'Ah, a token of your fond affection. I will cherish it the rest of the day. Shall I carry it in my waistcoat pocket?'

An undignified giggle, bordering on hysteria, escaped her. It was impossible to do a thing with him in this mood. 'You are quite fit for Bedlam, my lord. Please don't carry it in your pocket and ruin your waistcoat.'

'Very well.' He ate the strawberry and then set his plate behind him. 'What a lovely smile you have, Rosalyn. It lights up your entire countenance.'

'There is no need to offer me Spanish coin, my lord.' Nor to fix such caressing dark eyes on her face.

'I would never pay you idle compliments, Rosalyn.'

She dropped her eyes and stared fixedly at her half-eaten lunch. Perhaps she was unwell. Uneven pulses, trembling hands, and dizziness certainly could be signs of illness.

Fortunately for her peace of mind, Lord Hartman strolled by to announce some of the gentlemen wanted to get up an informal game of cricket. Michael rose to join them.

The ladies drifted out to watch from the side, parasols raised against the afternoon sun. The day was growing warmer by the minute. The men formed up teams and soon most of them had removed their coats, and several of the more daring their waistcoats.

Watching the game begin, Rosalyn could quite understand why men running about in nothing but breeches and shirts might prove unsettling to female sensibility. She could not keep her eyes off Michael. He was dressed most improperly, and she was fascinated. In addition to discarding his coat and waistcoat, he'd removed his cravat. Muscles as lean as a cat's rippled beneath the thin cambric of his shirt. Tight buckram breeches displayed the contours of his legs and thighs to perfection. Every movement was graceful and effortless. Even the sight of black hair curling over his white shirt in pleasing contrast was most engrossing.

She forced her eyes away, scandalised by her thoughts. Ladies did not stare at a gentlemen's physique in such an assessing and appreciative manner. The hot sun was undoubtedly affecting her reason.

Caroline came up beside her, fresh and pretty in jonquil and cream-striped muslin. She grimaced. 'This will occupy them for hours. It is too hot to stand here watching them tear up the lawn. Shall we go down to the lake? It is much cooler.'

Several of the other ladies agreed. The chattering group made their way to the small lake Rosalyn had glimpsed from the house.

The temperature seemed to drop by several degrees when they reached the water. The soft green lawn sloped down to the edge and tall trees provided welcome shade. A pair of swans drifted in lazy, graceful circles.

Caroline sat down and pulled off her slippers, stockings and gloves. 'I am going wading. Would anyone like to join me?'

Lady Cummings, a plump matron of some thirty-odd years, frowned in disapproval. 'Really, Caroline! What an improper idea and most vulgar!'

'I do it all the time. Giles does not mind. Beth, Rosalyn, want to come?'

'I don't know.' Rosalyn hesitated, but the thought of dipping her bare feet in cool water was tempting.

'Yes, I will go,' she decided. She hadn't done this for years, not since her marriage. John would not have approved. She immediately felt ashamed of her disloyal thought.

Three of the other ladies also declared cooling their toes in the water was a splendid idea. Rosalyn spotted Helena standing a little way off from the others. 'Would you like to join us?'

Helena smiled. 'No, thank you. I believe I will take a walk.' She wandered off towards a wooded grove near the lake.

Rosalyn hoped nothing was wrong, but Helena seemed contented. In fact, she had appeared quite happy since Mr Redding's arrival.

She sat down and removed her slippers and stockings. The grass tickled her toes, reminding her of the sense of freedom she experienced as a girl when she would daringly go barefooted. She pulled off her gloves and then started down towards the water.

Beth stood in the water, laughing. Caroline caught Rosalyn's hand and they gingerly stepped into the cool water, giggling like a pair of schoolgirls.

'Ooh! It is so cold!' Caroline exclaimed.

Rosalyn lifted the hem of her skirt which already dripped with water. 'Of course, I would wet this the very first thing!'

Caroline took another step forward. 'I used to love to do this.' Then she slipped.

Rosalyn grabbed her, steadying her small frame. 'Caroline! Please be careful!'

'I will. Oh, no!' Caroline cried. Her bonnet had slipped from her head into the water. 'Giles will scold me terribly!'

'Oh, Caroline!' Beth exclaimed. 'It is your new bonnet!'

Rosalyn dropped Caroline's hand and tried to snatch it. Her hand missed and hit the water, making small waves. The bonnet bobbed gently out of reach, its green ribbons trailing behind.

'Oh, dear,' Rosalyn said.

'Tis no matter. I can get it. I've often waded to nearly the middle of the lake.'

Rosalyn prodded Caroline out of the water. 'Caroline, no! You must certainly will not! Giles will really be furious then. Go sit down. I'll fetch it for you.'

'Rosalyn! I don't want you risking your life.'

Rosalyn laughed, suddenly feeling very adventuresome. 'My life? Caroline, I do know how to swim.'

'I can't let you. Michael will be livid!'

That decided her. Rosalyn turned and stepped back into the water. The wayward bonnet rested against the shiny round leaves of a water lily. It did not appear very far away at all. She took a few more steps and then gasped as the gentle slope gave way to a deeper pocket of water. She paused and hitched her skirt nearly up to her waist.

'Be careful, Rosalyn. It gets deep!' Caroline's voice held worry.

By the time she grabbed the bonnet, the water had reached her thighs. Thank goodness the bonnet appeared undamaged except for the edges where it rested in the water.

Squeals of feminine laughter and the deeper timbre of masculine voices reached her ears. She stopped and turned to look. The men must have finished their game for they now gathered around the lake edge. Why of all times, must they show up? She undoubtedly looked like a complete hoyden.

Water soaked her skirt and the bottom of her undergarments. Damp patches spotted her bodice. Her hair, having escaped from its pins, now hung about her shoulders in wanton disarray.

The trip back seemed to take forever. Rosalyn feared she had veered off course for she kept hitting pockets of deeper water. She could hear Caroline shouting something but could not make out the words. Her tender feet, accustomed to shoes and ball-room floors, felt bruised from the rocky bed. Twice, she nearly lost her balance on moss-covered rocks.

She almost reached safety when her big toe hit the edge of a large jagged rock. She squeaked and pitched forward.

Chapter Thirteen

Strong arms encircled her, breaking her fall, and then she felt herself being pulled up against a very familiar, masculine chest. She gasped.

'What the devil are you doing? Are you trying to drown yourself?' Michael demanded.

'I can swim. There is no need to clutch me like that,' she replied, attempting to push her hair from her face. She jerked out of his grasp. Thankfully, she still held Caroline's bonnet.

He glowered down at her. 'What are you doing so far out in the water? You were nearly in over your head.'

'I wanted to fetch Caroline's hat. Besides, the water was only up to my knees.'

'I see. That does make a difference, then. I hardly think Caroline would want you risking your life to get her bonnet.'

'Risking my life?' He was as absurd as Caroline. She stifled a giggle. 'How melodramatic! I can swim in much deeper water. I only wanted to retrieve Caroline's hat before it was ruined.'

'A gardener could have fetched it. I suppose this was one of Caroline's ideas, to engage in such improper behaviour.'

She stared at him, astounded. 'Improper behaviour, my lord? Pray, what exactly do you mean by that?'

He folded his arms across his chest, looking very much like her father when he had been about to deliver a resounding scold. 'You have no stockings or shoes on. You have discarded your hat and gloves. You are not properly dressed.'

She didn't know whether to laugh or hit him. It crossed her mind they must look like perfect cakes standing in the lake arguing, but she was too irate to care. 'Really? You are not properly dressed yourself.'

'It is different.'

'I see. Men are allowed to go about half-undressed, but women cannot remove their hats without being accused of impropriety.'

'I am hardly half-undressed, my dear.'

She coolly appraised him, letting her eyes travel from the damp shirt clinging to his chest down to the point where his ankles disappeared into the lake.

'Indeed? You have removed your coat, your waistcoat, your stock and I cannot see that you have any shoes or…'

'That is enough, Rosalyn. I am carrying you back to the house. You cannot go about with your dress clinging to you in that scandalous fashion.'

'I believe some ladies purposely dampen their dresses for that very purpose.'

'Not with muddy water. And that's hardly the style I wish my fiancée to adopt.'

His tone was so pompous she giggled. His brows

drew together most ominously. He caught her wrist, yanking her towards him. She shoved him away and then watched, horrified, as he fell backward and landed squarely in the shallow water. The expression on his face caused her to fear for her life.

She gathered up her skirts in one hand and waddled out of the shallow water faster than she imagined she could move. The entire company cheered and clapped. She wanted to dive back into the lake. Except Michael was there.

'Splendid!' cried Caroline, running towards her. 'I have always wanted to do that!'

'Better not give the other ladies any ideas,' exclaimed Charles who stood near by, watching the proceedings with a huge grin.

His fiancée cast him a sweet smile. 'Now I know how to keep you in line—I'll keep a jug of water on hand.'

Caroline caught her arm, mixed laughter and consternation written on her face. 'Oh, Rosalyn! Are you quite all right? I fear this was too much trouble for you.'

'Not at all.' She thrust the bonnet into Caroline's hand. 'I think I shall go back to the house now. If I don't show up for dinner, you will most likely find my body in the woods.'

Rosalyn could hear the men teasing Michael. She had best escape now. Completely forgetting her shoes, stockings and straw hat, she nearly ran across the lawn in the direction of the house. No footsteps sounded behind her. Not that she could have heard them anyway over her pounding heart and laboured breathing.

But what would she do when she reached the house? How to explain why she was alone, without her shoes, hat and gloves, and soaking wet? Her footsteps slowed to a walk. She gazed down at her ruined gown and flushed. No wonder Michael called her improper. The damp muslin revealed every curve. Mud splattered her arms. Her bare toes were every bit as dirty and now had pieces of grass clinging to them.

She limped towards a clump of trees edging the lawn. Her tender feet were bruised from the stones in the lake bottom. Her toe hurt. She leaned against an oak, thankful for its cool shade and closed her eyes in relief, her breath coming in short, shallow gasps. It was all she could do to keep from sinking down on the ground beneath the tree. Grass stains would only compound the damage.

Her relief was short-lived.

'Rosalyn!'

Her eyes flew open. Michael stood near the tree, barefooted, his breeches still wet from the lake, his damp shirt clinging to his chest. Droplets of water dripped from his dark hair. He looked wholly masculine and completely dangerous.

Rosalyn snatched up a branch and clutched it protectively across her chest. 'Don't come near me!'

He laughed and held up his hands. 'Put down your arms. What do you think I am planning to do to you?'

'Strangle me, perhaps. Or drown me.' She eyed him warily.

He came a few steps closer. His eyes danced. 'No, no. Have no fear, you are more valuable to me alive. I would hate to go to this much trouble for another fiancée. Shall we call a truce? I will promise not to harm you if you promise not to hit me with that stick—or push me in the next body of water we come across.'

Rosalyn dropped the branch, her heart thudding as he approached. That devilish glint in his dark eyes was much more worrisome than his anger. He stopped in front of her.

'I think we both need to go up to the house. I don't want you to catch your death from a chill.' He moved closer. She attempted to back around the tree only to find his two hands pressed against the tree on either side of her shoulders, effectively imprisoning her.

'It is far too warm for that,' she said, her heart pounding again. 'Michael, please let me go.'

'I think I should extract a price for your shoving me in the lake.' His eyes strayed to her lips. His voice was low and seductive. 'What do you think?'

'I think you deserved it…I mean being shoved. You were being most objectionable.'

His hand cupped her chin. 'Are you certain?'

She slapped his hand down. 'Stop it, Michael! You are being absurd. I am not going to flirt with you! It is not part of our bargain.'

He stepped away. 'Ah, yes. The bargain. I had almost forgotten. Let me see if I recall your terms. I am not to flirt with you. We are to address each other by our titles in private. And of course, I am never to think of kissing you.'

Her breathing returned to normal. 'No, most certainly not. I am not one of your women, my lord.'

'My women? How many women do you think I have, Rosalyn?' A lazy smile played around his mouth but his eyes held a dangerous glint. He leaned against a tree.

'I…I have no idea. It is none of my business.'

'None of your business? You do not care whether the man to whom you are betrothed keeps a mistress? It does not matter to you at all?'

She backed away. 'Since we are not really engaged I cannot object…that is, I have no claim on you, no claim over what you do.' Apparently that was not the right thing to say for his brows knit together alarmingly.

He folded his arms across his chest. 'We are betrothed, my dear. You do have a claim on me. But for the moment, let us assume you are to be married to a man you loved. Would you care if he had a lady under his protection?'

'Yes, of course I would,' she whispered. 'I would not like it at all.'

'I did not think so.' He shrugged. 'For all it matters to you, I would not insult you by keeping a mistress. Nor, if we were married, would I be unfaithful to you.'

It was the careful indifference in his voice that told her she had somehow hurt him. Without thinking, she moved to his side, touching his hand. He stared at her in shocked surprise.

'Michael, I am sorry. I did not mean to insult you. It is only that everything has become so very complicated. I…I hardly know what we are to be any more.' She feared her words made no sense. 'But thank you for telling me this. I feel very honoured that you would think of me in such a way.'

He dropped her hand as if it burned him.

'Michael? Is something wrong?'

'No.' He ran a distracted hand through his hair, mussing his locks further. 'You are right. This whole bargain has become incredibly complicated. Much more so than you realise, my dear.'

He suddenly seemed to recover himself. 'But I must take you back to the house. You need dry clothing before you catch a chill.'

'I don't think that is likely. The day is so warm that my dress is nearly dry now.'

He held out his hand, and she hesitated, then placed hers within his firm clasp. She winced at the first step. He instantly stopped.

'What is wrong? Are you hurt?'

'No, not really. My feet are a little sore,' she replied and then blushed as his gaze fell on her bare toes peeping from under the crinkled, dirty hem.

'No wonder. That lake bottom is enough to cripple anyone.' Before she knew what he was about, he had swung her up in his arms.

'Michael! Put me down. I can walk!'

'Yes, but I'm afraid if I let you walk now you won't be walking for the next week. No arguments, Rosalyn. I am carrying you to your room.' His mouth quirked at her expression. 'I won't drop you if that is what concerns you.'

That was her last fear. Cradling her against his chest, he headed towards the house. She had never been carried in a man's arms before. His heart beat strongly under her ear, his masculine scent enveloped her. The fine linen of his shirt caressed her cheek. He had rolled up his sleeves; the bare skin of his arms was warm against her own. She felt completely helpless and very, very vulnerable.

She made one last feeble effort to escape him. 'I am getting mud all over your shirt. You had best let me walk before it is ruined.'

He laughed. 'It was ruined from the dunking you gave me.' He tightened his hold, gazing down at her, his dark eyes lit with a hint of amusement and something else she shied away from naming. 'I like having you in my arms. I have no intention of letting you go.'

Rosalyn flushed and buried her face in his chest. He mounted the terrace steps as if she weighed nothing at all and strode through the drawing room. Lady Spence was just descending the grand staircase when they reached the hallway. She hustled forward, followed by the housekeeper.

'Whatever has happened?' Lady Spence asked. 'Dear child, you are soaked to the skin! And where are your shoes and stockings?'

Rosalyn wanted to disappear. Not only for her missing clothing but because she realised her skirt had become tangled, exposing most of her leg to the knee. 'It is nothing at all and entirely my own doing. I was merely wading in the lake and...'

'And nearly fell in. I am carrying her to her bedchamber.' Michael's arms tightened around her.

'I suppose wading was one of Caroline's ideas,' Lady Spence said resignedly. 'I will send a maid to help you change. I shall also have her draw a bath for you.'

'No, I...'

Michael frowned down at her. 'An excellent idea.' He started up the long curved staircase.

The trip to her room lasted an age. He finally put her down inside the door. She caught a glimpse of herself in the looking glass over the chest and was dismayed at the sight. Her wavy dark hair hung past her shoulders in wanton disarray. A small streak of mud marred her right cheek.

'Oh, dear. I look so disreputable.'

Michael stepped around so he was facing her. He brushed her hair back from her face with gentle fingers. 'Hardly that. You look utterly charming. I like your hair down about your shoulders in such disarray. You are a very beautiful woman, Rosalyn Jeffreys. Did you know that?'

'No…I scarcely think so. I am really rather ordinary.'

He laughed shortly. 'Hardly that, my dear.' He turned on his heel and quit the room, leaving her staring after him.

Rosalyn stood in front of one of the tall bookshelves in Lord Hartman's library. She had never seen such a magnificent collection of books. After dinner, while the ladies had gathered in the drawing room, Caroline had pulled Rosalyn aside. 'I know you adore reading, for Michael has told me. I must show you Giles's library; it is mine too, of course, but he is the one who is always searching for old books. I would rather read another tale by Maria Edgeworth myself.'

Caroline had shown her to the library and then left, telling Rosalyn to enjoy herself. And Rosalyn had, pulling out old volumes and settling down in the comfortable wing chair near the fire to leaf through the pages.

Her gaze settled on a familiar title, *A Treatise on Rome and the Punic Wars*. The author, Sir John Jeffreys. She pulled the book from the shelf, running her hand over its leather cover. It had been the last book John had completed before his untimely death in a carriage accident. He had worked for months on the manuscript, often forgetting to eat unless she reminded him. Most nights, she went to bed alone, while he stayed up working, sometimes until streaks of morning light crept across the sky. He had promised they would take a trip together, perhaps to Scotland, when he had completed the work. Instead, he had died.

Tears pricked her eyelids. She hugged the book to her chest, not wanting to cry. She had barely been able to cry when he was killed and now she seemed to erupt into tears at the least provocation.

'Rosalyn?'

She stiffened. Oh, no, why must Michael come upon her now? He'd think she did nothing but burst into tears like some wretched heroine in a novel. And he'd probably be nice to her again. The thought made her straighten her shoulders. That was the last thing she wanted. 'What is it, my lord?' she said without looking at him.

'My lord? Are we quarrelling again?' She could almost imagine his sardonically raised eyebrow.

'No.' She turned and gave him a feeble smile. 'Did you want something?'

'Yes, you, my dear.'

'Oh.'

He peered more closely at her. 'Is something wrong?'

'No, of course not.'

His gaze fell to the book in her hand. 'Another torrid tale?'

'Hardly. One of my husband's books.'

'I see.' His face lost all expression. 'I wanted to ask you to walk with me in the garden. But perhaps another time.'

His tone of voice held the same studied indifference it had this afternoon when she'd told him his private life was none of her concern. She couldn't imagine what she'd said now that could possibly insult him. 'Michael? Did you wish to discuss something with me?'

'No.' His voice was clipped. 'I will leave you to your books. I beg your pardon.'

'A walk would be very nice,' she found herself saying against all her better judgement. 'That is, if your offer is still open.'

'Yes.' Some of the tension left his face. He waited while she replaced the book on the shelf. 'Do you need a shawl?' he asked when she joined him.

'No.'

He opened one of the tall French doors leading on to the terrace running the length of the back of the house. A light breeze, sweetly scented from the pots of flowers along the terrace, brushed her cheeks. Instead of taking her arm as a proper gentleman should, he curled his fingers around hers in a firm, warm clasp.

'Where are we going?' she finally asked.

He smiled down at her, the tension gone. 'You'll see.'

'It is rather dark.'

'On the contrary, there is a full moon tonight. Most romantic, don't you think?' He was leading her down the terrace steps.

Romantic? They had no business even mentioning the word between them. She tried to draw her hand out of his clasp, but he held firm. To make matters worse, they encountered Caroline and Giles, standing at the bottom of the stone steps, locked in a passionate embrace. At their approach, the couple slowly drew apart. Caroline's lips curved in a knowing smile when she spotted her brother, not the least bit disconcerted to be caught in such an embrace with her husband.

'Are you taking Rosalyn to the maze garden? Don't keep her away too long, Michael, or I shall send Giles to rescue her. We don't want the other guests to be scandalised.'

Lord Hartman let out a low laugh. 'You should first ask Rosalyn if she wishes to be rescued. She may not. And anyone who is mad enough to marry into your family must expect a certain amount of scandal.'

Rosalyn's cheeks flamed. It was obvious Caroline and Giles thought they were escaping for a bit of dalliance. Michael merely laughed in passing. 'Don't scare her off, Giles. She is too prone to bolt as it is.'

'Michael! Please let go of my hand,' she said as soon as they were out of earshot.

'No.' His fingers closed more tightly around hers.

'Where are you taking me?' Her voice came out more desperately than she'd intended. They seemed to be heading much too far away from the house for comfort.

'Only to see a garden.' His voice held laughter. 'Rosalyn, you need not be afraid. I assure you, I am not leading you to some secluded spot where I intend to rob you of your virtue. I do have some scruples. Particularly where you're concerned.'

She bit her lip, chagrined he could read her so easily.

Michael seemed content to say nothing as they passed through a small rose garden and then through an adjoining flower garden. The moonlight, the scents, the warmth of his hand through her glove, enveloped her in a seductive velvet cloak.

The maze lay beyond the wall of the flower garden. By now only the moon provided the least light. Except for the soft sound of their footsteps on the grass, there was silence. They could be alone on their own private continent.

The twists of the maze only increased her sense of wandering into mysterious, unreal territory. And when they finally came through a wooden gate leading to the interior of the maze, she stopped, transfixed.

The light of the full moon bathed the garden spread before them in a soft magical light, touching the pale-hued flowers with silver fairy dust. Cherubs appeared to cavort among the shrubbery and next to a small shimmering pool. Behind the pool stood a summerhouse, built in the style of a small Grecian temple. Two goddesses in ageless marble robes flanked the entry, half-hidden by a curtain of vines.

Michael broke the silence, dropping her hand. 'Caro calls it her fairy garden. Most of the flowers are white or cream, chosen to reflect the light of the moon. If you will observe, many of the shrubs are grey or silver-leafed.' He touched her arm. 'Come and have a look.'

She followed him along the small grassy path dividing the beds. He paused next to some shrubbery and bent down to touch a tall plant with lacy silver leaves. 'See, here is an artemisia. Next to it grows a white rose. And here is a…'

'Gillyflower, my lord.' Any fear she'd entertained he had seduction on his mind evaporated. She suppressed a giggle.

'Gillyflower. Of course.' He glanced at her face, and his lips twitched. 'Is something amiss, Rosalyn?'

'Oh, no. Nothing at all. Do you always come here to discuss the shrubbery?'

'I've never been here with a woman, so I had no idea what I should discuss, particularly with such a lovely woman as yourself.'

'I find that difficult to believe,' she teased, inexplicably happy to learn he had never brought another woman to this lovely place.

He caught her hand again and drew her towards the temple. Near one of the statues, he stopped and pulled her around to face him. He gazed down at her, the laughter in his face evaporating. 'Of course there are things I would rather discuss. Such as how you resemble a beautiful, untouchable goddess yourself in this white gown. And your eyes; they are so wonderfully expressive, but tonight I believe I could almost see into your soul.' His gentle hands slid up her bare arms, coming to rest featherlight on her upper flesh.

She trembled, mesmerised by his touch. Perhaps

she was a goddess, but he was a sorcerer, bewitching her with his hands, his voice, his words. His own eyes were dark and mysterious and wholly seductive.

'What…what else did you wish to discuss? Perhaps we should return to the drawing room.' Her voice was oddly breathless. She shivered, and it was not only from the slight wind that fluttered her gown.

'You're cold. We should sit.' He led her to the temple and then pulled her close down beside him on the stone bench. 'Are you warmer now?' His warm fingers trailed down her arm.

'Michael, did you have something to say to me? Something serious, that is?' she added hastily in an attempt to bring the conversation back to sane, practical matters.

'I cannot remember what it was. Your presence is much too distracting,' he murmured.

'I pray you will not flirt with me, my lord.' She stared straight ahead, hands knotted in her lap. Perhaps if she did not look at him, she wouldn't be so susceptible to his dangerous spell.

He sighed and settled back on the bench. 'Why not? It is a very enjoyable pastime.'

'I hardly consider it a pastime. I fear I do not know how to flirt anyway.'

'It is not such a difficult skill. I should be delighted to instruct you, if you would like. I am considered something of an expert.'

'Thank you, but I must decline your offer. I fear any lessons you give would be far too advanced for me.'

'We can begin with the most simple techniques and then progress to more advanced lessons.'

'Michael!'

'Very well, I won't press you.'

'I think it would be best if I returned to the house.' She leaped up from the bench, intending to put as much distance as possible between them. She was not fast enough. Michael rose in one swift motion, catching her wrists in an iron grasp, and hauled her to his chest.

'Wh-what are you doing?' she gasped.

'Capturing your hands so that you don't hit me.'

'Hit you? Why would I want to hit you?'

'Because I'm going to kiss you. Properly.'

'No, Michael…'

'I've been wanting to do this for a long time,' he said, his voice husky. 'At least here we will not be interrupted. Do you object?'

He didn't wait for her reply. His face hovered over her for the briefest of moments, his eyes holding her captive, and then he lowered his head. His lips descended on hers, and began to move in gentle exploration over her mouth as if sampling its sweetness. He let her imprisoned hands flutter free and pulled her hard against him, moulding her soft curves to his hard frame, sending frightening shivers of desire through her body.

It was nothing like his other kisses. A sensuous languor flowed through her, robbing her of every vestige of willpower. She melted against him. Of their own accord, her arms circled his neck and her hands entwined in his thick, silky hair. Under his seductive pressure, her lips parted, inviting him to more passionate exploration. She felt drugged, light-headed; her senses spun out of control as if she were becoming one with him and one with the magical moonlit night.

So this is what it is like to be kissed by a rake, she thought dazedly. Rather like drinking too much wine.

Michael came to his senses first. Kissing Rosalyn Jeffreys the way he'd wanted was proving to be too heady an experience, even for him. The delicious taste of her lips and her light, feminine scent intoxicated him. Her gentle hands tangled in his hair and the soft curves of her breast against his chest threatened to push him beyond reason. If he didn't stop now, he'd be tempted to progress far beyond mere kisses.

Reluctantly, he broke off the sweet, intimate contact and lifted his head, his eyes searching her face. Her cheeks were flushed with desire; her expressive hazel eyes mirrored the same stunned surprise that he had experienced. With gentle fingers, he reached out and smoothed her tumbled hair from her face. As if jolted out of a trance, she started and pulled away. Her hand flew to her cheek.

'I think I should return to the house now,' she said, her voice shaking. She took two steps back, moving as far from him as possible, stumbling on the shallow step. Then she turned and fled.

A light wind had come up, whipping the skirt of her gown as she dashed away, a sprite in flight. Clouds drifted past the moon, casting the garden into shadow. He started after her, fearing she would lose her way or twist an ankle.

'I had best make certain you return safely. You should not be out here alone,' he said, as he caught up with her. He made no move to touch her.

'Thank you.' She said nothing more and for once

in their acquaintance he hadn't a clue to what she was thinking. Her face was nearly as expressionless as the statues in the garden.

They retraced their steps through the dark, silent gardens without speaking. At the retaining wall beneath the terrace, he halted by a fragrant climbing rose.

'Rosalyn. We must talk.'

'Talk?' She stared up at him, her face now filled with confusion.

'Yes, I thought you might wish to take me to task or perhaps slap my face,' he said, wanting to tease the bewilderment from her face.

'No. I don't think so.' He could visibly see her attempting to retain her composure. She added distractedly, 'I have never been kissed by a…a rake before.'

He nearly laughed. 'Haven't you? How did you find the experience?'

'It was rather interesting.'

'Interesting? Merely interesting? I must be losing my technique. Next time I must make sure you find it something besides interesting.'

'I…I don't think there should be a next time. That was not part of our agreement.'

'Agreements can be renegotiated. I would be quite amenable to changing the terms of ours…' he began, but stopped when he saw the panic on her face. He was going too fast for her. He added more gently, 'We can discuss this later.'

She tore away from him. 'No, there is nothing more to say! I do not want to change the terms of our agreement. I pray you will never kiss me again!'

He caught her arm, pulling her around to face him. 'What are you afraid of, Rosalyn? Are you afraid of me? I swear I will not hurt you.'

'Please! Don't touch me. I wish to be alone.' She wrenched herself away from him and flew up the stone steps to the terrace.

Michael watched her retreating form as he leaned against the retaining wall. He ran a distracted hand through his hair. He wanted to go after her; take her in his arms and show her there was nothing to fear, but he knew that would only drive her to further retreat.

Besides, he needed time to sort out his own chaotic thoughts. Since that day in the library, he'd tried to refrain from touching her, but free from the restraints of a London ball room, he'd found it difficult. Carrying her in his arms today had pushed him to his limit. And when he found her in Giles' library, tears in her eyes over her husband's book, he experienced the fierce desire to erase all thoughts of Sir John from her mind.

He nearly groaned aloud. Any hopes he'd had that kissing her would put his curiosity to rest had vanished. Instead, his smouldering desire had burst into flames. He had wanted many women, but never with the same mixture of desire and protective tenderness that Rosalyn aroused in him tonight.

He should have known he was in trouble when he attended balls and routs only to see her, when other women held little attraction for him. When he actually found his role of fiancé a pleasure rather than the painful duty he'd always imagined. And most of all, when he was filled with the murderous desire to put a bullet through Fairchilde for waltzing with her.

He feared he was too far gone to turn back. Offering her *carte blanche* was out of the question; she was not the sort of woman he could unscrupulously take for a mistress.

He supposed there was nothing to do but persuade her to marry him.

The irony of it struck him. Wanting her for his wife was the last thing he'd planned on when he'd forced this damnable bargain on her. But fate had played his own hand against him. Amazing to find he was looking forward to the chains of matrimony, if it meant he were chained to her.

However, one small problem remained—his fiancée would rather go to the devil than wed him. He had felt her sweet response tonight and knew she wasn't as indifferent to him as she wanted to believe. But convincing her of that…that was another matter. He had until September to convince her she did want to marry again. Him.

He moved up the steps and crossed the terrace. Lights blazed from the drawing room. Inside he could see his sister and several guests hovering around a table, undoubtedly engaged in emptying each others' pockets at loo.

He needed to plan his strategy carefully. He'd need to employ all his methods of persuasion to break down her resistance. He only hoped he was up to the task.

He smiled, a smile without humour. Now that he'd finally made up his mind to take a bride, he had no idea if the lady would comply.

Chapter Fourteen

After breakfast the following day, Rosalyn wandered through the gardens near the house, finally making her way to a bench underneath a small vine-covered pergola. She sat down, the air fresh and clean after last night's rainstorm.

In the rational light of day, she blushed to think of her eager response to Michael's kisses. His touch had erased all thoughts of John or, for that matter, anything else. This was dreadful. She felt as if she were losing control not only of her life, but of her carefully protected emotions.

She leaned her head against one of the pillars. Of course he was a flirt and undoubtedly kissed many women, but why would he want to kiss her? She couldn't fathom that a man such as the Marquis of Stamford would find her desirable. But afterwards, when he had lifted his head, all the teasing laughter gone from his face, she saw he'd been as affected as she had. He desired her.

And she desired him. The revelation hit her with shocking force. She closed her eyes. Oh, heavens, how had this ever happened? Somehow her initial dislike had turned into a devastating attraction. Worse, she actually like him, liked his humour, his intelligence, his charm, his unexpected kindness. She couldn't think of a more disastrous thing to have happened. She must not, could not, allow herself to fall in love with him.

A faint rustle made her open her eyes. Michael stood near the entrance to the pergola, handsome and all too masculine in his dark brown coat and breeches. He wore riding boots and in his hand carried a crop. 'Good morning, Rosalyn,' he said.

Her pulse quickened at the lazy, intimate tone of his voice. 'Good morning.'

He moved towards her with leisurely grace. 'I missed you at breakfast. I'm afraid I didn't rise as early as I had intended.'

'None of the men were up, so you are in good company. It makes one wonder what you do all night.'

He grinned. 'Nothing of significance, I'm afraid. Play billiards. Attempt to fleece each other out of our respective fortunes. Argue over the best way to govern the country, accompanied by a half-dozen bottles of brandy, of course.'

'How fascinating.'

'Sarcasm from the sweet Rosalyn Jeffreys? What other surprises do you hold under that innocent exterior?'

'None at all.'

'May I sit?' He indicated the spot next to her on the bench.

She shot up, unnerved by the thought of having

him squeeze next to her on the small bench. 'I...I was just about to return to the house. Lady Cummings has asked if I would like to accompany her on a walk.'

'I have other plans for you.'

She stared at him. 'Such as what? Are you not going riding?'

'Yes, but with you. My day is at your disposal. Or rather your day is at mine. We're going on a picnic.'

'A picnic? I haven't heard any plans for a picnic.'

'This will be a private picnic. Just you and me.' His mouth still curved in a half-smile, but his eyes were alert with an expression she could not fathom.

She flushed. 'I really don't think it is such a good idea. And what will the others think if we go off by ourselves?'

His smile was wicked. 'They will think we wish to be private, of course. Put your mind at rest, Caroline thinks it is a splendid idea, as does my aunt. Any other objections?'

Rosalyn could think of at least a half-dozen more. But her mouth had gone dry.

'Did you bring a riding habit?' he asked.

'Yes.'

'Good. I will walk with you to the house so you can change. What sort of mount do you prefer? Caroline has offered you the use of any of her horses.'

She found her tongue. 'But I haven't said I will go with you.'

'But you will.'

'Are you always this certain you'll have your way?'

He tucked her arm through his, then turned his

maddening smile on her. 'Yes, most of the time. If I set my mind to something, I generally get what I want.'

They began walking towards the house. 'You must have been a very disagreeable child,' Rosalyn said.

'Not at all. I believe I was considered a very charming child. I learned early there are many ways to achieve an end without throwing a tantrum. Often, a more subtle approach works best.'

She glanced up at his dark handsome face and his laughing eyes with their devastatingly long lashes. She could quite imagine how that worked. She could not keep the tartness from her voice. 'I see. You wind everyone around your finger by charming them into doing what you want.'

'Except for you. I cannot see that I have been able to charm you at all.'

'I believe we agreed you attempt to intimidate me.'

By now, they had reached the steps leading to the terrace outside the drawing room. He halted and looked down at her. 'I fear we are about to quarrel again. I don't wish to argue with you, Rosalyn. Admit you will go with me, or else I will be forced to persuade you by a different means.'

'Will you? And what method is that?'

He pulled her towards him. 'This.' He bent his head. His lips brushed across hers, sending a shiver down her spine. He lifted his head, a slight smile curving his mouth.

She backed away from him, giving a quick nervous glance towards the drawing room windows. 'Michael! Don't! What if someone sees us?'

'Will you agree or not? Otherwise I will be forced to take more drastic measures.'

The glint in his eye told her he was fully capable of doing so. 'Yes, I will go, but please don't do that again!'

He grinned. 'Then go change and hurry back.'

When she returned, after changing into her bottle-green riding habit, Michael was waiting where she'd left him. Philip stood with him. He looked up as Rosalyn hesitantly descended the steps. 'I'd best be leaving. I am most certainly *de trop*.'

'You would not be,' Rosalyn said, who was experiencing a moment of panic when she saw Michael. 'In fact, if you wished to join us, I am certain there would be no objections.'

'Perhaps not from you, but there most certainly would be from another quarter. No, thank you, I don't want a quarrel forced upon me.'

'Very wise of you,' Michael said drily. He glanced down at Rosalyn, a gleam in his eye that boded no good. 'Come, my love.'

Philip grinned as he started up the terrace steps. 'You'll be fine. Just shove him in a trout stream if he misbehaves.'

Michael and Rosalyn started down the path to the stables. 'There's no need to recruit a chaperon,' Michael said. 'Are you still convinced I mean to seduce you?'

'No, of course not.' She flushed uncomfortably.

'Although I might like to.'

'Michael!'

'You are very seducible, you know.'

She nearly walked into a rhododendron bush. He pulled her away. 'Seducible? Are you implying that I am a woman of loose morals?'

'Not at all. Merely that you are very desirable. It would be quite easy for a man's thoughts to stray when in your company.'

'How ridiculous! I have never had that effect on any man in my life!'

'Not even Sir John?'

'No!' Horrified at speaking of something so intimate, she said, 'Of course, he...he thought I was pretty.'

'That is not the same as desirable.'

'Michael...'

'He was a fool if he didn't find you so,' Michael said ruthlessly. He halted and pulled her around to face him. They stood in the shadow of one of the stable buildings.

She looked up at him. 'I don't wish to discuss my husband or my marriage. John was kind to me, and I...I know he loved me.'

'Of course.' His expression softened, and he traced a gentle thumb down the curve of her cheek to cup her chin. 'But you are more than merely pretty, you are lovely and intelligent and kind, and very, very desirable.'

Oh, no! Why must he do this to her? She nearly closed her eyes, wanting nothing more than to sway towards him, feel his arms close around her. Then sanity returned. 'Shouldn't we be going?'

He dropped his hand. 'Probably.' Then he gave her a half-smile. 'Some day I plan to wipe all practical considerations from your mind.'

'I hope not.' But his words made her pulse race all the same.

The groom had the horses saddled and ready. Next to Michael's bay gelding stood a smaller chestnut horse. 'Sir Henry's as gentle as a kitten,' the groom informed her as he helped her mount.

'Although I've had some nasty scratches from kittens,' Michael said. They had started across a pasture near the stables.

Rosalyn gave him an exasperated glance as she patted the horse's neck. 'I am certain Sir Henry doesn't scratch. He seems to have a very nice temper.'

Michael merely grinned at her. She smiled back, suddenly happy to be on a horse again, enjoying the smell of the country air after so many weeks in London. The sky was a bright cobalt blue, the trees and grass had the lovely dewy freshness that followed a night's rain. The air smelled clean and pure, the birds twittered in the trees, and a pleasant breeze caressed her cheeks. With a sense of wonder, she realised she felt more at peace than she had for a very long time.

She glanced at Michael and saw he was watching her. 'You look happy,' he said.

'It is a lovely day, don't you think?'

'Yes. I don't believe I've seen you look like that before.'

'Oh.' She coloured, a little embarrassed by his scrutiny. 'Where are we going?'

He slanted a glance at her. 'There's a secluded spot near an old cottage. I thought you might like it.'

'It sounds very nice.' She stole a glance at his

strong profile and thought he also looked relaxed, as if the day pleased him.

They rode in a companionable silence. The path wound by the lake and through a stand of trees. At last, they came out of the trees to a clearing where an old two-storey brick house stood. Vines rambled up a side wall and tall rhododendrons surrounded the front door. Michael reined his horse to a halt and waited for Rosalyn to amble up on Sir Henry. 'This is the cottage,' he told her.

'It is not occupied, is it?' she asked.

'No. It once belonged to a Dowager Countess who didn't want to reside very close to her son and daughter-in-law. Caroline sometimes comes here when she wants solitude. And she and Giles often come for a day or two. It's rather sparsely furnished, but the roof is in good repair.'

He dismounted in a graceful motion and then held out his arms to help Rosalyn down. She slid awkwardly off the horse and fell against him. 'I'm sorry,' she gasped, pushing herself away.

'I'm not.'

She heard the teasing in his voice and flushed. 'Where will we eat?'

'There's a spot behind the cottage or we can eat inside. I have a key. Whichever you prefer.'

'Outside. It seems a shame to waste such a lovely day.'

He secured the horses and then took Rosalyn's hand and led her around the side of the cottage. A small overgrown lawn lay behind the building, surrounded by tall bushes and trees. A rustic stone bench sat in one corner. Michael led her to the bench. She sat down and waited, wondering what to do or say next.

'Are you hungry or should we walk first?' he asked.

'I am actually quite hungry. I only had tea for breakfast.'

'Then we'd best eat. I'll retrieve the food.'

Looking around, she saw nothing resembling a basket. 'Where is the food?'

'It should be in the cottage. There's actually a more direct route here, but the longer ride is more enjoyable. I will get it.' He turned and strode toward the cottage. Rosalyn rose and followed him.

He thrust a key into the lock and then swore when the lock refused to budge. The door suddenly gave way. A sheepish look crossed his face. 'It wasn't locked.'

'I hope this doesn't mean our picnic has been stolen,' Rosalyn said.

He looked at her, his mouth curving in a smile. 'We'll just have to find something else to do to keep our mind off food, then.' His glance drifted to her lips. 'I can think of a few things,' he added suggestively.

Rosalyn flushed in spite of herself. Keeping him at bay was going to be difficult if he persisted in those sort of remarks. 'I'm afraid nothing will keep my mind off food when I am hungry.'

'Are you certain?'

'Perhaps we should look for the food, my lord.'

He heaved a mock sigh. 'I can see you're determined to keep me in my place.'

They found the baskets in the small dining room.

As Michael had said, the cottage was furnished very plainly, but its simplicity was inviting. It looked cosy and intimate, the sort of place one might go to meet a lover.

Her thoughts made her blush. What was wrong with her? She had never thought in such a manner before meeting him. And after his words near the stable, she'd best keep her thoughts on the practical.

She helped him carry the baskets over his protests that he could do it all. She found a cloth in one of them and spread it out on the ground. After removing her hat, she sat down on the cloth.

Michael joined her, then shrugged out of his coat. He rolled up his sleeves and leaned over one of the baskets to retrieve a dish. His wayward lock of hair fell over his forehead. Rosalyn swallowed at the sight of his bare, sinewy arms and the muscles stretched taut under his shirt. Perhaps a private picnic had not been such a good idea.

He removed another dish before she started out of her trance. She couldn't sit here and gape at him. Cheeks red, she reached into the other basket and pulled out a bottle of wine and two glasses, then plates and silver.

Michael set out the last dish and surveyed the spread before them. 'Good lord! There's enough food to feed Wellington's army.'

She laughed at the expression on his face. 'As long as we don't have to eat it all.'

He uncovered a dish. 'What will you have? There is chicken, ham, cheese and pickle, not to mention a cake and tarts. Shall I serve you?'

'You served me yesterday.' She reached for a plate. 'What would you like?'

He leaned back on one elbow and grinned. 'Anything. I'll let you decide since you made me do so yesterday.'

Perhaps she should have let him serve. He watched her every move as she dished out slices of ham and chicken, chunks of bread, pickles and asparagus. The ordinary act suddenly seemed extraordinarily intimate under his half-closed eyes.

He sat up as she moved towards him. She handed him the plate, her hand brushing his as he took it. She started to yank her hand away, but he caught it, giving her a lazy, heartstopping smile. 'This is very nice, Rosalyn. I like having you wait on me.'

Her startled eyes met his. His smile deepened. 'Last night you looked like a goddess; today you resemble a lovely fairy suddenly captured by a mere mortal.'

'Michael, this is ridiculous! I…I am not a fairy.'

'But you are. Weaving a spell around me.'

'Shouldn't we eat?'

'Only if you promise not to flit away.'

'I have no intention of doing so.'

He slowly released her. 'I hope not.'

She scooted back to her side of the cloth, heart pounding, heat flooding her cheeks. What was he trying to do to her? Certainly he was flirting; there was something more dangerous, more sensuous in his manner than she'd ever noticed before.

She helped herself to the food, wishing he'd pay attention to his plate instead of to her. She sat back, hardly knowing what she'd put on her plate.

She took a few bites. The food was good, and she

was hungry. They ate in silence, the sounds of birds and the nearby stream providing a pleasant accompaniment. Finally, Michael reached for the bottle of wine. He opened it, then poured two glasses. He handed her one.

She took it, pleased her hand did not tremble. 'Thank you.'

'Not at all.' He took a sip of his wine, then set the glass down. 'Rosalyn, we need to discuss last night.'

She spilled a drop of wine, her cheeks hot. 'There is nothing to say. I dare say we were both carried away by the garden and the moonlight, that is all.'

'So you think our passionate kiss was the result of smelling the roses or some sort of madness induced by a full moon?'

'Well, yes, something like that. It should never have happened.'

He set his wine glass down and looked at her with a great deal of speculation. 'An interesting theory. And why should it not have happened? Despite your attempts to deny it, there is some attraction between us.'

'We have a bargain, an agreement. We…we can't afford to do that sort of thing.'

'Can't we?'

She made a helpless gesture. 'Michael, please! Why must you be so difficult?'

He suddenly smiled. 'Because you get so delightfully confused.' He rose in an easy movement. 'Shall we walk for a bit?' He held out his hand.

She took it, allowing him to help her to her feet. His abrupt change of subject did nothing to restore her equilibrium. At least he seemed to have decided last night was a mere aberration. Which was exactly how she viewed it.

They left the lawn surrounding the cottage and strolled towards the stream. 'Shall we sit?' he asked, indicating a grassy spot under a tree.

'Perhaps a walk would be better.'

He deposited himself on the grass and leaned back against the tree, legs stretched out before him. 'But I'd rather sit. And I don't want you wandering off by yourself.'

'I have been on my own for some years.' Rosalyn sighed and finally sat beside him, careful to avoid the slightest contact with any part of him. Not that she could keep her eyes from straying to his well-muscled thighs encased in tight buckskin breeches. Or from noticing his strong lean fingers as they plucked a blade of grass. Her whole body tingled with awareness of his masculine presence.

He suddenly turned to look at her. 'So you think our kiss was nothing more than moon madness?'

'I really do not wish to discuss it.'

'But I am curious. Shall we determine if your theory is correct?'

'No. We should not.' Her voice did not sound at all convincing as he moved closer to her. She froze as one arm circled her back. His other hand tilted her chin so he could look into her eyes. His own eyes were warm, a half-smile hovered on his lips.

'If your theory is correct, this should have no effect at all.' He bent his head and kissed her.

She should have struggled, pushed him away as his lips moved over hers. Instead, she sighed and melted into his embrace as if she'd been waiting all day for this very moment. He ran a trail of kisses down her throat, pausing to nibble the pulse at the base of her neck, then lifted his head. 'What is your conclusion?' he asked, his voice husky.

'I...I don't know.' She made a supreme effort to regain control of her traitorous body. 'Our...our agreement.'

'To hell with the damned agreement.'

This time he pulled her hard against him, his mouth crushing hers.

Her arms went around his neck, pulling him closer, knowing now she had wanted this. Her lips parted under his, allowing him entry to explore the warm recesses of her mouth. His hands came up to pull the pins from her hair and her hair tumbled around her shoulders.

He lifted his head for a moment, but only to lower her gently to the ground. He braced himself on his elbows above her and stroked her cheek. 'You are beautiful.'

She closed her eyes, the intensity of his gaze burning through her. He fumbled with the hooks of her bodice and then deftly unbuttoned the shirt she wore beneath her habit, pushing it aside. All rational thought fled when the warmth of his hand caressed her tight, swollen breasts.

His mouth moved leisurely down her neck, leaving a trail of fiery kisses. He moved lower and when his tongue swirled over a peaked nipple, she gasped and arched against him.

His shirt had come loose from his breeches. She slipped her hands beneath it and ran her hands over his smooth, bare skin, revelling in the feel of the hard, taut muscles beneath. Her touch seemed to inflame him more. He groaned and his mouth moved back to possess hers.

Then he pulled up her skirt, his hand coming to stroke the silkily soft skin of her thigh above her stocking. But when his hand moved further to touch the sensitive cleft between her thighs, he suddenly pulled his hand away and rolled off her, pulling her skirt down.

Confused and ashamed by her own behaviour, she lay there, eyes closed until she felt his hand brush her cheek. 'Rosalyn? My sweet, did I hurt you?'

She opened her eyes to find him braced on one elbow, his face hovering over hers. A lock of hair hung over his forehead and his eyes were filled with concern.

'No. Please…move,' she whispered. He did so, leaving her feeling strangely bereft. She sat up, her face suffused with heat, attempting to compose herself.

Her hands trembled as she fumbled with the buttons which refused to cooperate. How could she be so foolish? If he hadn't stopped when he did, she would have let him make love to her. Not only let him, eagerly welcomed him.

Michael leaned over and gently pushed her hands away. 'Allow me.' With deft fingers, he fastened the buttons. She stared down at his dark head, aching with the need to touch him again.

He finished and stood up, and tucked his shirt into his breeches. Then he reached down to pull her to her feet. She could not look at him, afraid to see the look of contempt on his face. She pushed a strand of hair away from her face with fingers that still shook. How was she ever going to pin her hair up? Her hairpins lay scattered on the ground. She bent down to retrieve them, only to find Michael there before her. His hand brushed hers, and she hastily straightened up.

'I had best help pin your hair up, since I was responsible for its destruction,' he said. His voice was matter-of-fact.

She finally glanced at him, stunned by his calm. He sounded as if nothing had happened between them. But then, nothing had. He had made it painfully obvious he did not want her.

'Turn around,' he said.

'Turn around?' His words finally sunk in. 'I…I can manage my hair.'

'Isn't it difficult to do without a maid?' he inquired.

He wanted to discuss the finer points of dressing a lady's hair now?

'Well?' he asked. He seemed to really want to know.

'I suppose to do it properly it can be. However, I have done it before.' She frowned at him, not really wanting to attempt to pin it up with him watching her. It seemed a curiously intimate motion. But she could hardly return to the house with it tumbling past her shoulders. One look at her hair and wrinkled habit and everyone would guess what else they had enjoyed besides the picnic.

She turned her back to him and gathered her hair up, twisting it into a knot away from her neck. The next thing she knew, Michael was behind her.

'Let me help you. You have grass in your hair.' He plucked her hands away, untwisted the knot, then ran his fingers down the length of her hair as if to comb out the tangles. She froze, the feel of his fingers sending a languorous shudder through her being. Good Lord, what was he trying to do to her?

'You have beautiful hair. I noticed that the first time I saw you.'

'Di-did you?'

'Yes.' He lifted her tresses from her neck. 'What do I do next?'

What? 'Um, I...I usually gather it into a knot and then pin it on top of my head.'

'Like this?' She felt him knot her hair, then hold it while he fumbled with the hairpins.

'Yes.' The feel of his hands in her hair was producing the most exquisite sensations. She closed her eyes, praying she wouldn't do something rash such as throw herself at him, begging him to finish what he had interrupted.

He finally dropped his hands away. 'I don't think I am particularly talented at this. It looks rather lopsided. Perhaps I should try again.'

'No!' She nearly leaped around to face him. 'I...I am certain it is fine. And after I put my hat on, no one will even notice.'

'If you are certain.' He eyed her critically.

'Oh, yes. Thank you. I think we should go. Isn't it getting rather late?' She looked up at the sky as a cool breeze brushed her cheek. While they'd been occupied with other activities, heavy grey clouds were darkening the sky. 'I am afraid it might rain.'

'You're undoubtedly right.' He didn't move. 'Do I have grass in my hair?'

'I beg your pardon?'

'I thought you would like to perform the same office for me. Pull out any grass, brush your hands through my locks, remove any evidence of our day's activities from my person.' His mouth quirked.

'No, I...I think we've done enough of that sort of thing for today.'

'Will you at least see if all the grass is gone?'

He was utterly mad. They could stand here until dinner at this rate. She moved closer to him. He did have a piece caught in his thick hair. She reached up to remove it, feeling his breath on her face. He stood perfectly still until she stepped back. 'There. It is gone. Michael, we really must go.'

'Very well.' His voice sounded peculiar again. He retrieved his coat and shrugged himself into it, then in silence they walked back to the cottage, careful to avoid contact with each other.

Chapter Fifteen

To make matters worse, the clouds began to gather; by the time they neared the stables, light raindrops had started to fall.

Michael dismounted first and then went over to help Rosalyn down. He resisted the urge to let his hands linger on her waist, but instead quickly released her. She jerked away as if bitten by his touch.

They hurried back to the house, as the rain began to pour. Michael cursed himself. What in the devil had possessed him to practically seduce Rosalyn under the tree? He'd planned to take her on the damned picnic, talk with her, flirt with her, perhaps steal another kiss, not tumble her on the ground like a wench from a tavern. Then, in his clumsy efforts to help her rearrange her clothing and hair, he'd undoubtedly made a fool of himself.

He stole a glance at her. Her face was pale and quiet, and he had no idea what she was thinking. Her hair was falling out of her hat in a charming but rather untidy disarray. He'd never be hired on as a lady's maid if that was the best he could do.

Caroline was coming down the staircase as they entered the hallway. 'I saw you coming from the drawing-room window,' she said as she reached the bottom step. 'I thought I should warn you. Papa is here!'

'Good God!'

'He arrived only a hour ago. He is most impatient to meet Rosalyn.'

'Oh, no,' Rosalyn said faintly.

Looking over at Rosalyn, Michael saw her face had lost all colour. He touched her arm. 'He won't bite.'

'Really, he will not, Rosalyn,' Caroline said with a quick smile. 'Come, you only need to change and then you'll be quite presentable.' Caroline took her arm. 'I know he will quite adore you as we all do!'

Rosalyn looked stricken. She cast Michael a helpless glance as Caroline led her away. He gave her a reassuring smile.

Then Caroline stopped and turned back to him, her eyes full of mischief. 'I suggest you change also, Michael. You have grass in your hair.'

The Duke was standing near the long French windows in the drawing room when Michael entered. By now, the rain poured down in sheets. His aunt sat on the sofa next to Helena Randall. Beth and Lady Cummings sat together at a table playing cards. They gave him a curious glance when he entered, then turned back to their game.

Eversleigh turned as Michael reached his side. Tall and erect with a harsh, handsome face, he hardly looked his fifty-some years. He was still thin after his

illness, but Michael was relieved to see his colour had
returned.

'What brings you here, sir?' Michael inquired as
he joined his father.

Eversleigh raised a brow. 'A desire to meet your
fiancée. Since you do not seem inclined to bring her
to Eversleigh, I thought I'd best come here.'

'Are you certain you're fit to travel?'

'I am not quite on my deathbed yet,' he said.
'Where is Lady Jeffreys? I have been assured she
does exist, but I've yet to see her for myself.'

'She went to change from her riding habit.'
Michael glanced toward the doors. Where the devil
was she? Nearly a half-hour had passed since they
had arrived at the house. The idiotic notion she decided to escape through a window crossed his mind,
then was just as quickly dismissed.

The drawing-room doors opened and, to his infinite
relief, Rosalyn appeared with Caroline. Dressed in a
simple rose gown, her hair now properly arranged,
she looked cool and composed as Caroline brought
her forward. Only her hand going to her locket before
she swiftly brought it to her side betrayed her inner
nervousness.

Michael performed the introductions. Eversleigh
took her hand. 'I have looked forward to this moment,
Lady Jeffreys.'

'Thank you, your Grace.' Her voice held the
faintest tremor but Michael saw she kept her gaze
steady.

The Duke released her hand. 'I hope to see you
soon at Eversleigh.'

She looked startled. Michael moved closer to her.

'Perhaps I can persuade her to come for a visit.' It might be the perfect place to continue his courtship. Without too many picnics. The very thought made his mouth go dry.

He jerked his thoughts away from the images and realised his father was speaking. 'A visit is not quite what I meant. I hope to see Lady Jeffreys there on a more permanent basis.' This time Michael started. His father fixed him with a piercing stare. 'As your wife. That is why I am here. I see no reason to delay your marriage any further. When we return to London, we will proceed with the arrangements.'

Michael felt as much as heard Rosalyn's faint gasp. He turned and saw she had gone white. She looked as if she had been sentenced to death.

A cold pit formed in his stomach. It was obvious she had no desire to marry him, not even after their passionate lovemaking earlier. Now with his father's precipitate announcement, he had little time for the courtship he'd planned.

And no matter how much he desired Rosalyn, he had no intention of having his father force her to the altar.

Rosalyn had no idea how she made it through dinner. She sat between Michael and Philip, hardly tasting the food, hardly knowing what she said. She had never been prone to hysterics or swooning, but when Eversleigh announced that plans for their wedding should be made immediately, she had thought she might faint for the first time in her life.

Now she sat in the drawing room, anxiously waiting for the men to finish with their brandy and conversation. She hoped they were not planning to stay up half the night in the dining room. She must speak with Michael.

She rose from the chair, too agitated to sit. Michael had been silent and distracted at dinner, barely touching his food. He slanted no teasing glances her way, said nothing more than what was required for polite conversation. It was as if he already wished to put distance between them. Did he fear that after this afternoon she would take advantage of his father's words and insist he marry her?

Another hour passed before the men entered the drawing room. To her dismay, Michael was not among them. She excused herself from the others, and hurried from the room. He was not in the library, nor in the dining room. Finally, she saw a light in Giles's study. She pushed open the door, and stepped inside, blinking as her eyes adjusted to the dim light.

He sat behind Giles's desk, slumped back in the chair, contemplating a glass of brandy in front of him. From the scowl on his face, he seemed to be in no good mood. Rosalyn hesitated.

He looked up, surprise registering on his face. Then he rose to his feet a little awkwardly. 'My dear Rosalyn, I am quite amazed to see you here. I would have thought after my father's surprising announcement you'd wish to avoid me like the plague.'

'I...I had wished to speak with you, but perhaps later.' He was leaning rather heavily against the desk, his dark hair disordered. 'Michael, I think you should return to the drawing room. You do not look at all well.'

He laughed. 'I am quite well. What is it you wish

to talk to me about? Shall I hazard a guess? Our forth-coming nuptials.'

'I assure you, my lord, I have no intention of mar-rying you. There is no need to drink yourself into oblivion over it.'

His eyes glinted. 'Is that what you think? The pos-sibility of marriage to you is pushing me to the bot-tle?'

'What else am I to think? I have never seen you in this mood before.'

He laughed again, but there was little amusement. 'The notion of marrying me brings you little pleasure, I take it.'

'I do not want a loveless marriage. No more than you do.'

'How do you know what I want?' He stepped closer to her. She could smell the brandy on his breath.

'I suppose I don't really know. I…I think you've had more than enough to drink.'

He advanced a step closer. 'Do you? Since you are not my wife, I cannot imagine why you would care.'

Her hand crept to her locket. She had no idea how to reason with him in such a strange, wild mood. She moistened her dry lips and tried to speak in a rational tone. 'I should not like you to wake up with a head-ache, particularly since we are to leave tomorrow.'

'Always so practical.' He seemed to swoop down upon her. He crushed her against him, his arms bands of iron around her. 'So you don't wish to marry me?'

'No!' She struggled, truly frightened of him for the first time.

'No?' His face hovered before hers, dark and angry

and passionate, and then his lips crashed down on hers, demanding her surrender. She tried to break away, then sank against him as his kiss ravished her senses, sending her into a void where there was nothing but him.

He lifted his head, his triumphant eyes glinted down at her. 'What do you say now?'

'I think you are quite drunk! Let go of me!' She struggled against his iron grip.

He abruptly released her. 'Go, Rosalyn.'

She looked at him for an instant, hurt and anger warring in her breast, and then she left him, quietly closing the door behind her.

'Very well, I will be blunt: she doesn't want to marry me,' Michael said. He slumped back in his chair and observed his father grimly. His head felt like hell after last night's drinking, he'd had little sleep, and several cups of strong coffee had done little to abate the dryness in his mouth. The morning sun streaming through the windows of the study made a mockery of his black mood.

'Indeed. Then how did she come to be betrothed to you?' The Duke's voice held little surprise.

'I forced her.'

His father raised a brow. 'How?'

'Her brother lost his estate to me at Fallingham's. She came to me to ask me to return the estate to him—she offered to pay his debts. I refused, of course, and then, based on a passing comment of Charles's decided to return her brother's estate in exchange for a temporary betrothal. I wanted to avoid marriage with Miss Randall. I was in no danger from

Rosalyn expecting the engagement to end in marriage; she had made it clear she held me in dislike.'

'I see.'

'You do not seem surprised.'

'Not at all. Margaret had already suspected as much, particularly when she met Lady Jeffreys. Your fiancée's rather peculiar lack of enthusiasm over your charms, and reluctance to accompany you to the altar, aroused her suspicions. My only question had been what you held over her head.'

Michael laughed shortly. 'Now you know. I plan to release her from the damned betrothal as soon as possible.'

The Duke gave him a considering look. 'I suggest you marry her instead.'

'I have told you, she wishes me to the devil.' Particularly after last night.

'I rather doubt that. How long was this betrothal to go on?'

'Until September. Then she was to have the pleasure of jilting me.'

The Duke smiled dryly. 'You assumed Miss Randall would be safely married by then. However, what was to prevent me from attempting to arrange another match for you?'

'Nothing.' He scowled. 'I suppose you have someone else in mind.'

'Not at all. I think you and Lady Jeffreys are admirably suited. I see no reason why you cannot use your reputed charm to convince her to marry you. I will give you until the end of this month. After that I will take matters into my own hands.'

Michael gaped at him. Less than three weeks? He

shot to his feet. 'I won't have her coerced into marriage with me.'

'I have no intention of coercing her.' The Duke also rose, signalling the interview was at an end. 'I will leave you to plot your strategy.' He strode to the door and then turned, his hand on the knob. 'By the way, there was no need for this elaborate scheme to avoid marriage with Miss Randall. If you had indicated you had such a strong aversion to the idea in the first place, I would not have forced you.' He left, gently closing the door behind him.

Michael sunk back down in the chair with a groan. His father had the most interesting ways of accomplishing his goals. If he'd decided Rosalyn was to be the next Marchioness, she would be. Unless she managed to disappear from England. Even then his father would undoubtedly find her. The thought of her joining him at the altar with that white, stricken look on her face made his throat tighten.

But if his father did have his way...afterwards Michael would take her in his arms and assure her marriage to him wouldn't be a living death, that he would protect her and care for her. Then he'd gently kiss her, and she would respond... The hardness in his loins recalled him to his senses.

What the devil was he thinking of? He rubbed his aching head and stood, then paced to the window. He had to come up with something. Only the hell of it was, he had no idea whether he wanted to persuade Rosalyn she must marry him or to spirit her away, safe from his father's reaches.

Chapter Sixteen

'I don't care if she is still abed! I will see her now!'

Rosalyn stiffened. Oh, no! What was her grandmother doing here so early? She turned over and sat up just as the door burst opened.

Lady Carlyn looked livid. In her hand was a newspaper which she brandished about. 'How could you hide this from me? Your own grandmother! Tell me it is nothing but a pack of wicked lies!'

'What is?'

'This!' With a furious finger she jabbed at a point on the paper. 'It says that your brother lost Meryton to Stamford, who is forcing you to marry him as payment! Tell me this is not true!'

'I…I haven't married Stamford yet,' Rosalyn said in a faint voice.

'So it is true! And you never told me! How could you deceive me so!'

'I did not wish to worry you. At any rate, James has Meryton back so there is no need to overset yourself.'

'But to sell yourself into a loveless marriage! And

to a rake who would take such advantage! My dear child, there was no need for such a sacrifice! You should have come to me!'

'Lord Stamford has never taken advantage of me,' Rosalyn said stiffly, offended by hearing Michael spoken of in such terms, although a mere month ago she would have said the same thing herself. 'Besides, I…I am not going to marry him.'

'Not marry him?' Lady Carlyn asked incredulously. 'You have no choice now. If you jilt him, it will only prove the story is true. I won't have it bandied about that my granddaughter had to marry as…as payment for a debt. No, you must marry as soon as possible. I will see Lady Spence about it the first thing.'

A dull throb was beginning in Rosalyn's right temple. 'I would think a marriage would only confirm the story.'

'Nonsense. It will show you don't care a fig for such gossip.' Lady Carlyn eyed Rosalyn sternly. 'I hope you do not plan to stay in bed the entire day with a fit of the vapours. We have several calls to make and a wedding to plan. St James's, I think. You cannot wear white since you are a widow, but perhaps a grey would look becoming.'

'Grandmama! No! I am not going to marry Mi— Lord Stamford. I…I don't want to marry him, and he does not want to marry me. The whole betrothal was a…a farce! He only needed a temporary fiancée and said he would give the estate back if I would agree.' There! She had finally admitted it, but somehow the words gave her little comfort.

Lady Carlyn's mouth fell open, then she snapped it shut. 'Ridiculous!'

'But it is true. So you see, we cannot marry.' Oh, no! Surely she wasn't about cry in front of her grandmother.

Lady Carlyn sighed loudly. 'It is quite obvious that he is in love with you and I dare say, if you weren't so stubborn, you would admit you are in love with him.'

Rosalyn stared at her. 'But, did you not say you thought I was being forced into a...a loveless marriage?'

Lady Carlyn smiled blandly. 'I was merely overset by the shock of reading such a thing in the paper. But, of course, I have known for an age he is in love with you, as does the whole of London. I haven't been quite so certain about you, but now I see how it is.' She patted Rosalyn's hand. 'So there is no need to worry, I shall handle all the arrangements. Perhaps it would be best for you to stay in bed. You shall need all your strength for your wedding, and,' she added with a coy smile, 'your wedding trip.'

'Grandmama, no!' But Lady Carlyn had already risen from the bed and, with a bright smile, bustled out of the room, undoubtedly to arrange the rest of Rosalyn's life.

Rosalyn slumped back on her pillows. Could this whole situation get much worse? They had returned from Longbourne yesterday. She'd had no opportunity to speak to Michael since two nights ago, when he'd kissed her so ruthlessly in Giles's study.

She felt cold every time she thought of that night. His behaviour had been unfathomable to her; she could only think he feared he would somehow be trapped into marriage with her. Yet, he'd seemed so angry when she said she wouldn't marry him.

But her grandmother's supposition that he was in love with her was ridiculous! He could not be! Lady Carlyn always saw what she wanted.

And now the article in the paper! Who would do such a thing? A trap seemed to be closing around her, and around Michael. She must do something.

She had to break off their betrothal.

Watkins showed her into the drawing room, the same one where she'd been shown the very first time she'd ever met him. Butterflies fluttered in her stomach.

Sitting proved impossible. She rose and went to stare at the portrait above the mantelpiece. Now that she knew Michael so well, she could see the resemblance in the same dark, intelligent eyes, the arrogant tilt to the head, the shape of the sensuous mouth.

Then her stomach churned in a sickening manner as she heard his familiar, firm tread. She turned as he came into the room.

He observed her with an unsmiling countenance before coming forward. 'Rosalyn, I had planned to call on you.'

'Did you?' He looked tired, almost as tired as she felt. 'I didn't know, otherwise I…I would not have called on you in such a manner.'

'Since you had no idea of my intentions, I can hardly fault you for that.' His mouth lifted slightly and then he sobered as he observed her face. 'I suppose you saw the piece in the *Morning Post*.'

She nodded and tried to keep her voice from shaking. 'My grandmother called before I had even risen. She was not very pleased.'

'I imagine not. Nor was my father.' He looked at her more closely. 'What is it, Rosalyn?'

She took a deep breath, clutching her reticule in white fingers. 'I want to break off our…our betrothal.'

'Why?'

She stared at him, taken aback by the coldness in his voice. 'Why?'

'Yes, why?' His eyes were cool and wary and he'd folded his arms across his chest in a stance she knew only too well. 'You gave your word until September.'

'I know, but everything has changed. Your father seems to think we…we should marry as soon as possible, and my grandmother…'

'Yes?'

Rosalyn took a deep breath. 'Thinks the same thing after she saw the *Morning Post*. I am afraid that if we do not stop this we…we will find ourselves married.' She twisted her hands in her locket and looked away. 'So I am releasing you from our betrothal. I plan to leave London as soon as possible.'

'If you do that I will bring you back.' There was no denying the threat in his voice. 'Make no mistake, I have no intention of releasing you from our agreement.'

'But…'

'And furthermore, you *are* going to marry me.'

She gaped at him, feeling as if she'd been struck. Was he drunk again? No, he looked perfectly sober and deadly determined, his eyes cool and impassioned. 'I...I beg your pardon?'

'You are going to marry me.'

Marry him? Bewilderment, outrage and hurt flooded through her. And then pure fury. How dare he dictate to her as if she had no say in the matter! 'Marry you? I think not, my lord. I have told you I have no intention of ever marrying again, and certainly not you.'

He stepped towards her. It took every ounce of courage she possessed not to quail at the look on his face. 'Oh, yes, you are,' he said softly. 'Even if I have to force you to the altar.'

'But why? You can't possibly want to marry me!' she blurted out.

'Because after this damned article we have no choice, unless you want a scandal attached to our association. Because my father insists I do so, and moreover—' his eyes ran over her face and deliberately down her body in a way that made her go hot all over as if he had stripped her naked '—because I want you.'

She stepped back, coming up against a side table. The colour drained from her face, leaving her dizzy. 'No.'

'I promise you marriage to me won't be the hell you seem to think,' he went on ruthlessly. 'You will have my title, and you will have my fortune at your disposal. You may come and go as you please.'

'Those things mean nothing to me,' she whispered.

'There will be money to do as you wish with Meryton, then.'

'No, it...it is not worth this.'

'Isn't it?' He came to stand in front of her, almost touching her. She stared at him, helplessly trapped by the table boring into her back. Then he bent his head towards her.

'Michael, please! Don't!' she whispered. He wasn't going to kiss her again. Not in that angry, ruthless way he had last time as if he meant to force her to his will. She had no idea what was wrong with him. She could only think he was angry that he was somehow trapped. And that he felt a physical desire for her.

He jerked back at her whispered words and stared at her face. Then stepped back, his own face pale. 'Rosalyn, damn it! Don't look at me like that. I won't ravish you.' He moved away from her, running a hand through his hair, then looked back at her. 'I promise I won't touch you after we're married. Except for what is necessary to satisfy society, we need not see each other.'

'No! It…it is impossible.' A cold pit settled in her stomach. Not another marriage of disappointment and waiting, of loneliness. With a strangled sob, she pushed past him and dashed from the room.

Elinor caught her cousin's arm as he headed towards the card room. 'Edmund! I must speak with you! Now!'

Fairchilde looked down at her and gently removed her hand. 'There is no need to clutch me like that. I fear you are wrinkling my coat. Now, what has you in high dudgeon, dear cousin?'

'He is here with her! They are dancing!'

Fairchilde looked at the dancers performing the in-

tricate steps of a quadrille in Lady Carruthers's ball
room. His gaze fell on Rosalyn and Stamford, who
were circling each other, their faces stiff and unsmiling. 'Yes?'

'They should not be! I thought by now they would
not be speaking to each other!'

Fairchilde raised a brow. 'They don't seem to be
now.'

'That is not what I meant! They should not even
be looking at each other.'

'My dear, did you really think sending that little
piece to the *Morning Post* would put an end to their
connection?'

'What I meant is I thought you would have done
something! She certainly has not fallen into your
arms!' Elinor said.

'No.' His lips curled momentarily in a harsh smile,
causing Elinor to fall back a pace. Then his usual
bland expression returned. 'No, not yet. However, tonight our delightful hostess and one of our most malicious gossips will catch the proper Lady Jeffreys in
a flagrant act of impropriety. With myself, of course.'

'Delightful!' Elinor exclaimed, her eyes sparkling
with anticipation.

'I thought you would think so.' He gave her a
mocking smile. 'So go enjoy yourself with the dull
Lord Melton and leave Lady Jeffreys to me.'

Elinor bestowed an excited smile on him and hastened away. Fairchilde watched her for a moment,
then turned his attention back to the dancers.

The dance had ended and Stamford was leading
Rosalyn from the floor. He watched as Stamford
bowed over her hand, then stalked off. Head held

high, Rosalyn moved in the opposite direction. Fairchilde smiled. It was high time to make his move.

Rosalyn touched her grandmother's arm. 'I think I will go and sit somewhere. I am rather tired.'

Lady Carlyn turned from her conversation—or, rather, her monologue—with Miss Waverly, an elderly lady who was hard of hearing and whose conversations mostly consisted of nods and smiles.

'I must admit you do look rather out of curl,' Lady Carlyn said after glancing at Rosalyn's face. 'Well, go and sit, but do not disappear for too long. I don't want everyone to think you are going into a decline after that nasty bit of gossip.'

Rosalyn gave her a wan smile and, after pressing Miss Waverly's frail hand, made her way towards the door leading from the ball room. She was not really ill—so much as she wanted to be alone.

Lady Carruthers's ball room was small and extremely crowded. Rosalyn waited for a pair of giggling debutantes in white muslin gowns to move before she was able to reach the doors. Then she was forced to plaster herself against one of the doors to avoid being slammed into by a stout elderly man in an old-fashioned bagwig. As she stepped away, she felt a tug on the hem of her skirt and then heard an ominous rip. Looking down, she saw the lace on her skirt had caught and torn away.

Could anything else go wrong today? She made her way to the circular hall. She was thankful to see an empty gilt chair. She sank down on it and then bent down to inspect the damage to her hem.

A large strip of lace and ribbons had torn away

from the satin material. She would need to call for a maid and obtain some pins to secure the lace. She straightened back up and leaned against the chair with a heavy sigh.

She would rather call the carriage and go home. The only reason she had agreed to attend this ball was that her grandmother had insisted. 'It will be most noticeable if you do not put in an appearance. Not just for your sake and, of course, mine, but Stamford's family. And, my dear, Eversleigh is in town! Why did you not mention that! He would be most displeased if you are not there!'

In the end, it was the mention of the formidable Duke that decided Rosalyn. She had no desire to have him censure her. Perhaps she could escape this nightmare by fleeing to some remote village in Northumberland. She closed her eyes. They flew open as soon as she heard her name.

She looked up to see a bewigged footman standing in front of her. 'My lady, your grandmother desires your assistance. If you will follow me.'

She shot up from the chair. 'Oh, no! Is she not well?'

'I do not know, my lady.'

Worried, she trailed him down the staircase, holding her skirt so she would not trip on the lace. She barely acknowledged Miss Markham's greeting as she passed her and another lady on the stairs. The footman showed her to a door on the first floor. She thanked him and pushed open the door.

She saw no one at first glance in the dimly lit room. It appeared to be some sort of private study. She moved further in the room and saw the sofa in one corner was empty. 'Grandmama?'

'I have been waiting for you.'

She jumped as Edmund Fairchilde rose from a chair at one side of the doorway. He stepped behind her and shut the door.

She turned, her hand going to her throat in fright and confusion. 'Where is my grandmother?'

He shrugged. 'I have no idea. In the card room, I would imagine.'

'But the footman said she was ill.' He merely looked at her and suddenly she understood. 'You sent that message?'

'Of course. I am certain you are about to ask why. So I will tell you. I have wanted to speak to you alone and this was the only way I could think of to do so.'

'I have no idea what you want to say to me. My brother's debt has been paid.'

His smile caused her to shiver. 'In a manner of speaking, yes. But I still did not get interest. That is what I want to collect tonight.'

'I have no money on me.'

'I said nothing about money. I want something else entirely. Come here, Rosalyn.'

'Let me go. I…I will scream.'

'And I will stop you before you make more than a peep.'

'What do you want?' She had no idea what to do. He was standing in front of the door, blocking her escape.

'A kiss. Nothing more.'

She could scarcely stand to look at him. The

thought of his thick lips on hers made her shudder. 'No.'

'Come here now.'

She darted a glance around the room, searching for anything she could use as a weapon. The only item remotely useful was an inkwell sitting on the desk. She backed towards the desk, keeping a wary eye on him. He moved quickly towards her. She snatched up the inkwell just as he reached for her. She darted around the side of the desk as his hand closed around her wrist.

Her foot caught in the torn lace. She tripped backwards, his hand losing its grip on her wrist. He attempted to grab her bodice but she jerked away as his hand closed over the silk rose at her bodice. It tore off in his hand, ripping the silk of her bodice. She darted around the side of the desk, her breathing come in gasps, and held up the inkwell.

Fairchilde laughed, his eyes glittering with a peculiar excitement as if stimulated by the chase. 'That will hardly stop me, my dear.'

'But I will.'

Michael's voice came from the doorway, soft and deadly. Fairchilde turned towards him; for an instant his face registered a deadly hatred. Then his expression became hooded.

'Lady Jeffreys is hardly in need of your assistance,' Fairchilde said in a bored voice. He moved leisurely towards Michael. 'However, I suggest you keep a tighter rein on your fiancée. She is perhaps a bit too free with her favours.'

Michael glanced in her direction, his face filled with a cold, hard fury she'd never seen before. His glance rested on her bodice. With a sickening realisation she saw that the material had torn, revealing her shift beneath. She tried to pull the edges together, feeling as if she were in a horrible nightmare. And her hair had tumbled from its pins.

Michael turned back to Fairchilde. 'I warned you to stay away from her. I protect what is mine. I will have no regrets about putting a bullet through you.'

'You've only to name the place, my lord.'

Rosalyn found her voice. 'No, Michael. Please say no more. This is a misunderstanding. Nothing happened. I cannot bear another scandal.'

His mouth in a tight line, Michael looked over at her. She moved swiftly to his side and touched his arm. 'Please. He…he is not worth it!'

His own features softened slightly as he looked into her pleading face. 'Very well, my dear.' He lifted his head and stared at Fairchilde.

'I'm warning you, Fairchilde. If you come near her again, I will kill you without regret.'

'Is that a challenge?'

'It's a warning. If you value your life at all, you will heed it. I suggest you now remove yourself from the premises or I will throw you out.'

'Not very hospitable, are you? However, I can see I've overstayed my welcome.' Fairchilde moved lazily towards the door, but with a wary look in his eye. He stopped and glanced at Rosalyn.

'I hope you know what you are doing in marrying such a madman.'

Rosalyn closed her eyes, thankful there wasn't to be a duel but afraid Michael's temper would now descend upon herself. If she could have magically transported herself to another country at that moment, she would have done so.

Her legs trembled so hard she feared they would not support her. She swayed and the next thing she knew she was in Michael's arms. He held her for a moment and then asked, 'Did he hurt you?'

'No,' she replied, not looking at him.

'What did he do to you? Did he do this?' He touched her torn bodice and his gaze hardened as he saw the rent in the skirt of her gown, which by now was beyond simple repair.

'I tore my skirt in the ball room. I…I am fine, really.'

'And your bodice?'

She closed her eyes, ashamed. 'He…he tried to reach for me and…and when I tripped he…he tore the lace.'

She heard his sharp intake of breath. Opening her eyes, she saw he looked furious. 'Damn it, Rosalyn, what were you doing alone in here?'

'A footman said Grandmama was ill. Otherwise, I…I never would have come. Please believe me. I would never have…have willingly gone with him.'

'I know that.' His voice gentled. He stroked her cheek. 'But I fully intend to see he never so much as looks at you again. He will not dare insult my wife.'

'I…I am not going to be your wife.'

'Oh, yes, you are.' He pulled her close and then his mouth descended on hers, his hands tangling in her hair. She made a feeble attempt to shove him away, but his arms only tightened. And his lips, moving gently over hers, were warm and familiar and comforting.

'My dear Lydia! I am certain he said we should find it here. Let me…'

The small shriek caused Rosalyn and Michael to spring apart. Their startled eyes met those of Lady Carruthers and Mrs Bellwood-Smythe, one of London's most notorious gossips.

'I do beg your pardon,' Lady Carruthers gasped, her eyes wide. She backed towards the open door, but Mrs Bellwood-Smythe's fascinated gaze ran over Rosalyn's dress.

'Oh, my! Are you all right, my dear?'

Rosalyn flushed. 'Oh, yes. I…I merely tore my dress in the ball room.'

'Of course.' Mrs Bellwood-Smythe's expression was one of complete disbelief.

'Lydia!' Lady Carruthers grabbed her arm and pulled her from the room.

Michael stared after their retreating backs, his face stunned, then seemed to come to his senses. He strode to the door, closing it firmly behind them.

His gaze was impassive as he turned towards Rosalyn. 'That settles it. By tomorrow the entire *ton* will most likely think I was attempting to rip your clothes from your body and ravish you in Lord Carruthers's study. I'll be damned before I let you leave me with that hanging over my head.' A peculiar smile twisted his lips. 'You have no choice but to wed me after tonight, my dear.'

Chapter Seventeen

Rosalyn sat on the edge of her bed, dressed only in her shift and petticoat. She supposed she should ring for Annie to help her to dress for the dinner party she was to attend. She had only meant to lie down and close her eyes for a few minutes; instead, she'd slept for nearly two hours.

She heaved herself off the bed and rang the bell. Caroline was holding a small dinner party for family. Nothing very formal, she had reassured Rosalyn.

Ever since the Carruthers's ball five days ago, his family had gone out of their way to protect her from the gossip surrounding the whole disaster. Despite the efforts of Lady Spence and the Duke of Eversleigh, the rumours had run wild all over London. As Michael had predicted, Mrs Bellwood-Smythe had spread it about that Rosalyn had been locked in a passionate embrace with him, her gown ripped from her bodice, the rest left to everyone's sordid imagination. The more nasty-minded believed he had tried to ravish her.

Which was why she could not bring herself to run

away from London. Such action would only serve to confirm the rumours. And she could not do that to Michael.

She'd refused, however, to discuss the wedding. Lady Spence had unexpectedly come to her rescue, saying Rosalyn needed a few days to herself. She had been seen in public only once with Michael. Rosalyn had forced herself to smile and nod and take his arm as if nothing had happened.

'My lady, what will you wear? The cream gown or perhaps the one of sea-green?' Annie's voice interrupted her reverie.

'Oh, the green, I think.' She watched Annie bustle around. At least the Season had proved beneficial for one person—Annie had quite turned from a shy country miss to a very competent lady's maid. Rosalyn hadn't the heart to tell her yet that she would most likely never be the lady's maid to a Marchioness.

Annie helped her into the gown, then dressed her hair in an elaborate knot on top of her head. After that, she retrieved Rosalyn's jewel box and brought it to her. Rosalyn's eye fell on the rose brooch Michael had given her. She touched it, feeling unexpectedly sad.

Annie peered over her shoulder. 'It is so pretty, my lady. Do you wish to wear it?'

'I don't know. Yes, I think I will.' She pinned it to her bodice, her thoughts straying to Michael. She had spent no time alone with him, almost as if there was some sort of conspiracy to keep them apart. Either her grandmother was with her, or one of his relations. He had not once called on her. His manner was polite, almost too polite. He seemed a stranger.

After Annie finished with her toilette, Rosalyn picked up her gloves, fan, and shawl and went down to her drawing room. Her grandmother should be arriving soon and Rosalyn would share her carriage.

Lost in thought, she jumped at the sound of a rap on the door. She gathered her things and went to the hallway where Mrs Harrod had opened the door. 'And where is Frederick?' she was asking.

'E's been taken ill. I've come for her ladyship.'

Rosalyn gave Mrs Harrod a distracted smile as she stepped past her into the night air. A light misty rain was falling as she reached the carriage. She stopped, puzzled, for the carriage was completely unfamiliar. Her grandmother did not seem to be inside. She turned as a terrible uneasiness assailed her.

Then she screamed as a hand clamped over her mouth. She was pulled up against a hard chest, then shoved into the coach. The door slammed shut, and she fell against the cushions as the horses sprang away.

Michael stood next to the mantelpiece in Caroline's drawing room, every nerve in his body on edge, as Lady Carlyn was announced. He'd been waiting for Rosalyn, worrying about her. Always quiet, she had seemed to be in some sort of daze ever since that damnable night at the Carruthers's ball. He had no idea how to reach her, afraid if he touched her he wouldn't be able to stop. And like a coward, he'd avoided spending time alone with her. He had no intention of giving her the chance to tell him she would not marry him.

He frowned. Lady Carlyn had come alone. There

was no Rosalyn. Was she unwell? Or couldn't she bear the thought of facing his family one more time? Facing him? He'd hoped she would come so he could tell her he'd finally tracked down James. He hoped the news James had been at Meryton since he had left Newmarket would jolt her out of her trance.

He moved across the drawing room to Lady Carlyn's side. She was smiling and talking to his aunt, apparently unperturbed by Rosalyn's absence. 'I had the most dreadful time persuading her to accompany me to the dressmaker's! And then she would not look at anything! Sometimes I vow she is—' She broke off to address Michael. 'I really should not say such things about your bride-to-be! But really, she can be most difficult, I should warn you.'

'Where is she?' Michael asked.

Lady Carlyn looked puzzled. 'Who?'

'Rosalyn. I thought she was to come with you.'

Lady Carlyn looked surprised. 'Really? But you had sent a note around saying that you would send a carriage for her. I must admit I was rather relieved as it meant I needn't rush around so much.' She peered around him as if expecting to see Rosalyn behind him. 'But she is not here?'

'I sent no note.'

'Of course you did. It arrived—why yes, it arrived just as I returned from shopping. I remember because the footman gave it to me just as I stepped into the drawing room. I was quite surprised.'

'Where is the note?'

'I have no idea. I suppose I tossed it away.' His meaning finally seemed to penetrate her mind. 'You did not send a note? But who would?'

'Michael?' Lady Spence looked worried.

'I have no idea,' he said shortly.

Then his blood ran cold. Fairchilde? But would he stoop to such a thing? The man's cold determination, the vision of him reaching for Rosalyn, flashed sickeningly though his mind. And Fairchilde hated him.

'Michael? What is wrong?' Lady Spence touched his arm, her face full of worry.

'I must go.' He shook off her arm and started towards the door. 'I have to find her.'

He dashed down the winding staircase to the hallway, only pausing to call for his overcoat. He carried a pistol in its pocket. Outside he nearly collided with James Whitcomb, who was running up the steps. James's face was white, his cravat in complete disarray.

'Thank God you're here. He has Rosalyn!' James sounded sick with fear.

'Fairchilde?' At James's nod, Michael said, 'How can you be certain?'

'I just arrived in London. I wanted to call on her, apologise to her, but when I got there...the housekeeper said she saw him seize her. Or at least she thought it was him. But who else would do such a thing?' All trace of the cynical, wild young man had vanished. He looked more like a frightened school boy. 'It is all my fault! God! If I hadn't invited him to Meryton, hadn't lost the money—'

'Never mind that now! I will find her.'

'I'm coming with you!'

Michael looked at him. 'Very well. Then...' He spun around and saw Charles, Philip, and Giles behind him, their faces grim.

'Thought we might be of assistance,' Charles said. 'Where to?'

'Ask Rosalyn's housekeeper if she has any information. I'm going to Fairchilde's. Meet me there.'

And he was going to kill Fairchilde.

But Fairchilde was not there. His manservant, a beefy man with a surly expression, was disinclined to talk until Charles shoved him up against the hallway wall. Michael levelled a pistol at his heart.

'Won't do you much good if I'm dead, will it?' the man said with a smirk.

Michael cocked the pistol. 'It matters little to me whether you are or not. I'm certain there are others who'll be willing to tell me what I want to know.'

The bravado left the man's face as he looked at Michael's cold, unwavering gaze. 'Darley Hall,' he finally spat out.

Charles met Michael's eyes. 'Does that sound right?'

'Yes.'

Charles released the man, and they dashed from the house.

Darley Hall. Of course. It was Fairchilde's estate, a little more than two hours north of London. He prayed they'd reach her in time. For he dreaded to think what Fairchilde intended to do to her.

Rosalyn was jolted as the carriage hit a rut. Fear kept her immobilised in a corner as she tried to stay as far away as possible from Edmund Fairchilde. He had not tried to touch her, only watched her with his cold, hooded eyes.

They had left London. She could scarcely see where they were; the night was dark, the passing scenery only an occasional shadow. Fear combined with the lack of food and the motion of the carriage made her feel slightly nauseous.

She shivered, forcing herself to speak. 'Wh... where are you taking me?'

'You shall see when we get there,' he said.

'Why? Why are you doing this to me?'

She could barely see his mouth curve in an unpleasant smile. 'Revenge.'

'Revenge? I...I have done nothing to you.'

'Oh, you have, my dear. It would have been better for you if you had accepted my first offer. I do not like to be thwarted. And in this case, revenge shall be particularly sweet as I shall enjoy snatching you from Stamford. He has long been a thorn in my side, and his latest attempts to ruin me have most seriously displeased me. Instead, he is the one that will be ruined.'

Rosalyn wrapped her cloak more tightly about herself. 'I...I have no idea why abducting me would ruin him.' Perhaps if she kept him talking, she could discover some clue, some idea that would enable her to escape him.

'He is in love with you, my dear. Knowing that you are in my hands, at my mercy, knowing I am enjoying your delights, will cause him to suffer exceedingly. Particularly when he realises there is nothing he can do about it.'

'You are wrong. He does not love me. We are not going to be married.'

'You are correct in that regard. You will not marry Stamford.'

She moistened her dry lips. She had to ask. 'Wh…what are you planning to do with me?'

His eyes roved over her in a way that made her skin crawl. 'Bed you, of course. Perhaps I will marry you myself.'

Sick revulsion flooded her being. 'You cannot force me to do that.'

He laughed unpleasantly. 'Oh, I can. There are many ways. A dose of laudanum, perhaps. Whisky. None of it may be necessary. You may decide after a few nights in my bed you will be most willing to marry me.'

She lifted her chin. 'I doubt that.'

He laughed again. 'Shall we see? Come here, Rosalyn.'

'No!' Her stomach lurched along with the carriage. She tried to fold herself into the corner as far as she could.

'Come, or I will make you sorry you didn't obey me.' He made a move toward her.

'I…I feel quite ill,' she said faintly. Indeed, she did. She feared if he touched her, she would be sick all over him.

He stared at her, then settled back in his corner, apparently deciding she was serious. A moment later, he shot up as the coach lumbered to a halt.

'What the devil!' He grabbed a pistol hanging from its leather near his seat.

'Stand and deliver!'

'Blast it!' He turned and flashed a hard glance at

Rosalyn. 'Stay there!' He pushed his pistol through the window and fired.

The coach door on the opposite side was yanked opened. Rough hands pulled Rosalyn from her seat at the same time she heard more shots. She was vaguely aware of Fairchilde tumbling back. Frantic, she tried to aim a kick at her attacker.

'Rosalyn! Damn it! It's me!'

'James?' She collapsed into his arms, shaking. He hugged her close.

'My God! Are you all right? He didn't harm you?'

'No. Oh, James, what are you doing here?'

'I came with Stamford.'

'Michael?'

'Yes. I'm sorry, Rosalyn.' He pulled away from her, his face haggard with shock and worry. 'This is all my doing.'

'Oh, no! You…you don't know how I…I worried about you!' She clutched at him.

'Whitcomb? Do you have her?' She recognised Philip's voice.

'Yes. She's safe.'

'Bring her here. We need you to cover the coach. Michael's been shot!'

'No!' The sound was torn from her. She jerked out of her brother's arms, and stumbled around the back of the coach.

She saw his figure on the ground, heard a low moan. Philip, kneeling beside him, looked up as she ran to his side. She dropped to her knees, heedless of the muddy road. Fear clutched her when she saw the dark stain spreading down the left arm of his evening coat. 'Michael!'

He was sitting up, half-supported by Philip. He looked at her, his eyes glazed with pain. 'You're safe?'

'Oh, yes. Michael, please…' she whispered.

'We need to get him out of his coat. Can you help me?' Philip said.

'Yes.'

Michael swore. 'Get away, Rosalyn.'

'Be quiet,' she told him sharply.

She helped Philip ease him out of his coat, her heart in her throat. Philip ripped the sleeve from his shirt exposing his arm. A gasp escaped her at the sight of the raw ragged hole in his arm just below the shoulder.

'We need to stop the bleeding.' Philip was making a pad of his neckcloth. 'Ask the others for cravats, shirts, if we must, anything.'

'Yes.' She rose, almost running into Charles. He heard her request and without a word removed his cravat. She took it, then kneeled.

Caught in a nightmare, she tried to help as Philip attempted to stem the blood seeping from the wound. The voices of the others, the mud of the road, the light misty rain receded from her consciousness as she passed strip after strip of dry cloth to Philip. Michael said nothing, but she could see from the way he gripped her hand and the set look of his mouth it was all he could do to remain silent.

At last, Philip bound the arm with a strip of her shawl. He looked up as Charles approached.

'How is he?' Charles asked.

'It should hold, but we need to get him to a surgeon. The shot is still in his arm. Where's Fairchilde?'

'Bound up near the coach. Giles shot him in the leg after he shot Michael. Only a flesh wound,' Charles said. His easy manner was gone, his eyes were hard. 'What should we do with him?'

Michael struggled to sit up. 'I shall be glad to dispose of him,' he said grimly.

'Although I fully comprehend your sentiments, we don't need a murder to complicate matters,' Philip said. He stood. 'How far is Darley Hall?'

'Michael?' Charles asked.

'A half-hour's ride,' Michael said. He had slumped back against Rosalyn, his face drained, the spurt of energy he'd shown at Fairchilde's name now spent.

'We'll leave him a horse and take the carriage. He can make his way to Darley Hall,' Philip said. He looked down at Rosalyn. 'Can you manage him for a moment? Don't let him move.'

'No,' she said.

The rest of the trip passed in a haze. Michael could not be laid in the coach, so they made him as comfortable as possible, tucking coats under his head so he could rest his head in one corner. Rosalyn sat at his side, refusing to leave him, trying her best to cushion the jolts. He remained conscious, and then finally collapsed in the corner, eyes closed. Philip sat across from her, James next to him, pale and worried.

Once Philip leaned forward and touched her knee. 'Don't worry, Rosalyn. I've seen worse. He'll pull through.'

She nodded, her heart numb. Because if he didn't, she had no idea how she would survive. For she realised, with utter overwhelming clarity, she loved him.

Chapter Eighteen

His arm ached. He slowly opened his eyes and realised, with some wonder, he was in his own bed. He had no idea what time it was or the day. He vaguely remembered voices coming and going, but time had passed in a hazy, drugged stupor. The last thing he remembered before fainting as the surgeon cut into his arm was Rosalyn's white face hovering over him.

He must have made a sound for he heard the rustle of skirts, and then his eyes focused vaguely on a familiar figure.

'Michael, are you awake? Do you know me?' His aunt Margaret hovered over him, lines of concern on her drawn face.

'Yes,' he managed to whisper.

She passed a gentle hand over his forehead. 'Your fever has finally broken.' She knelt by him. 'We have been so worried. I am so thankful you are awake.'

'How long…?'

'Three days. You developed a fever after the surgeon removed the bullet. You have been very ill,

Michael.' She brought him a glass of water. 'Can you drink?'

She helped him take a few sips, then he fell back on the pillows, willing himself not to drift into another sleep.

He closed his eyes, then they shot open. 'Rosalyn. Where is she?'

'She is here. She has been staying with us since the night you were wounded. Can you take a little more water?'

He pushed her hand away. 'I must see her.'

'Michael! I think it would be best if you waited.' She sighed as he attempted to throw back the covers. 'Very well, don't agitate yourself. I shall fetch her.'

Rosalyn quietly closed the door behind her. Michael lay very still, his eyes closed. He turned his head as she approached the bed and opened his eyes. His usually olive skin was pale and his hair, unruly under the best of circumstances, tumbled over his forehead in complete disorder.

'Rosalyn.' She had to bend to catch his voice. 'Did he hurt you?'

'No, I am quite safe.' His pallor and weakness alarmed her. She fought back tears that were all too close.

'I am glad.' He fumbled for her hand. 'Sit by me. I must talk to you.'

She sunk down in the chair by his bed. 'Not now. You need to rest. You have been very ill.'

He focused on her, his eyes drugged from the laudanum he'd been given to dull his pain. 'Stay with me.'

'I will. Please try to rest, Michael.' She smoothed his hair back from his brow, and he closed his eyes.

Rosalyn sat with him for a long while, as she had for the past few interminable days. The candles slowly burned down, casting a soft glow in the room. His breathing was slow and even, and he no longer tossed and turned in feverish delirium as he had been doing during the past few days.

She stroked his hand, then brought it to her cheek for a moment, tears of thankfulness streaming down her face. For the first time since that terrible night, she had hope that he would live.

After a while, Caroline tiptoed in to relieve her, touching her hand in passing. Unable to sleep, Rosalyn wandered down to the library. She was startled to find the Duke still up, idly browsing through a book. He laid it aside when she entered.

After a few days in his company, Rosalyn could understand why his family found him daunting. Although his dark hair was flecked with silver, he very much resembled his sons, possessing the same handsome, aristocratic features. But it was his inborn air of self-assurance and command, coupled with the penetrating look in his grey eyes, that inspired awe in those around him. At first she had thought him a very hard man, but she had seen the lines of worry in his face for his son and knew he would be devastated if Michael were not to live.

'Lady Jeffreys,' he said politely, as he rose to his feet. 'How do you find my son?'

'He is much better; not so feverish and restless but so very weak. I still worry for him.'

'The surgeon assured us once the fever has broken,

the worst is over. Stamford is a survivor with a will of iron.' He put a hand on her shoulder. 'You should go to bed, my dear. You look peaked.'

She tried to smile. 'I do not think I can sleep.'

'What is troubling you?' he asked quietly.

'I cannot help but feel this whole affair is my fault. If it had not been for me, he would not have nearly been killed.'

'I do not believe you deliberately attracted Fairchilde's attentions, did you?'

'No, never.' She shuddered. 'He was quite the most repugnant man I have ever met.'

'You surely cannot hold yourself responsible for the harm he wished to do you and Michael? That would be most foolish and quite unnecessary. You are only fortunate that Michael and the others found you in time.'

'Yes.' She was silent and looked directly at him. 'It is not that, your Grace. You see, Michael and I, we…we really were never betrothed. It was only a temporary bargain between us. He wished to avoid marriage with Miss Randall, I wanted my brother's estate back…' Her voice trailed away as he held up his hand.

'I know this, my dear. Michael told me before we left Longbourne.'

'Oh, dear.'

'He feared I would coerce you to the altar so he felt he should inform me of the truth.'

'Oh, what must you think of me?' she whispered. Her hands crept to her burning cheeks. 'I am so very sorry for such deceit. And then for Michael to almost lose his life because of it.'

'My dear, this is nonsense. You have nothing to reproach yourself for. If anything, I am grateful he has met you.' He smiled slightly, his eyes kind. 'I suggest you retire now. Wearing yourself out with worry will not help.'

He held the door open for her, and as she passed he said, 'I trust you care for him?'

She looked up at him, a blush heating her cheeks. 'Yes, very much.'

He touched her cheek. 'That is all that matters. Good night.'

Four days later, Rosalyn stood in the doorway of the sitting room off Michael's bedchamber. He sat in a wing-chair, facing the window looking out over the garden behind Eversleigh House. He did not turn until she came into the room.

'Rosalyn.' He made a move to rise.

'Please don't. I know you are still not recovered.' He looked much better, but she could see he was still pale. He wore a dark-green silk dressing gown over his loose white shirt and breeches. His arm was in a sling under the gown. 'I will not stay very long.'

'No. I did not think you would.' He looked at her with that unreadable expression he'd had on his face the last two days, ever since he started to recover from his fever. He was polite, but remote, as if his whispered request for her to stay at his side had never happened.

She swallowed her despair and managed a smile. 'I know James has thanked you, but I also wanted to thank you for what you have done for James.

Particularly after he did lose more money at Newmarket. You did not need to return Meryton.'

'I have no great desire to worry about another property. I thought it fitting punishment he should learn how to manage the place properly.' A cool smile touched his lips. 'We will see how grateful James is after a few months. Rutherford is one of my best stewards, which is why I have sent him to Meryton. He is a good man, but a hard taskmaster. James will find there is little time for gambling. However, he could not have a better tutor for learning how to run an estate.'

'I am certain it will be quite good for him.'

'I hope it keeps him out of trouble.' Michael returned his gaze to the window.

'Yes.' She moved next to his chair. 'He felt responsible for Fairchilde's obsession as he invited him to Meryton. It is nonsense, but it seems to have sobered him considerably.'

Michael glanced up at her. 'If he ever does anything else that puts you in danger like that, I'll have him whipped.'

'I doubt he will.' She took a deep breath, clasping her hands together. 'There is something else I must tell you. I…I think I will go to Meryton for a while.'

'Why?'

'There is no point in continuing here. Your father knows about our agreement, and Miss Randall is to marry Mr Redding. I am so grateful to you…'

'I don't want your gratitude,' he interrupted her. He turned to look at her, a dark look on his face. 'Nor do I care about Miss Randall's nuptials.'

'What do you want?' she whispered.

He rose from the chair, staggering a little. Alarmed for him, she caught his arm. He shook her off and before she could think, caught her to him, his good arm pulling her tight against him. He looked down into her face, his eyes no longer indifferent, but dark with passion. 'This is what I want.'

His lips crushed hers in a fierce kiss, surprisingly masterful for a man who was still convalescing. Not wanting to struggle for fear of doing him further injury, Rosalyn decided she had no choice but to yield to his embrace.

He didn't let her go until a slight sound made them pull apart. He lifted his head, and they both turned towards the door.

Eversleigh stood there, eyeing them with an unreadable expression. 'I would not interrupt you longer than necessary. I take it, however, you have no objections if your wedding takes place tomorrow.'

Rosalyn felt the colour drain from her face. She stole a glance at Michael, who had turned to stone. Then an odd smile touched his mouth. 'But I do, sir. If you will excuse me, Rosalyn, I would like to speak to my father alone.'

'Yes.' In a daze, she left the room.

Michael watched her go, then turned to his father. 'This is impossible.'

The Duke walked over to the chair. 'I suggest you sit down before you faint. Then you may tell me why. After the embrace I just witnessed, I could be forgiven for assuming the matter has been settled.'

Michael flushed, and sat down. 'Hardly. I told her after the damnable ball she must marry me in order to save her reputation and mine. She probably would have looked more delighted if I'd informed her she'd be facing a firing squad.'

'Your usual address seems to have been somewhat lacking,' Eversleigh said. 'However, I trust you will remedy the matter after you are married.'

'We are not going to be married.'

'I am loathe to contradict you, but you will be. You are quite correct in attempting to save your reputation, particularly if you persist in kissing her in your bed-chamber or in private rooms at balls.'

'I promise to stay away from her. She wishes to leave for Meryton at any rate.' He ran an agitated hand through his hair as he saw his father's imper-turbable expression. 'It's impossible! I won't have her coerced. I know how persuasive you can be.'

The Duke raised thin brows. 'I have no intention of coercing her. She will not be unwilling, I think. I am correct in assuming you love her?'

'I love her more than anything. Too much to force her into marriage.'

'The wedding will be small. Family and a few friends. I suggest you rest.'

Michael rose, agitated. 'I must talk to Rosalyn. I must make certain this is what she wishes.'

His father moved to the door and paused, his hand resting on the doorknob. 'You may speak with her tomorrow. There will be time enough to settle your concerns after you are wed.' He closed the door firmly behind him.

Michael sank down into his chair and buried his head in his hands. She should have made her escape while he was unconscious. Once his father decided on a course of action there was no thwarting him. Michael only prayed she did not hate him too much.

Tension filled him. Not so much with worry that there would be a wedding tomorrow, but from fear there would not.

Rosalyn sat on a sofa in the library, her gaze fixed on a statue of Shakespeare. She started when she heard soft footsteps, and turned to see Lady Spence enter the room.

Lady Spence smiled down at Rosalyn, then seated herself next to her. Her eyes held sympathy. 'Are you all right, my dear? I fear my brother can be somewhat overwhelming when he has his mind made up.'

'He…he wishes us to be married tomorrow,' Rosalyn whispered.

'I know. I will admit it is rather sudden, but I do think it is for the best.' She touched Rosalyn's hand. 'Michael loves you very much, you know.'

'He…he has never said anything.'

'Perhaps he is not certain of your feelings. He worries about forcing you into a marriage you don't want.' Her gaze was direct. 'If you are certain you don't wish to marry him, if you can say you do not love him, then I will put a halt to the wedding.'

'No, I…I cannot say that,' Rosalyn whispered. 'But surely the Duke told you. We never meant to marry.'

'I had already guessed that, even before Alistair confirmed it. My dear, I know this is not what either of you had planned. But sometimes fate plays us a much different hand than we expect. We cannot control everything, even the events we set in motion ourselves. You and Michael will be married. You are meant for each other. I have thought so from the first. Sometimes it is no use trying to run from our lives; you could go on like this and both of you would be unhappy. It will be best to wed tomorrow and start your lives together.'

Further argument seemed futile. In her own quiet way, Lady Spence was as strong as her brother. No wonder Michael had resorted to a false engagement to avoid an unwanted marriage. And when Watkins announced Lady Carlyn, and Rosalyn saw her grandmother bustle in, a pleased and determined look on her face, Rosalyn knew her fate was sealed. Fighting the three of them would be impossible.

And in her heart, she had no desire to do so.

Chapter Nineteen

Annie fastened the tapes of the dove-grey silk wedding dress Rosalyn wore and then bent to arrange the skirts. Lady Spence and Caroline fluttered around her. Her hair was tied in a knot at the top of her head and fell in dark ringlets to her shoulders. Caroline wove a circlet of fragrant lily-of-the-valley through her hair. Lady Spence fastened a strand of pearls around her neck.

Lady Carlyn entered the bedchamber and bustled forward to catch Rosalyn's hands. 'How lovely you look! So like your mother, I vow I could cry!' She kissed Rosalyn's cheek, her own moist with tears.

She stepped away, pressing a small picture frame into Rosalyn's hand. Rosalyn saw it was a miniature of her mother as a very young woman. She looked up at her grandmother with misty eyes. 'Thank you.'

'I only hope you will be as happy as your mother was in her marriage.'

'Grandmama?'

Lady Carlyn smiled sheepishly through her tears. 'Well, I could see she was. Anyone could.'

Rosalyn hugged her grandmother, tears springing to her eyes.

And then Caroline was kissing her on the cheek and telling her how beautiful she was and how she looked forward to having her for a sister. Lady Julianna, Michael's youngest sister, came in and presented her with a bouquet of fragrant pale pink roses to carry and pressed her hand. Finally, Lady Spence pronounced her ready and took her arm.

Michael stood at the front of the drawing room where the guests were assembled, waiting for his bride. Only vaguely aware of the others, his eyes were fixed on the doors. Time seemed to tick by ruthlessly and still Rosalyn did not come. Perhaps she had managed to escape after all, he thought with sick despair.

Finally the doors were flung open, and his sisters and aunt entered, followed by Lady Carlyn and James, and to his great, overwhelming relief, Rosalyn. She was beautiful; her dark hair tied in a loose knot tumbled to her shoulders, the colour of her dress enhanced the pale perfection of her skin. She drifted towards him like one in a trance, and he briefly wondered if they had drugged her.

He took her hand as she joined him in front of the priest—it was ice cold. Her gaze, as she met his own, was bewildered. He wanted to take her in his arms then and there and comfort her, but it would have to wait until after the ceremony.

For Rosalyn, the wedding passed in a dream. The only solid and real thing was Michael, standing pale and still beside her, his arm in a sling under his morning coat. His hand was warm and firm around hers as the priest began to recite the words of the age-old ceremony. She heard Michael repeat the vows, 'I, Michael Stephen Elliot...' and then the priest turned to her. She must have hesitated too long for Michael squeezed her hand. He leaned toward her, 'Rosalyn, please.' She saw the vulnerability in his face and snapped out of her inertia to obediently repeat her vows. He slipped the ring on her finger.

And then they were pronounced man and wife. Michael bent over her and his lips were on hers, gentle and comforting.

The guests adjourned to the dining room. On such short notice, Lady Spence, with help from her nieces and Lady Carlyn, had organised an elaborate wedding breakfast. Lady Spence instructed the bridal couple to sit at the centre of one of the long sides of the heavy mahogany table.

Glancing at Michael, Rosalyn thought he appeared unnaturally pale. He had not said much to her, and appeared as shell-shocked as she felt. Had his father caught him in a moment of delirium and told him he was to marry her? The thought was too awful to contemplate.

'You are not eating, Rosalyn,' said Michael.

She glanced at his plate, which was as untouched as hers. She could not remember how the food came to be in front of her. 'Neither are you.'

He grimaced. 'I find I have little appetite. It is difficult to eat when one is the centre of so much attention. We should have eloped and avoided the fuss.'

She laughed shakily. 'I don't think your father would have liked that. Or my grandmother either.'

'You are quite right. And in my condition I don't think I could have managed to escape out of the window, unfortunately. It would not be very romantic to have your bridegroom faint on you.'

'Very unromantic and very inconvenient.'

He leaned towards her. 'Would you have come with me, Rosalyn?' he asked softly.

She caught her breath, sudden shyness overtaking her, and looked down at her hands.

'May I propose a toast to the bride and groom?' Rosalyn started as Charles's voice boomed out over the chattering of the guests. He grinned at them, lifting his champagne glass.

Several more speeches followed, expressing wishes for future happiness and congratulations, and then Caroline and Lady Spence were at Rosalyn's side. Caroline took her hand and whispered they would escort her upstairs. She rose from the table, and Michael stood up.

Lady Spence frowned at him. 'You had best repair to your chamber. You look as if you are about to collapse. That will hardly do.'

'I have no intention of collapsing.' But Rosalyn did not like the white look about his mouth. 'I would like to speak with my wife in private, if you please.'

'You may later. After you rest,' Lady Spence replied firmly.

'Do not worry. We are not about to spirit her away,' Caroline told him patting his arm. 'She also needs to rest.'

'Of course.' He fixed Rosalyn with an anxious

gaze—almost, she thought in surprise, as if he thought she would vanish.

She gave him a small, reassuring smile, then turned to go with Caroline.

'Is there anything more you need, my lady? I hope the room is satisfactory' the housekeeper said, giving Rosalyn an anxious glance. Rosalyn started from her daze, realising she had said nothing since entering the bedchamber.

'Thank you, it is lovely.' Some time during the afternoon, her belongings had been moved from the guest chamber she had occupied to the room adjoining the sitting room next to Michael's chamber. It was a beautiful room, decorated in shades of rose, cream and gold. After the housekeeper departed, she sank down on the four-poster bed hung with rose and cream hangings. Strange to think this was now her home, her room.

Lady Spence knocked and entered. She came to sit next to Rosalyn, touching her hand. 'You must be exhausted. I shall send your abigail to draw your bath and help you into your nightclothes.' She smiled gently at Rosalyn. 'We thought it would be best if you and Michael had some time alone without the others. Particularly since Michael will not be able to travel for a few more days. I know everything has been very confusing for both of you and there has been little time to recover yourselves. Eversleigh and Julianna shall stay with me. If you need anything, you have only to send a servant around.'

'But Michael…he is still not very well,' Rosalyn stammered, panicked. How could she stay here with him alone? She had thought at least his family would be here until they could sort through this mess.

'He will be fine. Just make certain he doesn't over-exert himself and keep him in bed as much as possible. I am certain you'll have no trouble managing him.' She arose from the bed and kissed Rosalyn's cheek. Eversleigh and Julianna entered, and bade her goodbye, and then she was quite alone.

Annie came in to undress Rosalyn and draw her bath. After that she helped Rosalyn into an ivory nightdress and dressing gown.

'How very pretty,' said Annie, touching the fine lawn material. She noticed her mistress's expression. 'Lady Carlyn gave me the package. She said it was for you to wear tonight.'

'I see.' Oh, dear. Why had her grandmother given her such an intimate gift? No, she knew why.

The room felt deserted after Annie left. The ticking of the clock emphasised the awful quiet. She stared out the window and wondered what she should do next. Never had she felt more alone in her life.

She had not seen Michael since the wedding. Did he not wish to see her? Or perhaps he had fallen ill again. As much as she wished she could avoid him, she could not. She must talk to him.

She looked down at the soft folds of her night-clothes and wished she was wearing something more practical, such as a high-necked cotton dress. If she went to his bedchamber dressed like this, he might think she wanted to seduce him. How humiliating! She had no idea what their relationship was to be.

Rosalyn searched through the wardrobe and finally found a large paisley shawl and threw it over her gown. She opened the connecting door and nearly collided with Michael. She gasped.

Michael caught her with his good arm. 'It is only me. My dear girl, whatever is wrong?'

'I am sorry. I did not expect to see you there.' She backed away from him and pulled the shawl more firmly about her shoulders, then folded her arms across her chest. He closed the door behind him and stood with his back to it.

'Were you by any chance coming to see me?' he asked. He wore a dressing gown in a rich shade of burgundy. The light from the candles gleamed off his dark hair. He was partially in the shadows, and she could not see the expression on his face.

She felt her knees tremble but tried to keep her voice calm. 'I must talk to you. It could wait until tomorrow, however. I am certain you must be quite tired. I know I am.'

He advanced towards her, and she backed away. He caught her hand. 'Come and sit down. I think we should talk now and not put this off any longer.' He pulled her down beside him on the side of her bed. She clutched the shawl with nervous fingers.

'There is no need to look so frightened, Rosalyn,' he said with gentle amusement in his voice. 'Tell me what's troubling you.'

'Michael, I am not certain how this happened. We were not supposed to be married,' she said faintly.

'Isn't it obvious? My father decided we were to be married and we were. I only hope he did not cow you into this.'

'Oh, no,' she replied on a slight laugh. 'Not your father, your aunt. She seemed to consider the matter settled, and I could see no way of arguing with her.'

He brushed the hair back from her face with gentle

fingers. 'We hadn't a chance between the two of them. They can be thwarted, but one usually needs a little time to plan a strategy. In this case, time was short—and I did not wish to thwart them.'

He caressed her hand, making slow circles around her thumb with a finger. It was very distracting. She pulled her mind back to the subject at hand. 'But you didn't wish to be married. You wanted this bargain so you could avoid it.'

'Yes, caught in my own trap.' He moved closer to her. 'But I think I shall like my trap very much as long as I am trapped with you.' He reached up and slowly slipped the shawl off her shoulders. 'Must you wear this? If you are cold there are other ways to keep you warm.'

Actually, she was not cold at all—she felt hot and vulnerable. He slowly caressed her cheek, sending little sparks of fire down her spine. 'Will it really be such a terrible fate to have me for a husband, Rosalyn? I take my vows very seriously. I fully intend to love, honour, and cherish you, to remain faithful to you for the rest of my life.'

'You wished to marry me?' she whispered.

'Yes, more than anything, for a very long time. Perhaps even from the first.'

'Michael, I...'

He bent and gently kissed her lips. 'I know you have doubts about marriage. I vow I will not leave you if that is what you fear. I plan to live a long, long time. And I will not desert you in any other way. You will not be alone and left to your own devices. You are my wife and a part of me, as I wish to be a part of you.'

Tears sprang to her eyes. 'Oh, Michael,' she whispered.

His hand slid the robe off her shoulders. 'I love you. Do you suppose you could learn to love me more than a little, Rosalyn?'

'Yes, I think so.' Somehow, she found herself eased against the pillows and Michael stretched out fully beside her. His dressing gown had fallen from his shoulders revealing a dark mat of hair curling on his bare chest. She glanced down and blushed to see he was wearing nothing at all under his robe. Her stomach tightened as he pulled her to him and kissed her with fierce, hungry passion.

Her eyes closed and she moved her hands shyly down his chest, then over his arm. Her lids snapped open when she came in contact with the dressing on his arm. He was not wearing his sling. She had nearly forgotten how weak he still was. 'Michael, I…what are you doing?'

He raised up on his good arm so he could look at her. His lips curved in a slow smile that made her weak all over. 'Seducing you, my sweet. We are married, you know. I must perform certain duties as your husband to ensure your happiness. I thought I should start tonight.' He looked more deeply into her face. 'What is it? Am I going too fast for you? I promise I will be gentle. I won't hurt you.'

'It is not that. I might hurt you. You are still not well. Your aunt said you should not exert yourself.' She was finding it difficult to breathe—his touch was a drug, but she could not let him continue.

'She said you were to keep me confined to my bed as much as possible. It will be much easier for you if you are with me. Otherwise I shall be forced to trail you about the house.'

She stroked his beloved face with a gentle hand. 'But your wound, I do not want to aggravate it.'

He caught her hand and pressed it to his lips. His eyes were dark with passion. 'You won't hurt me. My love, I want to be with you tonight. I want to make love to you. I want to make you mine.' He cupped her face in his hands. 'Tell me that's what you want also. Tell me you love me as much as I love you.'

A small sound halfway between a sob and a laugh escaped her. 'I do love you, Michael.' And then he pressed her back against the pillows, his lips possessed hers, and his hands cupped her breasts through the soft fabric of her gown. She murmured a faint protest when he lifted his head but it was only to ease her nightdress over her head. Then there were no barriers between them.

The early light of dawn glimmered across the bed. Michael stirred and turned to wrap his arm more firmly around the soft warmth of the precious woman curled up against him. His wife. He liked the sound of that more than he'd ever imagined. Never had he dreamed union with a woman could be such a joining of soul and spirit as well as body.

She moved in his arms and he pressed his lips to the nape of her neck, burying his face in her silky tresses. She half-turned; her eyelids fluttered open. She looked at him with sleep-filled eyes.

'Good morning, my love.' He kissed her lightly. 'I hope you slept well.'

She gently caressed his face and returned his kiss.

'Yes, very well. Better than I have for weeks. But you, your arm, does it pain you?'

'A little, but I will survive.' He smiled, stroking the soft silky skin of her upper arm. 'I shall have to ensure you sleep well every night, then.' A delicate pink stained her cheeks. The shy modesty concealing her passionate nature intrigued and delighted him. 'So did last night persuade you marriage to me might be tolerable?'

'I shall have to see.'

'So you don't know yet? I can see I must try a little harder to convince you.' He shifted so his mouth and body covered hers. Her hands came up to pull his head to her.

Three-quarters of an hour later, Rosalyn lay with her head on his chest. He softly stroked her hair. 'What do you think now?' he inquired.

She smiled shyly. 'I think I shall find it much more than tolerable. In fact, I think I will like it very much.'

*　*　*　*　*

A KIND AND DECENT MAN

by

Mary Brendan

Mary Brendan was born in North London and lived there for nineteen years before marrying and migrating north into Hertfordshire. She was grammar-school educated and has been at various times in her working life a personnel secretary for an international oil company, a property developer and a landlady. Presently working part-time in a local library, she dedicates hard-won leisure time to antique-browsing, curries, and keeping up with two lively sons.

Also by Mary Brendan
in Mills & Boon Historical Romance™:

MR TRELAWNEY'S PROPOSAL★
THE SILVER SQUIRE★
A ROGUISH GENTLEMAN★
WEDDING NIGHT REVENGE^
THE UNKNOWN WIFE^

★ novels have linking characters
^ novels have linking characters

Look for Mary Brendan's
A SCANDALOUS MARRIAGE
Coming February 2005

Prologue

'I'm begging you to hear me out, sir!'

'Remove yourself. I have nothing further to say to you and will listen to no more.' The words snapped out, the frail man showed his visitor a slumped-shouldered back.

'You *will* hear me out.' The quiet determination had the elderly gentleman twisting unsteadily about. Undisguised alarm in weak grey eyes elicited a sardonic tilt to the youthful supplicant's mouth. Talk of fighting had obviously also reached his ears. The doddering fool probably believed him disposed to hitting someone almost thrice his age. He reined in his temper, politely but firmly requesting, 'Please, let me at least speak to your daughter before I leave…'

'My daughter is removed to Hertfordshire with her aunt.' The information was bitten out in icy triumph. 'She seemed unaware of your true character but I have now told her of your revolting habits and morals. Moreover, she knows her duty to her father.'

Fierce blue eyes bored relentlessly into watering grey. A white line traced around the young man's thin, compressed lips and a cord of muscle formed, jerking a lean cheek.

Instinctively the girl's father stumbled back a few steps. He knew of his dangerous reputation. Oh, he had heard every sordid detail gossiped abroad, and he knew this was not a man to trifle with. But his contempt was impossible to contain, and finally exploded in a hissed, 'You have the effrontery to come here and offer for my daughter? You? The younger son of a bankrupt viscount, with no prospect of title or wealth to recommend you? You, with your gambling, your whoring, your brawling...your disgusting breeding? If your parents were struck down dead in the street I doubt that carrion would risk the taint of picking them over.' He had gone too far, he was sure, and his bloodless, puckered lips pressed so firmly shut they disappeared.

A flash of even white teeth revealed the young man's appreciation of the imagery and the mirthless smile terrorised the elderly man more than the leashed rage he could sense radiating from him.

'Remove yourself before I call Brook to eject you.' The words were pushed out, emerging in a strangled whisper.

The threat provoked no more than a careless elevation in the young petitioner's thick dark brows. But he exhaled a steadying breath through set teeth. 'I am aware, sir, that at present I have little to offer. But within two months I will have. I have several deals on the table and the prospect of much more. I can raise considerable finance through a private source...'

'You think you can buy my daughter?' the elderly man spat, hoarse with outrage, bony fists quaking at his sides.

Exasperatedly snapping back his dark head, the young man finally yielded and pivoted on his heel. He turned by the door and leaned his tall, powerful figure back against its mahogany panels. Sapphire eyes narrowed in his handsome, angular face, riveting into his gaunt, stooped tormentor. 'Oh, I know I can,' he softly promised, before quietly closing the door behind him.

Chapter One

'Promise you will, Victoria.' The whispered words were thready and Victoria Hart inclined her head closer to her husband.

A thin-skinned, thick-veined hand trembled out and rested upon the crumpled black satin of her hair. He stirred it beneath his fingers. 'Promise me, my dear, that you will write to him and tell him. I want you to do it now…this minute.'

'Hush,' Victoria soothed, closing wet grey eyes to shield her grief from him. 'You can write yourself when you are feeling a little better.' The words were gasped out as she battled against the tears threatening to close her throat at such futile comfort. She half turned for a sideways glance at Dr Gibson by the shadowy doorway. Leaping flames in the hearth revealed his stooped silhouette and the negative swaying of his head.

Her husband attempted a wry, appreciative laugh at her sweet, hopeless encouragement but it made him wheeze and he fought to regain his breath. 'Will you do it now, for your poor old Danny?' he eventually squeezed out on a long, painful sigh. 'And will you promise that Samuel takes it today for the letter-carrier? For I want him to receive it in time. He is all the kin I have, apart from you.' As he sighed into the silence, there was a faint, appealing smile for his beautiful young wife.

Victoria nodded her dark head beneath his fleshless palm and cold, dry fingers drifted across her warm, wet cheek before falling back to the coverlet.

'Thank you, Victoria.' Relaxing at her wordless vow, Daniel Hart allowed speckled lids to droop over colourless eyes. 'You know what you have promised me, my dear. No widow's weeds…not for your Danny. Nor moping about indoors away from the young people you like. Never deprive yourself of your youth, or anyone of your sweet company. It is what I want, you know that, and others will too. It is a condition of my bequest, witnessed and sealed.' A dry chuckle preceded his next words. 'What care we for convention…you and I…eh, my dear?' He patted her slender white fingers in a gesture of dismissal.

As the rustling of her skirts told him she had risen from kneeling by his bedside, he murmured, 'There is something else you have to promise me, Victoria.' Into the rasping silence he finally breathed, 'Promise me you won't cry any more…'

David Hardinge, Viscount Courtenay of Hawkesmere in the county of Berkshire, paused while dictating and smiled. So infrequent a show of consideration and humour was this that Jacob Robinson, clerk and general factotum to the Viscount, actually ceased his frantic note-scribbling to stare at his master. He peered through his dusty spectacles at the lean profile presented to him as his employer settled broad shoulders comfortably back into his leather wing chair and brought the source of his amusement closer, savouring it. Startlingly blue eyes scanned an ivory black-edged card as he shoved back his chair and leisurely settled his highly polished top-boots on the edge of his highly polished ma-

hogany desk. He reread the few lines of elegant black script
while his long fingers sought on the desk for the cheroot
curling a gentle drift of smoke towards the lofty ceiling of
his walnut-panelled study. With the cigar stuck between his
white teeth, his narrowed blue eyes flicked upwards, contemplating the ornate plaster coving. As his mind sped back
seven years, the card was tapped idly against a manicured
thumbnail. A few seconds of reminiscence had his teeth
clenching on his cheroot and the card flipping casually
across the desk to land in front of Jacob. 'Send condolences
and usual regrets at being unable to attend.'

Juggling his lapful of letters and ledgers, Jacob finally
freed an index finger, stabbed it onto the card and slid it
closer. Once he'd read it, he wondered what it was about
a distant cousin's funeral, notified to him by the man's
widow, that could possibly give the Viscount cause to smile
in that unpleasant way. 'Sad business…' he volunteered,
hoping to find out.

His sympathy was ignored. David Hardinge leafed impatiently through a lengthy document. 'Have this delivered
back to Mainwaring by hand this afternoon with a note
stating that if he alters terms and conditions again the deal
is off. The contract of sale I issued last month is the only
one I will sign.' Piercing blue eyes fixed on the clerk as
David realised the man had noted nothing down but was
apparently fascinated by the notification of Daniel Hart's
demise. 'Have you got that dictation?' he enquired silkily
past the cigar clamped at one corner of his thin mouth.

'Sad business…' Jacob persisted, meaningfully pointing
his sharp nose at the card on the desk.

'Is it?' David Hardinge asked, feigned concern spuri-
ously softening his tone. The cigar was jerked from his
teeth and he studied its glowing tip.

'Oh, *yes*…' Jacob opined, pulling his lips into a sorrow-
ful droop. 'Poor Mrs Hart. Not married more than seven

years, I'll warrant. Widowed so young. I met her just the once, you know, at your brother's funeral. So charming a young lady, I recall.' He shook his greying head, reflectively sucking his teeth. 'Of course you were fighting alongside Wellington at the time, were you not, and missed laying your brother to rest, so perhaps you wouldn't know her. It's hard to believe that young master Michael's been gone these five years and that I've worked man and boy for the Viscounts Courtenay for more than twenty-five years and—'

'And there's no real need for it to continue beyond today,' David mildly threatened, while long fingers ground out his cigar so thoroughly that he singed them, shook them, swore audibly and scowled at Jacob's censorious look.

Oh, he knew charming young Mrs Hart, and she could damn well go to hell alongside her husband for all he cared. But he didn't, he reminded himself. He hadn't cared for seven years or more, not since her father had unceremoniously tossed his marriage proposal back at him and sneered in his face for his effrontery. David had known his youthful hell-raising was a minor consideration; it was his lack of money and status that was the genuine stumbling-block. Vice in bridegrooms was customarily overlooked so long as the prospects were right.

But, in fairness to the man, all of Charles Lorrimer's objections had been quite valid. And, in his own defence, in the six months he had gently courted eighteen-year-old Victoria Lorrimer, his behaviour and morals had been impeccable. Those of his parents, however, had continued to swill around in the gutter, to the vicious amusement of the *haut ton*. Paul Hardinge and the courtesan, Maria Poole, he had scandalously married by then had no further affluence or influence to buy acceptability.

In the distant days of childhood, he had been fiercely

loyal to his parents, believing them to be the butt of malicious gossip. But the craving for reciprocal love and attention had slowly eroded, finally extinguishing in his midteens when he'd abruptly had to accept that his mother *was* an unreformed whore and his father a drunken sybarite who had gambled away practically every asset the Courtenays had amassed over two centuries. Henceforth David had unswervingly believed what he was often maliciously told—that his destiny must be tainted and shaped by theirs—and had lived his life accordingly.

Until he'd seen Victoria Lorrimer. For six months he'd believed in salvation. He'd lived in daylight hours and serenity.

Within a month of his proposal the only woman he had ever believed himself capable of loving had married Squire Hart of Ashdowne in Hertfordshire, who, with typical bitter irony, happened to be some distant relation of the Hardinges. His father's great-aunt had married into the Hart clan in 1680, as he recalled.

Daniel Hart had a comfortable estate and wealth, and, at fifty-two, was some thirty-four years Victoria's senior and a mere fifteen years younger than her own dear papa.

His own dear papa had been dead of syphilis within six months and his older brother Michael had inherited the viscountcy and the escalating debts bequeathed by their wastrel father. When Michael had succumbed to smallpox two years into his birthright, after a valiant but unsuccessful battle to repair the Courtenay fortune and standing, David had gained nothing other than a title he didn't want and continuing ignominy. But he had risen to the challenge. If there was one thing David Hardinge had learned by the age of twenty-five, as he then was, it was how to survive, need no one, and decimate adversity through cunning and doggedness. He was grateful to Paul Hardinge for one solitary thing: his traditionally thorough education. His honed intellect was applied to his business affairs with the diligence of any trained banker. With the same typical irony, now he no longer cared, he found he had the respect and admiration of his peers, who ruminated enviously on how astonishingly he had turned about the Courtenay fortunes.

And now that David had money enough, he liked to enjoy the fruits of his interminable labour. He even allowed others to enjoy at his expense. He knew he had a reputation for being a generous man and was thus persistently targeted by women who, through necessity or choice, kept company with gentlemen. In short, he had a thoroughly pleasurable, if licentious lifestyle, and no intention of moderating any of it…ever again.

The devastation that had ripped into him on learning Victoria Lorrimer had married was now simply a hazy memory. Since then he was sure he had barely spared her an idle thought. He reluctantly conceded that odd; after all, thinking of her had for six months monopolised every waking hour and kept him hot, frustrated and celibate the night through. But then, at just twenty-three and still surprisingly reluctant to fully relinquish youthful idealism, despite the sewer in which he was reared, courting a beautiful, enchanting virgin to marry and play house with had seemed so appealing. A wry choke of laughter escaped him at the fairy-tale quality of it, causing Jacob to launch a quelling look his way and sniff, 'I don't see any humour in funerals myself.'

'Jacob,' David gently threatened, 'if we don't get through this correspondence in the time I have allocated to it, which is—' he consulted his gold fob-watch '—five minutes more, you'll be unamused to find yourself seeking alternative employment without a character.' Abruptly swinging his long legs off the desktop, he shoved back his chair and stood up. He stretched and flexed his powerful shoulders before wandering idly to the large casement window. A hand eased a niggling cramp at his nape as he gazed down onto the quiet elegance of Beauchamp Place. Creamstuccoed Palladian splendour soothed his restless gaze before blue eyes met a scene that elicited a smile of genuine amusement.

Richard Du Quesne, splendidly attired in a striking burgundy greatcoat trimmed with luxurious gold frogging, was sauntering towards his residence as though he hadn't a care in the world. This despite the fact that clutching at the man's arm was the mistress he had been trying to offload. Dickie Du Quesne was his closest friend—a true companion of similar taste and habits who shared a good deal of David's history, time and vices.

Sensing eyes on him, Dickie glanced up at the study window and grimaced his bored disdain for his friend.

A shrug of exaggerated sympathy met this. David drew a long finger leisurely across his immaculate silk cravat before closing his hand and explicitly indicating with his thumb along the street. She might be a countess, the wife of an impecunious, much cuckolded earl, but he had no intention of enduring her presence in his house this morning. Roberta Stewart knew her relationship with Dickie was in its death throes and had been casting about for an equally wealthy replacement. David knew himself as prime target. Since he had finished with her some months before Dickie had taken her on, her constant pathetic attempts at seduction aroused disgust rather than lust.

David currently had set up two fresh, eager young mistresses, one at either end of town; that way, whether finishing the evening at Cheapside or Mayfair, he had a willing body close by should he require it. When neither Annabelle Sharpe's creamy skin and thick auburn tresses nor Suzanna Phillips's rosy charms and wispy blonde curls held any allure, he allowed himself to succumb to sexual enticements. And he received plenty. Ambitious seamstresses, impoverished widows, bored titled ladies all constantly prowled in his vicinity, flirtatiously displaying their interest and availability. As he was so popular, he could afford to be choosy…and cautious. He had no intention of losing his own robust health to a dose of the pox or risking the appalling ravages that had preceded his father's death.

Thinking of widows brought Victoria Hart's pale, pointed face, smoky eyes and silken black hair floating into his mind's eye. A self-mocking twist of thin lips acknowledged that, seven years it might be, but he certainly hadn't forgotten her delicate beauty. Lean hands braced at either side of the casement showed steadily blanching knuckles. She was probably grown fat and matronly in her wedded bliss, and had several brats clinging to her rustic skirts.

He casually pushed himself back from the window, concentrating on his promenading friend. Once rid of Roberta, Dickie and he would take their usual stroll to Watier's for an afternoon of cards, dice or whatever pursuit took their jaded fancy. He idly pondered whether the bare-knuckle fight on the cobbles in Haymarket would go ahead this afternoon, but it occupied his mind only briefly. He collected his thoughts with iron discipline. His meeting with his clerk was not yet finished and business always took priority.

He had grown up having very little money, now had more than he was ever likely to need, and knew which state of affairs he preferred. Unlike a lot of his peers, commerce was accorded serious respect: he oversaw the execution of every single enterprise. He had a reputation as a fair yet unforgiving master. Those keen to feather their own nests at their employer's expense gave Viscount Courtenay an extremely wide berth.

His boot had once sent an amateur opportunist sprawling down his elegant front steps, causing Dickie to say admiringly that it took one to know one. That irreverence had earned his friend a playful cuff…David was professional…especially when devious. He slanted a glance at the old retainer who had stayed with the Lords Courtenay through fair, foul and fair again. Jacob was an inquisitive, irreverent old buffer, but he was extremely efficient and unwaveringly loyal and trustworthy. David knew that his half-hearted threats to put him off were now a source of amusement to them both. In fact, he'd really grown quite fond of him.

'Make sure that Mainwaring has that response regarding the sale of the property in Chelsea and deal with all other matters as we discussed.'

Jacob's short, wiry body carefully unfolded from the chair. He cradled his day's work in one arm while the other hand sprang to catch his spectacles before they slid from the end of his nose.

Reaching over his desk for another cheroot, David lit it and drew deeply until the tip ruddied. He speared long fingers through his dark mahogany hair, aware of the length of it and that he should get to his barber some time this week. In all other respects he was immaculately turned out as usual: a shirt of finest white lawn, a deep chestnut silk cravat similar in shade to his thick hair, and buff breeches of excellent quality and a style that snugly emphasised the considerable muscular length of his legs.

'Mr Du Quesne,' Jeremiah Clavering, his butler, intoned from the doorway, allowing David's comrade, well wrapped into his exquisite greatcoat, entrance to the cosy study.

As he caught the draught from the corridor, David stirred the glowing coals with the tip of his expensive leather boot. It had been a long, hard winter and these February mornings were invariably solid with frost. A sideways grin at Dickie acknowledged his glowing red nose, white cheeks and blond hair, lank with cold. His freezing friend immediately sought a place by the roaring fire.

'Nippy out there?' David needled.

'I'd taken two extra turns of the square with that silly bitch before someone hove into view and I managed to dump her. I'm not sure Wainwright will still be speaking to me... Damn!' he exclaimed, through chattering teeth. 'He'd best not consider returning her home a favour and cancel my duns.'

David laughed down into the leaping flames. As the chill from his friend's body permeated his comfortable warmth, he shifted to allow Dickie the best position in front of the hearth. 'You did well,' he soothed. 'Had you brought her in here, I would not have been best pleased. You'll get your money from Wainwright—' He broke off, noting Jacob was hopping from foot to foot, shifting and balancing documents in his arms while making grabs at the door handle. He strolled over and held the door wide. As the clerk exited under his braced arm, David instructed, for no reason he could understand, 'Forget that letter to Mrs Hart. I'll convey condolences myself at the funeral.'

It was certainly comforting to see so many paying their last respects to her dear Danny, was Victoria's consoling thought as she buried her small, trembling hands further into her sable muff.

This February morning was bright with winter sunshine but bitterly cold; the grave-diggers had laboured long and hard to scoop out her husband's final icy resting place.

Parson Woodbridge dropped a fistful of dark soil into the grave and it hit Daniel Hart's coffin with a splattering thud. He inclined his head at her and she stepped unsteadily forward on numbed legs at the signal. The mixed sheaf of fragrant herbs and flowers she had collected that morning was released into the earth-dark void. Despite her solemn promise to Daniel that she would not cry, she felt melancholy tears heating her hastily closed eyes. Withdrawing her gloved fingers from their warm nest, she pressed them to her eyelids, chafing delicate skin with the black lace veil shrouding her small, sculpted face. Damp, inky lashes slowly unmeshed to expose luminous damson-grey eyes and she raised her head, again composed…and saw him.

She squinted through a teary film and an involuntary gasp of recognition was heightened by fierce frosty air abrading her throat. He was standing a way off, absolutely still—a solitary figure divorced from those by the graveside stamping frozen feet and huddling close together for warmth. She was sure he was staring at her as intently as she was at him, despite her veil and matted lashes distorting her view. And she quietly knew that after seven years he would look as she remembered him even though his features were indistinct. He looked statuesque outlined against a washed winter sky, and quite frighteningly imposing. He seemed more powerfully built. Perhaps he had grown broader, or perhaps it was just an illusion created by his heavy black greatcoat. A steamy haze froze before his face and this undeniable proof that he was not a figment of her imagination but a living, breathing man simultaneously cheered and alarmed her.

He must have just arrived, walked up alone from Hartfield to the chapel, for he hadn't left with the mourning party. He was a head taller than any man here and impeccably attired; she would never have missed him.

Victoria dragged her gaze back to Parson Woodbridge's kindly face as he concluded the funeral service and indicated to her that the pair of grave-diggers would like to continue about their business.

It was too final! She couldn't yet relinquish the man who had cared for her, provided for her and her relatives. It was too soon.

Despite the empathy radiating from the friends and neighbours grouped about her, she felt alone and frightened, and that stomach-churning anxiety was now oddly intensified by the shadowy, remote figure on the edge of her vision. She suddenly wished that Daniel hadn't insisted she write and ask him to come. Why had he? There had been no bond between them other than a distant kinship that neither man had ever sought to acknowledge or build on.

She became conscious of people looking more purposefully at her. Stiff fingers were being warmed with puff-cheeked breaths and chilled cloaked bodies batted with rigid arms. They were patiently awaiting a signal to leave.

'Are you ready, Victoria, my dear?' the parson enquired kindly as he took a pace towards her. 'Come, my child, you'll freeze,' he coaxed, taking her arm gently and turning her about. 'You can return later, when these men have done their work, with another pretty posy and a nice hot toddy inside you.' He lifted a bony gloved hand to his bulbous nose set in a curiously gaunt face. 'I do believe this is twice its normal size,' he gently joked as he led her away. Sheeny grey eyes raised to his painfully purple proboscis and Victoria choked a hysterical giggle. She gratefully held his arm as they slowly made their careful way back down the frost-glistening grassy hillock to the shingle path that wound to Hartfield. The mourning party, approximately a score in number, fell into step behind them. A quiet murmuring among its members could be heard, conveying gladness that the ceremony was satisfactorily accomplished, and that a fire and a warming drink awaited them at Hartfield.

They would pass close by him, Victoria realised, for he had not so much as budged an inch from his isolated spot. Raising her head as she drew level, she turned; courtesy decreed she acknowledge him. Glistening grey eyes were immediately entrapped by a steady sapphire gaze. Powerless to break free, she glided on until looking across at him became impossible and she finally twisted her veiled face away and exhaled.

The blonde woman climbed the last mound. Pausing to draw a spiteful breath, she spied the snaking trail of mourners trudging away towards Hartfield. But her narrowed green eyes were almost immediately skimming back to the churchyard, targeting the sole remaining figure. Her interest quickened at his virile attractiveness, but it was his obvious affluence that drew forth a calculating smile.

Ignoring the open grave, the tall, impressive man strolled the rimed grass towards the shingle path. Feline eyes tracked him until he latched the lychgate, when they pounced forward onto the slightly built young widow far in the distance and close to the saintly parson.

The woman's generous mouth thinned in malice. Wrapping herself more closely into the warmth of her thick cloak, she picked a careful path across the slippery turf. She glared boldly at the two labourers who began whispering as she approached. Leaning on shovels, they watched curiously as she stared down at the coffin partially obscured by a few scoops of rich dark soil.

Muttered curses, loud and crude enough to make the grave-diggers exchange an appreciative look, preceded earth piled along the edges of the grave being sent hurtling unceremoniously back into the void by a small booted foot. Then, with a dramatic swirl of her cloak, the blonde woman was hastening back across the fields in the opposite direction to the mourners and Hartfield.

'Here, drink this,' Laura Grayson urged her friend as she held out the glass of mulled wine.

Victoria gave her a grateful smile but her eyes were discreetly watching the door, sliding over familiar faces to find one she hadn't seen for so long.

She felt neglectful now and ill-mannered. She had not so much as nodded to him in welcome or recognition. All she had done was stare like an idiotic fool. She so hoped he would enter the house and take a little refreshment before leaving. He had no doubt travelled from London. He must be tired…thirsty. Guilt and shame suddenly swamped her. He obviously felt shunned; she had written and invited him to attend the funeral, as Daniel had bidden her, yet done nothing to greet him. Daniel would have been rightly horrified by such lack of hospitality.

Her aunt Matilda entered the drawing room and immediately made for the roaring fire, a glass of warm wine grasped in each hand.

'Your aunt Matty seems in fine form,' Laura said wryly, but her troubled hazel eyes searched Victoria's strained countenance. 'Daniel would hate to see you looking so peaky. Remember those promises you made,' she gently reminded her.

Victoria gave her friend a wan smile, then directed a speedy, searching glance at the ancient gentleman ensconced close to the wide hearth. It judged him to be quite comfortable and cosy. 'Would you mind my papa, Laura, while I ensure everyone has some refreshment before they leave? It is so terribly cold and some have travelled far.' Having received an immediate affirmative to this request from her friend, she hurried away.

People waylaid her to sympathise, making her pause to graciously thank them, but as soon as possible some inner desperation had her hastening on. She was sure he was here solely from his own sense of duty: he felt obliged to pay his last respects and would probably leave as soon as he deemed that achieved. The notion that he might go before they had even exchanged a few words, before she had even thanked him for attending, had her running.

Her black crape skirts were gripped in small white fists as she flew out into the chilly hallway and came upon him immediately, talking with the Reverend Mr Woodbridge. She stopped dead, her heart thumping so hard it was as though she had sped up three floors while searching for him in each of the fifty-two rooms that comprised Hartfield.

She paused to compose herself, noting that Jonathan Woodbridge had the appearance of a scrawny crow beside the expensively attired, athletic physique of the man who stood head and shoulders above him. He was listening with his lean, handsome face politely inclined towards the cleric's sunken features. Both men saw her at the same time and as she moved forward again she silently gave thanks to Jonathan Woodbridge for his thoughtfulness. No doubt he had noticed the stranger in their midst and had taken it upon himself to welcome him. The people of Ashdowne were naturally hospitable folk. As she now classed herself amongst them, and was the largest landowner, she felt sadly lacking in duty. And duty was something Victoria had never shirked.

'Mr Hardinge.' She warmly greeted him, extending a small, gloved hand which he courteously, fleetingly touched. The extreme brevity of the contact made her withdraw it quickly and shield it amongst her stiff black skirts. But she cordially continued, 'I'm so glad you have joined us today. It is an honour that you have travelled in such perilous weather to attend Daniel's funeral. You are very welcome. Please come through into the warm.' Perhaps he had misunderstood her invitation to seek the fire in the drawing room, she thought when he neither moved nor spoke, but she felt the intensity of his blue gaze prickling the top of her head. 'May I fetch you some mulled wine? Something to eat? There is a spread upon the dining table,' she coaxed huskily, including Jonathan Woodbridge in this invitation so she could avoid those penetrating sapphire eyes.

'That sounds very good, Victoria,' Jonathan said, with a twinkle to his watering eyes, his skeletal gloved hands clasping together before him as he purposely made for the drawing-room door.

Left alone in the marble-flagged hall, Victoria realised that now the parson had withdrawn there was no one else on whom to focus. She summoned a firm smile as her eyes finally raised to meet his and the breathtaking sight of him stopped her heart.

He *was* as she remembered but every feature, every hard, angular plane of his face, seemed more intense, more roughly hewn in maturity. There was none of the bright freshness of youth left in him. But his eyes seemed bluer, his jaw leaner, his mouth thinner—crueller, she realised. His hair seemed deeper in colour, bronze-black in the dim hallway light, and so long it curled thickly onto the collar of his coat.

'Please have something to drink at least,' she quickly rattled off, aware that she had been staring. 'I would hate you to set back on the road having partaken of nothing at all.'

'Well, I'll accept a little refreshment, then, Mrs Hart, for I'd hate to offend you,' David Hardinge smoothly said.

Victoria visibly relaxed and smiled at him with an unconscious sweet familiarity that hinted at their distant courtship. For a moment the charm bound him. Long fingers were raised to her face, lifting and slowly folding back the lacy veil over the crown of her hat, revealing her features.

His eyes scanned her countenance and she watched his back teeth meet, shooting his jaw out of alignment. Her smile and budding confidence faltered as she waited for a comment or sign as to how their reunion would proceed.

As the silence between them tautened, she obliquely recalled addressing him incorrectly and seized on that for further conversation. 'Oh, I'm so sorry. You are now Lord Courtenay. How stupid of me to have forgotten. I knew, of course, because I attended your brother's funeral with Daniel. It must have been…five years ago. But I didn't see you then…you weren't there… I believe you were abroad…the war…' She was babbling, she realised wildly, and abruptly clamped together tremulous lips and bit down on the lower one.

David's eyes were drawn immediately to the small white teeth gripping at that soft full curve. His lids swept down, shielding the expression darkening his eyes to midnight, and a muttered curse was hastily choked in his throat. Fat? Blowsy? Matronly? If she had children and this was how they'd left her…

She was everything he remembered, but so much more. More beautiful, if possible: she'd lost the youthful fullness in her face and now had cheekbones like ivory razors. Her inky lashes seemed lusher, her eyes more storm-violet than grey, her hair gleaming, glossy jet. Her nature seemed as sweet; that poignant melancholy she was trying to disguise with tentative friendliness made him want to do something idiotic like comfort her; cuddle her against him in a way he remembered doing so long ago…

His eyes ripped from her upturned face to stare across her dark head. The sooner he was out of here the better. He'd been a fool to come. There had been no need. A simple note of condolence would have sufficed. He'd take a glass of wine then get the hell out back to the Swan tavern at St Albans and pray that Dickie had found them some diversion to occupy his body and mind before they set off on the road back to London in the morning.

'Lord Courtenay?' a male voice queried uncertainly.

Victoria and David both immediately, gratefully looked

about, glad of the distraction as the tension between them strained unbearably.

Sir Peter Grayson, Laura's husband, had just entered through the great arched oaken doors of Hartfield and was clapping together his leather-gloved palms to warm them. He brushed flakes of snow from his caped shoulders and knocked them from the brim of his hat.

'It's snowing…' Victoria murmured.

'I thought I recognised you,' Sir Peter said at the same time, directing a huge grin at David Hardinge.

David smiled as recognition dawned. 'Peter, how nice to see you.' He gripped the hand extended to him, while trying to block the memory of the last time this man and he had socialised. It had been about a year ago at a discreet private salon run by a personable widow. The evening of music and cards had terminated in its customary drunken orgy. The amusing memory of this young buck, cavorting naked except for his cravat, was difficult to banish.

As though abruptly recalling the same event, Sir Peter flushed, making Victoria look curiously at him. An embarrassed cough preceded Peter's hasty, 'I must introduce you to my wife, Lord Courtenay. Where is Laura, Vicky? Have you seen her?' He chattered on. 'It must be more than a year since last I spoke to you. How have you been? I rarely get to London now, you know. I spend all my time here in Hertfordshire. I was married in October of last year…and have never been happier.'

David inclined his head, acknowledging the caution. 'Of course…' he soothed.

'Ah, here she is…' Sir Peter said with a mix of relief and horror as Laura's slim, black-clad figure drifted into the hallway from the drawing room.

Aware that a perfect opportunity for her to escape and compose her thoughts and a perfect opportunity to waylay David Hardinge longer had presented itself, Victoria appealed to her friends. 'Please show Lord Courtenay the fire and the refreshments. I must just check that my papa is comfortable.

'It is freezing out, Papa, and snowing again too,' Victoria consoled her father a few moments later. 'It is bitterly cold. Far too cold for you.' She raised a cool, pale hand and laid it gently against his papery cheek. 'See how chilled I still am, and I have been indoors for some while. Daniel would not have wished you to endure such inclement weather by the graveside. You know it would make you cough.' She tucked in the rugs more closely about his bony frame but he grumbled incoherently and plucked at the blankets as she neatened them.

'I'm hungry. Is there some wine?' he demanded testily, making Victoria smile wryly. At times her poor, confused papa had no difficulty at all in making himself understood.

'I'll fetch a little porter for you,' she promised, while removing his spectacles from where he had wedged them in the side of the chair.

He suddenly stiffened and leaned forward to hiss, 'Who is that? Do I know him?' Victoria half turned, still bending slightly over him, and even before she saw him, she knew to whom her father referred.

David Hardinge was grouped with Laura, Sir Peter and several other neighbours who, curious as to his relationship with the deceased, had come forward to be introduced to this handsome, charming stranger.

And he was both, Victoria had to acknowledge. His manners and appearance were exceptional. He had removed his greatcoat and handed it to Samuel Prescott, her male servant, on entering the drawing room, and now stood, superbly attired in black superfine tailcoat and trousers of expert cut and finest quality. A large black pearl nestled in a silver silk cravat at his throat. That he was now fabulously wealthy was beyond doubt. Everyone in his vicinity was focussed on him, and although he returned conversation his attention soon drifted elsewhere. He raised his glass of warm ruby wine and tasted it while watching her and her father over the rim.

'Who is that?' her father demanded stridently, making several people close by turn and sympathetically smile at her. 'I recognise that devil…'

'Papa…hush…' Victoria soothed, feeling her face heating. As she turned away, she caught sight of a strange, humourless slant to David Hardinge's thin lips, and heard his murmured excuses to his companions before he strolled over.

He looked down impassively at the brain-sick, elderly man for several seconds before quietly saying, 'Hello, Mr Lorrimer.'

Charles Lorrimer peered up at him. He dug frantically in the sides of his chair for his spectacles but, finding nothing, he simply squinted foxily. 'I suppose it's been two months, then,' he finally snapped, running his rheumy grey eyes over the man's supremely distinguished figure, 'and you've come back to buy my daughter.'

Chapter Two

'You have a fine memory, Mr Lorrimer,' David Hardinge quietly, drily commented.

Long, sooty lashes swept to shield the horrified embarrassment darkening her eyes before Victoria snatched a glance through them. David's face gave nothing away. He was watching her father with what could have been wry amusement twisting his hard-moulded mouth. Any anger or umbrage was admirably concealed. Victoria steeled herself to hold the narrowed blue gaze that sliced to her, hoping he could detect in her expressive eyes her heartfelt regret at her father's indiscretion.

'Hah, you see, I have a fine memory.' Charles Lorrimer smugly emphasised his point by clawing at his chair with skeletal fingers and inclining his fragile frame towards them. 'She will not believe me when I tell her so,' he conspiratorially confided to David Hardinge. 'She says I am confused. But it suits her to say such things…to be cruel to her father and to lie to me.'

'Papa!' Victoria gasped, hurt and shame hoarsening her voice.

'I remember she said she would fetch me a nice glass of

warm brandy, but she has not,' was next sniped craftily at his white-faced daughter.

'I said a glass of porter, Papa. And I will fetch it, or get Sally to do so, if you are just patient a moment—'

'And where is Daniel?' Her father tetchily cut short her hushed placation. 'Danny said today I could have snuff. Where is my son-in-law? He treats me better than my own flesh and blood; I swear he does. He is a true friend, a fine fellow. He will fetch me snuff and brandy...'

'What is up with you now, Charles?' a female voice boomed into his senile self-pity. 'What are you blathering on about?' Matilda Sweeting's black-bombazine-clad figure pushed forward and she thrust one of her glasses of mulled wine towards her brother. 'Here, take this and cease crabbing,' she ordered him bluntly. 'And don't guzzle it so or 'twill make you cough. No doubt your lungs will then be my concern...'

As Matilda continued to upbraid her brother good-naturedly while tugging at his blankets to neaten them, and Charles ignored her advice and gave hearty attention to his wine glass, Victoria instinctively withdrew. The past few fortifying minutes had drained her complexion and dilated her pupils to glossy gunmetal. She thankfully noticed that none of those standing close seemed to have overheard her father's impropriety. Or, if they had, they were paying scant attention to Charles Lorrimer's latest odd ramblings. Indeed, there was an atmosphere of pleasant gregariousness about the mourners now that Sally and Beryl had set to and mulled wine was being freely distributed and imbibed. Victoria finally allowed her dusky eyes to glide up to David Hardinge's face, for she was aware he had moved away from her father's chair as she did.

'I'm so sorry...' she breathed.

'I have to be going...' he said.

Their quiet words collided and they fell silent together

too. After an awkward pause, Victoria resumed her low apology. 'I assure you he meant no real offence. He cannot help the way he is. I sincerely regret if he has caused you—'

'He has caused me nothing. Nothing at all,' David interrupted lightly, his eyes on a spot on the ceiling. 'But you have every right to feel slighted. Is he often so?'

Victoria glanced hastily away from eyes that had swooped to hers, feeling more humiliated by this man's pity than by her father's rudeness. She simply nodded quickly, casting about in her mind for a change of subject in case he enquired further.

He did not. He repeated mildly, 'I have to go now, Mrs Hart. I'm not offended, I promise. My leaving has nothing to do with your father…'

David glanced down into her beautiful, solemn face. Well, that's the whole truth, ran self-mockingly through his mind as he forced his eyes away again. It certainly was nothing to do with her decrepit father. It was everything to do with her. If he stayed longer she might tempt him to do or say something he was sure to regret. The urge to touch her was tormenting him. He longed to discover if her hair was as silken; even now he could recall its fine texture slipping beneath his fingers. He wanted to glide his thumb across her sculpted jaw, the delicate ridge of her cheekbones—repossess skin that looked so incredibly pale and soft.

But he could control it, he sardonically reminded himself, because he was different now. He readily acknowledged burgeoning lust; more worrying was a stirring of emotional commitment. But it was a while since that had mangled him and the notion of ever again allowing such vulnerability was so ludicrous, it almost prompted him to laugh.

So what if her father treated her ill? It was none of his

concern. So what if she was now widowed? It was hardly
the time or place to capitalise on it. Propositioning a woman
on the day she buried her husband was beyond even his
amoral sensibilities.

So he was still leaving, right now, and going back to
what he knew he wanted: a good tavern, a good friend and
a good night of uncomplicated roistering. Because that was
what he was good at. And then tomorrow, as he journeyed
home to Mayfair and his life of luxury and debauchery, he
could leisurely castigate himself for ever being idiotic
enough to come here at all. God only knew why he had.
Travelling in freezing weather to watch earth shovelled
atop some distant relative he barely knew…sheer madness!

David flicked a glance at the elderly man he had once
despised and felt nothing. No disgust, no hatred. But he
avoided looking back at that man's daughter, because he
knew he couldn't pretend the same apathy, much as he
wanted to.

'I shall just find one of the servants to fetch your coat,'
Victoria politely informed him, feeling ridiculously hurt
that he would not stay longer; that he could not even seem
to look at her for longer than a second.

Cool hallway air fanned welcomingly against her flushed
cheeks as she sped to find Samuel. Her head hammered
with tension and haunting words she'd believed she had
successfully buried so long ago but never would stay forgotten.

*'He wanted to buy you…he said he would do it. He
wanted to buy my daughter as though she was some common whore. But then that is all he is used to and all you
mean to him…'*

Her father's bellowed words of seven years ago throbbed
in her head. She had dismissed it all as lies. Everything she
had heard whispered abroad about David and his family
she had rejected as vile rumour. She was aware that the

beau monde loved nothing better than to maliciously dissect reputations, especially those of their peers. Even when Aunt Matilda had tendered cautions about her socialising with roguish David Hardinge or his wayward friends, Victoria would have none of it. She was too much in love, too obsessed with this man who wooed her with a captivating, tender passion yet never once attempted to coerce or take advantage of her. And she knew there had been times when he could have, when fate and obliging friends had allowed them a stolen hour alone, and she would have summoned little resistance had he decided to seduce her.

During their short, six-month courtship, David had shown her more affection, more gentleness and respect than any other man she had known. Even her own father. And she'd told her father that, earnestly, and it had earned her a hefty blow and her immediate banishment from Hammersmith to Hertfordshire. Following her father's ranting censure, still she would not believe that David Hardinge was a callous rogue who did not love or want her.

Unknown to her father, she had managed to smuggle out two letters to David and had been certain he would soon rescue her. In them she'd made so plain her love for him, and the fact that she was prepared to wait, to elope, to do whatever he wanted, so long as he still loved her and would soon come for her. Yet the weeks had passed with no message, no reply…

Then one afternoon, when her father was away from home, Matilda had managed to sneak to her room to gently break the news that David had left the country and was believed to be travelling abroad. With those few whispered words had come real despair. The first inkling that she had been duped…abandoned had iced her skin and made her stomach churn so violently, so indelibly that she could taste the fear again now. Curled on her bed on that autumn afternoon, she had finally given way to a keening, draining

grief that no amount of calming draughts or soothing plat-
itudes from Matilda could ease, and only exhaustion could
curtail. The redolence of that earthy, rain-spattered October
day teased her nostrils anew; the memory of the incongruous perfection of the rainbow that had later bridged the
house dazzled her mind. Swollen-eyed at her window, she
had watched the drizzle soften into a harvest evening of
such serene beauty that somehow she had found the
strength to weep again.

Yet still she would have waited…so desperate was she
to believe David honourable and her trust in him justified.
But the empty days had crawled by, her father's rancour
had escalated to new, demented heights and a final, painful
decision had had to be made.

And now she finally knew the truth of it… The awful
fear that she had been wrong to marry so soon, that she
should have suffered in that harsh, soulless environment
longer, had evaporated. Her decision to accept Daniel's offer of shelter in an unconventional marriage had been vin-
dicated.

'*I suppose…you've come back to buy my daughter…*'
her father had just said in his painfully honest way, and
David Hardinge had simply smiled and complimented him
on his fine memory.

Her black lacy veil tumbled forward onto her brow and
Victoria swiftly unpinned the hat, dropped it carelessly onto
a hall table and hurried on.

What did any of it matter now? It was all seven years
old! she impressed upon herself, furious that a wedge of
melancholy was blocking her throat. How could she even
dwell on it? She had just buried her dear husband. He had
been a fine, generous husband for seven long years. David
Hardinge had been a reprobate playing a convincing role
for just six months.

Daniel's selfless goodness had stirred feelings of guilt:

he might have made a second marriage to rival the consummate success of his first. But whenever Victoria had mentioned such doubts he would smile, with his pale eyes distant, and tell her that such love came but once and that once was a privilege. But a daughter to care for… God had never been that kind to him…until now.

Victoria sighed, dragging her thoughts to the present. If only Daniel had not made her promise to write to David Hardinge, she would have been as oblivious to his disturbing presence today as she had been last week…last month…last year. But for the worry of Danny's illness and her papa's worsening dementia, she had been virtually content with her lot in life here at Hartfield. Now she felt hot and restless…and queasy, as though a nest of vipers writhed in the pit of her stomach.

Nearing the kitchens, she spied Samuel's broad back huddled close to the short, plump figure of Sally, one of the domestics. She had believed Sally still to be serving refreshments in the drawing room. A sigh of impatience escaped her.

'Samuel, Lord Courtenay is leaving. His coat, please…' The young couple immediately shifted away from each other. Sally bustled past with a deferential dip of her brunette head but her face was blotchy from weeping.

Victoria closed her eyes in sheer exasperation. She could not countenance dealing with any histrionics from the servants…not today. She already felt as though she was wound as tightly as a spring. Just one more twist and she would snap; of that she was sure.

Samuel tried to pass her too with a gruff, cooperative, 'I'll fetch it straight away, ma'am.'

Victoria placed a restraining hand on his beefy arm. 'Samuel…this is too much today. Can you and Sally—and I suppose it's Beryl involved too—can you not at least cease your bickering on a day such as this?' she stressed in a voice quivering with emotion.

'Sorry, ma'am…' Samuel mumbled, his coarsely attractive features ruddying in embarrassment and remorse. Straightening his waistcoat with a businesslike jerk, he sedately walked on.

Victoria stared at the kitchen door then momentarily closed her eyes, composing herself, before swishing about and calmly retracing her steps.

She emptied her mind. Nothing was allowed other than the need to get through this day. She concentrated on whether any mourners would expect bed and board. The weather was now so inclement it would invariably come to that, she decided. That would entail arranging chambers and linen, further meals… She was exhausted and desirous of solitude, not extended company. But it was her duty and she would deal with it, just as she always had since Danny's illness had shifted such mundane matters onto her slender shoulders. For with his declining health had come declining fortune when he'd no longer devoted attention to his business affairs. And as their income had reduced so had the number of servants they could employ at Hartfield. But she had been happy to take over housekeeping duties when Mrs Whittaker had retired and gone to live with her sister in Brighton. And thus the first economies had been made.

Victoria completely ignored the reflexive jump of her heart as she rounded the corner into the main hallway and immediately spied David Hardinge's tall, imposing figure. He was chatting to Sir Peter by the double arched entrance doors. She focussed on being relieved that Samuel had speedily set about the task of returning the Viscount his coat. That comforting emotion was immediately whipped from her as she anxiously noticed Beryl's neat, black-uniformed figure sidling up to Samuel by the hall table. But

they both appeared fully occupied attending to guests'
cloaks and gloves and quite oblivious and uncaring of each
other.

A grateful sigh escaped. Any further embarrassing do-
mestic situations and she was sure she would scream or
weep. Instead she stifled a wry laugh at the very idea; such
selfish indulgence was a luxury, and there would be no
more of those.

Having cordially shaken hands with his old acquaintance,
Sir Peter turned back to the warmth of the drawing room.
Victoria received a friendly, slightly inebriated grin as he
passed.

'Thank you once again, Lord Courtenay, for being good
enough to attend Daniel's funeral. I hope the weather im-
proves for your safe journey home.'

David inclined his dark head, acknowledging her civil
good wishes, even though they held the same arctic quality
as the air outside. His eyes reluctantly shifted from her face
to gaze at something distracting behind her. 'One of your
servants seems a little upset,' he mentioned impartially.

Victoria felt a stinging surge of blood heat her cheeks.
So Beryl and Samuel had not contained their differences,
not even for the five short minutes that would have been
necessary for David Hardinge to have taken his leave. Narrowed blue eyes scanned her pink, tense face as he said,
'You already know about it…?'

The hint of mild concern in his tone snapped up her
glossy black head. She had no use for his pity and would
have liked to tell him so. Instead she murmured stiffly,
'Yes, I do know, thank you,' while wishing the floor would
open up and swallow her…or this taciturn man who assuredly never tolerated tantrums from his domestics.

Pride aided her swift composure. 'It has been a very sad
time for us all. My husband was well liked and respected
by the servants…by all who knew him.' It was a quite

truthful prevarication. The rustling of Beryl's stiff skirts as she scurried away was all that broke the ensuing silence.

'I believe I've been remiss in not yet offering condolences on your loss, Mrs Hart,' David eventually said. 'Was he a good husband?'

Grey and blue eyes linked then strained. 'I'm sure there was never better,' Victoria quietly stated, and something about the way he found that cool sincerity amusing twisted her stomach.

He extended a hand in farewell and she allowed him one of hers for the briefest moment. His smile quirked sardonically as she exactly matched his reaction to her touch earlier. Then all that was left with her in the hallway was an icy draught and a dusting of snowflakes melting on the marble flags.

The sun was lost early today, Victoria realised glumly as she glanced out through the casement window in Hartfield's small library at the clouding sky. She finished totting up the column of figures in the household accounts before pushing the ledger away from her and laying the quill back on the blotter. It mattered little how many times she did the sums; the balances never looked any healthier. But she had made economies before; it was simply a case of cutting back a little further.

Daniel had always praised her housekeeping skills, in the early days of her undertaking the task, marvelling at the way she could make do and mend, bargain with tradesmen and generally pinch a penny until it squeaked. As he'd grown weaker, she'd known he no longer had strength enough to worry or enquire as to how she did.

She had no idea where her talents for parsimony came from: until her marriage she'd had no experience of household budgeting or hiring servants or paying wages. But she had been reared on thrift. Her father had never been a generous man where she was concerned—either in his time, his affection or his coin.

She withdrew her mother's locket from the pocket of her serviceable serge gown and laid it on the blotter. A finger traced the carved gold surface before she opened it with gentle reverence and looked at the miniature portraits of her parents. The likenesses had been painted shortly after their marriage, some twenty-eight years ago. Her father was strong and handsome, his hair as black as her own, despite the fact that he was then in his forties, and his eyes bright and alert. Her mother looked serene: her luxuriant auburn tresses swept back from the delicate bone-structure of her ivory-skinned, heart-shaped face. She had been more than twenty years younger than her husband.

Whenever Victoria feasted her hungry eyes upon the beautiful mother she had never known, she understood how awful it must have been for the man who'd doted on her to have lost her. She understood why her father resented her; why she had grown up shunned as an unwanted burden rather than a cherished child. For her mother had relinquished life in order that Victoria could have hers and she knew her father had found that impossible to forgive. The sad irony was that her late husband had lost both his newborn daughter and his first wife in childbed and had cherished Victoria as his child-wife.

In her early years, her dear aunt Matty had done her best to substitute herself as the mother Victoria had never known. She had also upbraided her brother many times for his coldness and neglect of his only child. Victoria had overheard their cross words on occasion, and knowing she was causing her father that family pain too had served only to turn the screws of the awful guilt that racked her. And she marvelled at her aunt Matty's temerity. For she had been, during their days in Hammersmith, an impecunious widow reliant on her brother's charity, and to scold him as she did, and on another's account...

Matilda Sweeting's life had never been easy. She had married a penniless scoundrel who purported to be a naval officer, given birth to a son and been widowed all in the space of two years. Despite her wastrel husband having frittered away all his own money and then hers too, Matilda had managed to retain her pride and her sanity. And then when her only son, Justin, had disappeared in his sixteenth year, she had again drawn on that unbreachable resilience to overcome the disaster. He had been press-ganged, or so they believed, for there was no other credible solution to his disappearance some eleven years ago in the vicinity of the London dockland. Matilda spoke rarely of him now, but when she did it was as though he was alive and well but just too busy and successful to visit yet awhile.

Victoria focussed again on her parents' youthful, attractive faces. There had been a lot of heartache for the Lorrimers in the past twenty-five years. A troubled sigh escaped as she dwelt on her father's dementia. Heartache wasn't yet over.

A bar of warmth gilded her clasped hands on the desk as the sun escaped cloud. She turned her dark head to the window. The bitter winter was extending into late March but had not prevented spring bulbs spearing the frozen ground. The sight of yellow and mauve crocuses interspersed with snowdrops bobbing their drooping heads prompted a wistful smile. The sky was clouding again already, slowly obliterating the lucid sunlight, but she resolved to go. Each afternoon in the hour between finishing her bookkeeping duties and organising preparation of the evening meal, she would walk the short distance to the chapel and tend her husband's grave.

'I thought I might find you here.'

Victoria started, gasped and twisted about so quickly that

she almost pitched forward onto her knees. She shielded her eyes as she peered up at the man standing a few paces away on the shingle path. He stepped jerkily forward, belatedly steadying her with a meaty hand.

'I'm so sorry, Mrs Hart; I didn't mean to frighten you,' he earnestly apologised. 'Samuel said you're to be found here most afternoons. I…I needed to speak with you…' He looked at the grave, the pretty arrangement of pastel spring flowers atop the cropped grassy mound. 'I apologise for intruding on a private moment… I just… I'm afraid it is important.…'

Victoria banged earth from her gloved hands. 'Please don't apologise, Mr Beresford. In any case, I was just about to return to Hartfield. 'Twill soon be time for dinner. Will you stay and dine?' she pleasantly invited her late husband's attorney.

Alexander Beresford reluctantly demurred but with grateful thanks for the kind offer as he gallantly helped Victoria to her feet. She was surprised to see him. He usually made the trip from the town of St Albans to the village of Ashdowne about once every six weeks to advise her on Daniel's investments and her current financial situation. She was sure not yet a fortnight had passed since last she had seen him. He was a pleasant, stocky man of perhaps thirty-five. He seemed efficient in all he did and had been a great deal of help to her in the weeks following Daniel's death, patiently explaining exactly what provision Daniel had made for her and that, with careful administration and a tight grip on the purse-strings, the funds would prove adequate to frugally maintain Hartfield.

She noticed he seemed more nervous than usual. Despite the chill afternoon air, a beading of perspiration glistened along his hairline. 'Is something amiss, Mr Beresford?'

He cleared his throat, thrusting large hands into his great-

coat pockets while gazing off into the distance. This was
to be a momentous day for both of them and he still wasn't
sure how or where to start. So he didn't. 'You have made
that look very nice indeed, Mrs Hart. Those bright flow-
erheads can be seen from beyond the chapel gate.' His
praise was fulsome yet not once did he glance at the crocuses he so admired.

'*Is* there something amiss, Mr Beresford?' Victoria persisted, seeking contact with his evasive brown eyes.

'Yes, Mrs Hart, there is,' Alexander Beresford told her
bluntly, his gaze finally colliding with hers. 'But I think we
should leave further discussion until we're back at Hartfield.' With a solemn air of finality he offered her his arm.

'Surely the warehouse ought to have been insured against
fire?' Victoria demanded of Alexander Beresford, seated
opposite her, his papers spread across her small library
desk.

The man raked some chubby fingers through his brown
hair. 'It seems it was not, Mrs Hart. I have to admit to
being equally amazed and angry at this discovery.' A
stubby finger poked between his neckcloth and his red-
mottled throat. 'The clerk charged with dealing with insurance cover on the premises at the East India Dock had not
paid over the cash to the insurance company. In short, the
man appears to have fraudently used the money as his own
and allowed the policy to lapse.' Mr Beresford clapped both
hands down on the table, pushed himself back in his chair
and issued a hearty blow of mingled annoyance and resignation. 'None of which helps your cause, I'm afraid, Mrs
Hart. Practically all Daniel's stock was lost in the inferno.
The rogue could possibly be punished, if the theft was
proven and his whereabouts discovered. I have it from a
reliable source that the coward is gone to ground. No doubt
he trusted the theft would go undetected.'

Victoria gazed at him with wide grey eyes. The enormity of what he was saying was slowly penetrating her mind, in terrifying fragments. 'Just how badly will I…will Hartfield…be affected by this loss, Mr Beresford?' she asked quietly, determinedly.

His thick fingers plucked distractedly at the papers in front of him before clasping together. 'To pay off creditors Hartfield must be sold,' he eventually burst out.

'Never!' Victoria whispered in fierce astonishment. She certainly had not anticipated that things were as bad as that. 'Daniel bequeathed Hartfield to me to provide a home for us all. And also to retain the servants who have served him…us so faithfully. Some have been at Hartfield for twenty years or more. Samuel was but nine years old when he commenced work in the stables. I would feel I had utterly failed Daniel…betrayed him, and so soon. It is barely eight weeks since his death. No! There must be some other way…'

'I have searched for other ways, I assure you,' Alexander Beresford stressed quite truthfully, his fleshy face ruddying in indignation. 'The bank that forwarded loans to Daniel for the speculative purchase of those silks and cottons, now mere ashes, is pressing for payment. I need to forward some cash soon. An interim payment might appease them for a short while. I suggest sale of the last of the sterling bonds…' He swivelled some papers towards her as he spoke, but they barely received a cursory glance. Her grey eyes were pinned back on his face, desperate for some reassurance that this awful, unexpected situation wasn't as dire as it seemed. None came.

'I'm sorry, my dear, but Hartfield will need to be sold. And as soon as possible. There is no stock now to sell to meet the interest or the principal. You probably know that during your late husband's illness his finances declined quite considerably. There is the matter of the overdue rent from the Holdbrook farm, but I know Daniel was not keen to sue for that while the family were suffering such tribulations.'

Victoria nodded, murmuring her wholehearted agreement with Daniel's forbearance. The tenants at that farm were experiencing dreadful hardship: two of the sons had been taken with consumption and just before Daniel had died of the same pitiless condition they'd had word that the youths' mother was also afflicted. Adam Holdbrook, a man in his late forties, was now struggling to run his farm single-handed and rear three young children under five years of age. To insist on payment of overdue rent at such a time would have been beneath humanity. In fact, it was time she visited the family with a little of Hartfield's butter and cheese. Samuel had told her only that week that, in desperation, Adam Holdbrook had sold the family's last dairy cow. At one time, Daniel had been in a position to help luckless villagers. It had cemented good relationships between landlord and tenant. Now there was very little she could offer at such times. Her thoughts raced back to her own predicament. The awful truth was that she might soon be in need of a little charity herself.

'Will there be any residue from the sale? Enough to provide a home for myself and my father and aunt?'

'There will be very little, my dear…very little indeed.' Alexander knew there would be nothing but voicing as much was beyond his courage.

Victoria stared at him, obliquely aware that he was kindly trying to comfort her. He had done so before on the fateful evening Dr Gibson had told them that Daniel would be dead before morn. And when reading Daniel's will to her and explaining that everything her late husband owned was to be hers.

Hartfield was to be hers to keep or sell as she would but no other man would ever lay hands on it. Codicils had been added to the deeds to Daniel's estate so it could be bequeathed to her yet never pass out of her control and into the unworthy clutches of a future husband, should she remarry.

Alexander Beresford's brown eyes settled on the woman he secretly desired and admired. He strove for the boldness to voice his proposal. 'There is another way, Victoria.'

The immediate bright hope in her eyes made him blurt quickly, 'You could…you should remarry.'

Victoria frowned across the library table at him. 'Remarry? My husband is barely eight weeks buried. It is far too soon; besides, I have no wish…'

'I realise, my dear, that so soon might seem indelicate but in circumstances such as these…desperate circumstances…people understand such behaviour. What choices have you? A man to support you or employment are the only options if you are to avoid the parish relief.'

'Well, which man would take on a widow with an estate and property to upkeep that will never be his own? He would need to be a wealthy saint. No such man exists.'

'Well, naturally, Victoria,' Alexander Beresford said mildly, 'no man would burden himself so. Hartfield must be sold to meet your debts, for no man would take on such losses. But you still need protection and security. And any amount of gentlemen would be proud…happy to have you grace their home…' *And their bed,* ran involuntarily through Alexander Beresford's mind, making his chubby features perspire at such lustful thoughts. He repeated quickly, 'No, Hartfield must be sold to pay your debts and I expect you would feel obliged to make provision for your relatives before you wed, if at all possible.'

'My relatives? You mean my papa and Aunt Matilda? Well, naturally they would live with me…'

'Daniel Hart was indeed philanthropic. But a new husband might not countenance such an arrangement, my dear,' Alexander warned firmly. His brown eyes roved discreetly over her fitted buttoned bodice. Even the drab mourning grey and serviceable material could not deflect an appreciative glance at her slender ribcage and small rounded breasts.

He was determined to make his offer and in the circumstances was reasonably confident of it being successful. But his means and generosity would never stretch to her extended family. He earned a reasonable salary, had good prospects, and a comfortable home in St Albans. Victoria was very welcome to share it as his wife but his duty ended there. He had no intention of charitably boarding and lodging her brain-sick father or her outspoken widowed aunt, no matter what precedent Daniel Hart had vexingly set.

She would lose Hartfield. She had debts to pay and would thus lose the home her husband had had in his family for three generations. This was all that dominated Victoria's mind. Daniel had left it in her safekeeping and within two months of his death it was to be lost. But how could she have prevented it? She could never have averted this disaster. Was there sense in Alexander's proposal that another good man might be her salvation? She had married one kindly husband who had cared for her and her family. But then Daniel Hart and Charles Lorrimer had been old acquaintances: she had known her late husband all her life. She had always liked him…trusted him implicitly. It was the reason she had agreed to marry him when her future looked so bleak. She sighed dejectedly. 'My papa and my aunt are settled here. I so wish my father could see out his remaining days at Hartfield.'

'Well, I would do all in my power to please you, my dear,' Alexander said. 'But retaining Hartfield even for one more month is, I believe, quite beyond me.'

Victoria looked at him with wary grey eyes. Surely he didn't mean…?

'I see you have guessed, and I can't say I'm surprised for I know I have difficulty at times in shielding my feelings for you. I have long admired you, Victoria. To my shame, I held you in great affection even when Daniel was alive. I envied him so...' The admission seemed ripped from him.

'Please, I feel I should stress that I...that I...' Victoria could think of nothing to add quickly to make him stop.

'No, let me finish. I must say these things, my dear. I have loved and admired you for a long while. It would make me the proudest man alive if you would consent to be my wife. I have a comfortable villa in St Albans and good prospects and salary. I have my business premises there and ambitions to expand and take on a partner—'

'Please, I have to speak.' Victoria softly interrupted him. She smiled and it prompted the florid-faced man to spontaneously reach across the table and grasp one of her small-boned hands in his pudgy fingers. The instinct to withdraw from his moist palm was not easily curbed. 'I truly thank you, Mr Beresford, for your proposal. But I cannot...I cannot even countenance remarrying at present. Your kindness in offering to share your home with me does you great credit and me great honour. But at present I cannot consent...'

'I understand; of course I do. A year at least to mourn one's dear departed is usual...indeed expected. I have spoken too soon in the normal way. But circumstances are no longer normal. People understand that financial hardship countermands such codes. But I understand you need time to think.' He gave her a rather sweet smile. 'I pray you will consider quickly and favourably, Victoria.' He hurriedly collected together his papers and within five minutes was gone from Hartfield.

As Victoria pivoted on her heel in the hallway after the great door closed behind him, she pondered on all he had told her. She thought of her father and her aunt and, because he was a kind man, she knew Alexander would provide for them. She turned back and stared at the arched oaken doors of Hartfield. He was quite right: her circumstances were exceptional. Protection for herself and her family was a priority; clinging to social niceties was not. She suddenly felt sorely tempted to run after him and give him her answer now.

Chapter Three

'Well, I think it is an admirable idea!'

'You do?' Victoria quizzed her aunt, amazed.

'Of course. What you have to bear in mind, Vicky, my dear, is that you are property-rich but income-poor. You need an alliance with a man who is the reverse. That would solve everything.'

'I am not property-rich, Aunt Matty,' Victoria patiently explained. 'The bank will seize Hartfield, and Alexander Beresford is hardly rich…'

'Tush, not him!' Matilda Sweeting dismissed, contemptuously flapping a hand. 'We can do better than him, I'll warrant. We want a man of serious wealth, not reasonable prospects. No, what we will have to do, my dear Vicky, is take a trip to London and put you on the marriage block!'

'You are simply priceless, Aunt Matty,' Victoria censured on a giggle. 'In case it's slipped your mind, I am not a debutante of eighteen with an enticing dowry but an impecunious recent widow in her twenty-sixth year. Husband-hunting so soon and so blatantly would be frightfully unseemly. Besides, how many rich saints do you know that we can impose upon? For such a man is indeed what we need. Someone willing to take on all the responsibilities of

Hartfield, and yet be content never to own it himself. A man prepared to support with equanimity a wife and her relations…' Victoria glanced anxiously at Matilda's reaction to that; she hadn't meant to imply her aunt was a burden.

'Keep your head still,' Matilda ordered, unperturbed by Victoria's tactless comment. She gently drew a silver-backed hairbrush through her niece's thick hair, fanned ebony tresses over the shoulders of her white cotton nightgown and teased strands to frame her ivory complexion. Satisfied with her artistry, she curved her age-spotted hands over Victoria's silken scalp, showing her her reflection in the glass. 'Now tell me which man would not like that beautiful sight greeting him nightly.'

'Aunt Matilda!' Victoria admonished in an outraged squeak.

'Now don't get prudish with me, my girl. What you have to bear in mind is that what always counts with gentlemen when the chips are down—or more importantly aren't down in our case, as we are all now so poor—is the lure of beauty. I suppose that tubby solicitor courting you told soppy tales of admiration and respect,' Matilda fawned, contorting her lined cheeks into further wrinkles. 'Pah! He desires you. So does every lusty male who claps eyes on you…that's the truth of it.'

Placing her elbows on the dressing table, Victoria rested her slender chin in her cupped hands and looked. Limpid grey eyes roved across her creamy brow from where ebony satin hair curtained her small, heart-shaped face. She swivelled her pointed chin in her palm, examining her features. Her nose was too short and narrow, she was sure, and her mouth too full and wide. But throughout her life she had been told she was pretty. Even her papa had once grudgingly admitted that she mirrored her mother's pale beauty and not a scrap of him…apart from his black hair. But she could only recall him complimenting her that once, when mellow with brandy and *bonhomie* after a successful afternoon's gambling at his club. There had been very few such cheering incidents. He'd invariably lost, and heavily. Yet he would return to St James's confident of recouping the previous day's misfortunes.

Daniel had constantly said how proud he was of his child-wife, as he affectionately termed her. But the man who had pleased her most with his quiet compliments…she no longer thought of, she firmly reminded herself, abruptly sitting back in her velvet chair. But her grey eyes held with her reflection. She rubbed at her high cheekbones, stirring some colour into them.

'Leave yourself be!' Matilda whipped pins from her own greying locks in readiness for retirement. 'You weren't meant to be one of those milky-pinky misses with yellow hair and baby-blue eyes,' she lisped through the pins lodged temporarily between her teeth. They soon scattered on the dressing table. 'You're just fine as you are. I noticed David Hardinge couldn't keep his eyes from you…when he thought you were looking elsewhere, of course. I swear you quite took that *wealthy bachelor's* breath away,' she innocently declared, sliding a pale blue eye sideways at her niece.

Victoria stood up abruptly. 'Indeed I did,' she admitted sourly. 'So breathless was he in my company, he had difficulty speaking at all. We barely exchanged a dozen words, in the short while he deigned to stay at his kinsman's wake.'

'Well, the memory of him has certainly cured the lack of roses in your cheeks,' Matilda lightly remarked, eyeing the becoming flush warming Victoria's face. 'I've heard from my sources in London that he is now so eligible he is sought by all the top hostesses, yet shuns most in favour of carrying on regardless. Of course his affluence and title ensure he is welcome whatever his character and reputation.' A reflective pause preceded her next words. 'I thought he seemed much older and rather cynical about the eyes and mouth. But then it hasn't detracted at all from his looks; quite the reverse. Maturity sits well on some men: gives them presence and sophistication. To look at him, so handsome and dignified, you would judge him a paragon of propriety.'

'Perhaps he is,' Victoria remarked lightly, as though, truth or not, it concerned her little.

'Indeed, he's not!' Matilda scoffed. 'Last time I sat down to a hand of brag with Colonel Whiting and his lady, I overheard the gentlemen tattling about Viscount Courtenay. Never mind.' She drily anticipated and answered Victoria's unspoken inquisitiveness. 'They sounded quite green with envy and were no doubt vastly embellishing it all. They must have been! The few snippets I caught would have shocked the devil himself!'

'How can you intrigue me so then refuse to say more? You have to tell me now,' Victoria petitioned with a brittle little laugh.

'Indeed, I shall not! It's not fit for these old ears.' Matilda batted at them in emphasis. 'I'll certainly not repeat such lewd, shameless behaviour to a genteel young female.'

'It concerned his lady friends, then?' Victoria probed, dipping her head and brushing her hair.

'Friends, maybe…ladies, never!' Matilda snorted. 'And you'll prise no more from me, my girl. You've tricked me into saying too much as it is. Now I'm off to find my bed. These old bones need some rest.' She halted with her hand on the doorknob. 'What you have to bear in mind, Victoria, is that there are far worse things than marrying a libertine for his money and his title. After all, once you were prepared to marry him when he had neither,' she added wryly, closing the bedroom door.

* * *

'I thought I ought to bring this to your immediate attention, my lord. Albert Gibbons had it hand-delivered. As you and the lady are almost related, he probably guessed you'd be concerned at the news.'

David Hardinge frowned at this cryptic comment and immediately took the proffered note. It had to be news of some import from his solicitor, he supposed, breaking the seal, that had brought Jacob out in the sleety rain to seek him at his club. A frown and narrowing of incredulous blue eyes were swiftly followed by an exceedingly contented smile. As David relaxed back into his chair, leisurely re-reading the note, he gave a throaty, satisfied laugh, thereby prompting Jacob to sigh and give an imperceptible shake of his head. He had anticipated a mood of shock and sorrow at the calamitous information contained in the missive, but his master was merely surprised…and pleased.

He had always believed he knew this Lord Courtenay well. He would have held him up as a charitable man; not one apt to crow over others' misfortune. It was true he was ruthless in his business dealings, especially with any foolish enough to attempt trickery. Nevertheless, he could be outstandingly generous. William Branch, not even one of his closest chums, had fallen foul of the dice once too often, yet had been saved from the Fleet by the Viscount's funds forwarded at a paltry percentage. Was not his lordship also invariably generous to his women, past and present? Redundant paramours were amply compensated. In fact, Jacob was prone to tut and mutter about economies every time he dealt with such pension funds.

Yet Lord Courtenay learned of disasters affecting his late cousin's family and it gave him cause to chuckle. Jacob had heard about the inferno that had decimated a warehouse on the East India Dock and knew, unofficially, that Mrs Hart was now destitute because of it. Well, perhaps the hard-hearted devil wouldn't find it quite so amusing if his kinsman's widow decided to petition for his charity. Jacob glared through his spectacles at his master's hard face. Yes, that might just test his generosity and his humour, for he'd heard her losses were colossal.

Having folded his hand of poker and taken leave of Dickie Du Quesne and various other acquaintances at White's, David Hardinge walked back through the cold drizzle towards Beauchamp Place. His thoughts would have surprised his clerk, half running beside him to keep up with his long stride, had Jacob but known them. Far from maliciously relishing Victoria's fate, what he sardonically savoured was his own.

At one time, and not so many years ago, nothing in his life had ever gone the way he wanted. Now luck ran so persistently in his favour that it tended to rouse his sceptical amusement.

During the past two months, a plausible reason to approach Victoria Hart and offer her his protection would have had him bartering his soul. And now he had one. Not only that, but after what he'd just learned he was quite confident she would be readily amenable to his overtures. Contrarily that disappointed him: nothing and no one seemed to be a worthy challenge any more.

In the first month following their reunion he had striven daily to exclude her from his mind. Finally accepting that as utterly impossible and therefore utterly infuriating, the second month he'd given in, succumbed to self-torment and had cast about desperately for some tenable excuse to return to Hartfield.

Now he had it, and just in time: this irritating obsession he had with possessing her had vexed him long enough. Deliverance from it lay in indulging it until it palled, and that was exactly what he intended to do. So her impending bankruptcy aroused little sympathy for it suited him and need never harm her. She would be well cared for. His women always were.

Dwelling on her delicate beauty softened the hard set of his features. Despite her grief on the day of her husband's funeral, she had clung tightly to her composure, admirably dealing with her servants and her deranged father. She had dealt admirably with him too. Yet she had wanted him to stay longer and had poignantly lacked the guile to conceal it. Pride had made her try, he allowed with a wry smile, recalling her aloof civility and how sweetly vulnerable it had made her seem.

From the moment he had walked away and into the snow he had wished himself back with her. It was only later, at the Swan tavern, that he'd grudgingly accepted he'd run for cover. No other woman had ever rattled him the way she did, or made him feel simultaneously lecherous and caring.

On hearing another low, private chuckle, Jacob muttered beneath his breath, sprinted ahead up the steps of his master's magnificent town house and rapped impatiently on the enormous stately door. Turning back, he watched his employer stroll on through the icy mist as though promenading on a summer's day, hands thrust deep in his pockets, a vague smile about his narrow mouth.

'It's fate, that's what it is. The stars have decided the matter for us,' Aunt Matilda announced breathlessly on entering the dining room two mornings later.

Victoria enquiringly raised dark brows, while carrying to her father his tea and toast. She placed his breakfast close by him, retrieved his napkin from the carpet, replaced it on the polished mahogany table, then gave her aunt her full attention.

Matilda held out a letter towards her niece, shaking it excitedly. 'See what the express has just brought. There, read that!' she ordered. 'It's a sign. I swear it is. Charles, if you drop it again, you remain jammy-mouthed,' she warned her brother as he furtively lowered white linen towards the persian rug.

'Where are the kippers?' Charles Lorrimer demanded, through the napkin scrubbing at his mouth. 'I don't want this…' He sent the plate of toast and jam skidding away across the table's glossy surface. 'Where is my proper breakfast?'

'You know kippers give you indigestion, Papa, and the bones catch in your teeth,' Victoria calmly answered, while reading the letter in her hand. It was from her aunt's sister-in-law, Margaret Worthington, and its purpose was to invite Matilda and a companion to Cheapside in London to attend her daughter's birthday celebration in two weeks' time.

'Well, you must go, of course,' Victoria told her gleeful aunt as she handed back her letter.

'*We* must go,' Matilda stressed for Victoria. 'You and I now have a reason for a trip to town and the perfect venue to socialise. Margaret has some very influential friends. You must remember her daughter, Emma. Nice enough but a plain little thing. I'll warrant Margaret must be fair despairing of ever shifting her. She must be twenty-four now if a day. But the girl always was too much of an opinionated blue-stocking…' Matilda halted mid-flow. 'Of course! She has probably invited every eligible man for miles around to attend. It will be just perfect for us. You'll outshine every female there. Margaret will be spitting mad…'

'Aunt!' Victoria cautioned, noticing that her father was leaning towards them in his chair, straining to listen, a crafty look crinkling his eyes and mouth. 'You must go and enjoy yourself, Aunt Matty, but much as I would love to join you it's impossible,' she stated quietly and firmly as she noticed her aunt about to protest. 'I am a recent widow. I know I promised Daniel not to mope and weep but extravagant socialising is too much. Besides, Papa needs me and so does Hartfield.'

'Well, what you have to bear in mind, my girl, is that this might be your last chance for either of them to need you,' Aunt Matilda hissed in an undertone. 'There will soon be no more Hartfield to concern you. Every stick of furniture, every acre and barn will be sold…gone unless you find a man to take it all on. And as for your papa…' She nodded meaningfully at her brain-sick brother, polishing the dining table with his napkin dipped in tea. 'How long do you think he will stand the rigours of the parish relief? Or a lunatic asylum, for that matter? Your chubby solicitor suitor has no intention of burdening himself with either of us old 'uns, you know.' She gave Victoria's arm an encouraging shake. 'Daniel doted on you. He would want you safe and happy. With his last breath he decreed you enjoy your youth. You know that's the truth. Besides, Margaret is my late husband's half-sister and it is an age since we met. We are not gadding, simply visiting relations.'

Victoria started awake from her snooze as the carriage jolted. As it slowed a small exclamation of dismay escaped her. But mercifully it picked up speed. If they had halted once again and she had had to endure George Prescott pacing to and fro mumbling and grumbling that he was *in a bit of a quandary*, she was sure she would have resorted to hysteria.

Her tapered fingers whitened on the battered upholstery of Hartfield's travelling coach as she leaned forward to blink sleepy eyes at the passing shadowy scenery.

The cottages were getting closer together and there were fewer intervals of wooded countryside—a sure sign that they were approaching the outskirts of the city. They had already lost several hours while Samuel's uncle had dithered about going this way or that.

As Samuel could not be spared from managing Hartfield or caring for her papa in her absence to drive them to London, he had suggested that an uncle of his, now retired, would be happy to take on the job for a small consideration. A reciprocal small consideration from Samuel's uncle would have been very welcome: to wit, an admission that the man had not travelled this route either as coachman or passenger for more than sixteen years and that his sight and his memory were useless.

Twice they had turned into narrow lanes leading nowhere. Manoeuvring their small carriage and two elderly greys about had proved arduous and almost impossible.

Twice Victoria had suggested cancelling the trip and returning to Hartfield. Then later in the week they could catch the stage from St Albans and travel to town in a sane and relaxed manner.

Beryl, for her own reasons, had heartily concurred with this. Her aunt had told Beryl to mind her business before impressing on Victoria, with a cautionary wag of the head, that they *bear in mind* the importance of this trip. Also, that Margaret Worthington was expecting them and would be horrified should they not arrive, suspecting all sorts of devilry had befallen them on the journey. This genuinely concerned Victoria. There was no way a message could speedily be sent to their hostess, who was kind enough to be putting them up for a week at Rosemary House in Cheapside. She was probably even now preparing for their arrival.

When George Prescott had then insisted that he was out of his quandary and into his stride, Victoria had relented. So they persevered towards London but were several hours behind schedule.

She glanced across at her two female companions, one propped in either corner of the creaking carriage, both sleeping soundly. Neither had spoken a word to the other since the clash of opinion about continuing to London. Thereafter, simmering resentment was limited to ostentatiously shifting as far apart as the small travelling coach allowed.

Beryl had sulked from the moment she had learned she would be acting as maid to Victoria and Matilda on this trip. Victoria knew it was not the thought of dressing a head of hair, which she did remarkably well, but the thought of Sally exerting influence over Samuel in her absence. But it would have been impossible to leave the two women together, sharpening their claws on each other while vying for Samuel's favours. Separating the housemaids was the only option in her absence from Hartfield.

The carriage juddered and slowed. Victoria immediately pulled herself towards the window and peered out. There were two conveyances in front of them now and, on the right-hand side, a row of grimy building tenements.

London! At last! A few hawkers' shouts were audible amongst the rattling of carriage wheels and as they proceeded they merged into a thrum of sound. Victoria inhaled carefully, sure she could detect tar and brine in amongst the pungent whiffs assaulting her nostrils. She squinted into the gloom and in the distance made out rigging and masts rising like grey skeletons against a velvet night sky. They were obviously near the Thames.

A young boy, perhaps seven years old, caught her attention by waving a hand; he then held it out, calling for coins. Even in the twilight, Victoria could discern his ragged, emaciated body and it tweaked her heartstrings.

The babble and stench of the city increased, permeating the coach. A mouth-watering aroma of savoury pies became submerged beneath the stomach-churning stink of ordure. Victoria drew the leather curtain over the draughty window. She glanced at her female companions; neither was in the

least disturbed by the city hullaballoo and both gently
snored on.

The thought of Rosemary House—warm refreshment and
a soft bed close at hand—made Victoria simultaneously
contented and conscience-stricken as she thought of the
filthy urchin she'd just spied. As she shifted to find a comfortable spot on the cracked hide seat, her weary head lolled
back into the squabs and her eyelids drooped.

They flicked up within a few minutes. The coach had
stopped. She waited tensely, then felt the vehicle rock on
its axle as George Prescott descended from his perch. Victoria fought to budge the coach window to speak to him;
he was now conversing with someone by the greys' heads.

George looked searchingly about in the manner of someone locating their bearings and Victoria groaned despair-
ingly. He scratched his head thoughtfully, then, urged by
his rough-looking companion, walked towards a crowd of
people.

Without sensible thought, Victoria was out of the coach
and running to apprehend him. 'Mr Prescott!' she called
loudly, holding her skirts as she skipped and dodged the
debris in the street. 'What is happening? Where do you
think you are off to? Are we arrived at Cheapside? Why
have we stopped here?' Her queries and accusations came
tumbling out.

'I'm in a bit of a quandary, you see, Mrs Hart...' he
began sheepishly. 'Now you get yourself back in the coach
while I finds out from these folks jest where we are. This
kind gent reckons Rosemary Lane be up there and a turn
back towards the Ratcliffe Highway where I believe we jest
came through. Er...we've been around in a circle, like...'

'We're lost again?' Victoria demanded incredulously,
and then, horrified, corrected, 'We require Rosemary
House, in Cheapside, Mr Prescott. Not Rosemary Lane.'
She glanced warily at the scruffy, stocky man with George

Prescott. His features were virtually lost beneath a tangle of beard that seemed almost attached to scraggy brows. His sharp black eyes were distinguishable: they slipped assessingly over her fine clothes before sliding sideways to the unattended carriage behind her.

Victoria stiffened. Two sleeping women were left there alone and unprotected. She attempted to divert the man's astute stare. 'Are there street entertainers?' She was sure her voice sounded squeakily unnatural and quickly indicated a crowd of people forming a circle. Raucous shouts and laughter crescendoed as people began spilling onto the cobbles from brightly lit inns and gin shops situated on either side of the narrow street. Flares formed moving pools of glowing gold amid flickering patches of darkness. She watched in increasing alarm as drunkards linked arms, holding each other up, yet still up-ended tankards and tots. Two blowsy, rouged women passed close by and subjected Victoria to a spiteful-eyed stare.

'Look at 'er…proper Miss 'Oity-Toity, ain't she?' one spat coarsely. They both screeched with laughter as the scruffy man gave them a playful shove and told them to mind their manners. Before weaving on, they swore and gesticulated good-naturedly at him.

'Why not look, my lady?' her unkempt champion challenged her. 'We gets people o' quality about here on cock-fighting night. Lords 'n all sorts. They comes to wager and partake o' the sport. Jugglers in the market there. Plenty to see 'n buy. Yer'll judge us proper decent folk compared to the Ratcliffe Highway scum. Come, yer'll not be alone wi' ruffians. I'll look out fer yer and finds out direkshuns to… What was that address agin? Rosemary sumthink?' He solicitously lowered his head for her response but his intention was closer inspection of what delightful promise Victoria's cloak concealed.

Cautiously stepping back, Victoria glanced appealingly

at old George Prescott. Her driver was scratching at his head again. 'As I recall, Cheapside is…' He rotated on the spot with a searching finger in the air.

'Cock-fighting, you say?' Victoria gulped, feigning interest in the barbaric pastime. Their carriage was still intermittently drawing this rough stranger's acquisitive attention, and, hoping to distance him from it, Victoria said breathlessly, 'I've never before seen such a spectacle…'

The man obstructed her as she made to speed past him. 'Nor never likely to see agin, I reckons. What you doin' 'ere? Sweet little lady like you? Come fer the sport, did yer? Bored little lady, is yer?' he breathed close to her face with a foxy smile. 'Well, I'll shows yer some better sport than yer'll get off them cocks…' He howled with laughter, painfully tightening dirty fingers about an evasive arm.

'Unhand me at once,' Victoria demanded, her alarm now backed by anger, her grey eyes sparking jet-black in her white face.

'Unhand you…is it?' he mimicked. 'You ain't in Mayfair now, duckie. Yer on my manor and yer'll…'

Victoria was no longer listening. She was staring wide-eyed past her tormentor and at that precise moment the focus of her amazement turned, laughing, from his male companion and saw her.

'David…' Victoria whispered in shock and stupendous relief.

'Victoria?'

She was too far away from him to hear her name, but she saw it on his lips, just as she saw her own disbelief and astonishment mirrored in his face. His blond companion took money from his unresisting fingers then wandered off towards some stalls set up.

There *was* a small group of gentlemen present, clearly distinguishable by their arrogant bearing and expensive dress. And they were, indeed, wagering, she obliquely realised. This local ruffian hadn't lied on that score. As though sensing he was favourably considered, the man fumbled two large hands inside her cloak.

For little more than a second Victoria desperately fended him off, then he was savagely spun away from her and sent tottering back on his heels.

David Hardinge stood facing the giddy Lothario with his back to her. 'Not your type, Toby,' he stated, in an odd mix of lazy drawl and steely threat.

The man regained his balance, simultaneously shaking his shaggy head and whipping up ham-like fists in aggression. But, instead of charging, grimy fingers scraped across his bristly, bashful face. 'Sorry, milord. Didn't know she was yours, honest.' He shifted uncomfortably then executed an incongruous sort of bow-cum-curtsey before sloping off, muttering, 'Some looka.'

Before Victoria could draw breath to thank him, she was propelled backwards, fast up against the licheny brickwork of a building. Two rigid, barring arms slammed at either side of her, shielding her face from view.

Everything once dear and familiar about him bombarded her senses: his warmth and muscular strength, his fresh cologne, so welcome a fragrance in the hotchpotch of odours. Instinctively she swayed closer then started back.

'What the hell are you doing here?' David Hardinge bit out so ferociously through his teeth, his thin lips barely parted.

Victoria winced as though he'd hit her. His intense, almost tangible fury dried her mouth and her head throbbed with tension.

The shabby stranger had alarmed her; this elegantly dressed man she believed she knew terrified her. Yet, paradoxically, a serene sense of safety let her rest back against the brickwork and raise languid eyes to his. Flickering torchlight threw into stark relief his fierce, anxious expression. Fear for her safety had prompted his anger. The instinct to protect radiated from him. It was in his rigid stance, in the way he used his body to shield her as people pressed close by them.

Hard, unsteady fingers lifted to her cheek before sliding across her jaw.

Mesmerised by the soothing caress, Victoria simply stared up at him. She had thought this all forgotten, banished from her life for ever. This touch…this man inclined towards her, his mouth close to hers.

Long sooty lashes parted to reveal tortured relief in his sapphire eyes. 'What in damnation do you think you're doing here?' he gritted out.

'Looking for you,' Victoria answered with rash honesty.

Chapter Four

'Looking for me?' he repeated.

Victoria dipped her head, feeling her face heating at her unguarded confession. But it was honest, she remotely realised. It was the absolute truth. She now accepted in this noxious London marketplace what she had refused to acknowledge in the quiet sanctuary of Hertfordshire: the only reason she had agreed to leave her papa and Hartfield in the servants' care was to come to London with her aunt, seek out this man and ask him to marry her. To save them all from destitution, she needed him to want her again.

'Looking for me?' David persisted, a light finger sliding beneath her oval chin to try to make her meet his eyes.

Victoria subtly shielded her chagrin by turning her face into his shoulder. Everything had gone so awfully wrong! And so soon! He would naturally expect some explanation for such an outrageous declaration. She had seen this man but once in seven years. That reunion had hardly been auspicious, yet, despite it, she had just freely implied searching an insalubrious London district for him on a chilly spring night.

Subconsciously she had planned a far more favourable meeting. Perhaps when she was finely dressed in her beau-

tiful lilac silk gown, when she could attempt to charm him
as she once had. As it was, she knew she looked fatigued
and dishevelled. Her grey velvet bonnet had been discarded
in the carriage and dusky tresses wisped untidily about her
face in the biting night breeze. Her dark woollen travelling
cloak had been chosen for warmth rather than fashion. Oh,
there couldn't have been a worse time for her to have let
slip such vital information!

'I'm flattered, Mrs Hart, that you wanted me so desperately you tracked me to one of London's most notorious
rookeries. Nevertheless, a visiting card delivered to Beauchamp Place would definitely have been wiser.'

His bored irony and the way he formally addressed her
both froze and fired Victoria. So she was 'Mrs Hart', and
no doubt a tiresome nuisance who was ruining his evening's entertainment.

Her cool, dignified expression clashed with one of sardonic intensity. 'I intended to do exactly that, Mr Hardinge.
I have certainly not sought you out specifically this evening. How could I possibly have known of your whereabouts?' she demanded on a derisive little laugh. 'I had no
idea *you* would be here...I had no idea *I* would be here,
for that matter. We are lost and...' Her scornful defence
faltered. 'We are lost' ran back through her mind. Oh, God!
She had completely forgotten about her aunt and Beryl, still
in the coach. Oh, she hoped they were still in the coach.
They could have been abducted or robbed or murdered because she had been foolish enough to abandon them defenceless and sleeping.

'Thank you for your aid, sir. I apologise for detaining
you,' tumbled from her lips as she attempted dodging past
him.

It was impossible to go anywhere. His arms remained
stationed at either side of her. Her small hands rose, yanking desperately at his forearms to remove them. Iron muscle

flexed within the fine wool of his coat as he thwarted her attempts to shift him.

'Do you really want to roam unescorted through this drunken rabble, Mrs Hart?' he quietly asked. 'You've met Toby and should deem yourself fortunate: in comparison to some of the stevedores around here, he's a reasonably decent chap. He, and many others about here tonight, are also in my employ. Were they not, both you and I and my companions would now be fighting to keep our valuables…and our lives. You haven't the vaguest idea where you are, have you? This isn't a charming Hertfordshire village, Mrs Hart. There's a deplorable lack of chivalrous squires in these parts.'

'I am being made perfectly aware of that, Mr Hardinge,' Victoria tartly retaliated, incensed by his ironic allusion to her dear, late husband. 'Please allow me to pass. I have to return to my companions and I have no wish to detain you from rejoining yours.'

'Companions? There are more of you?' David demanded on an incredulous laugh.

'Indeed. And I am anxious for their welfare after what you have told me…' Her voice quavered as her fragile composure finally cracked. She heard him curse beneath his breath and frantically blinked away the betraying, humiliated tears glossing her eyes.

She had been such a stupid fool! In every single way! She railed at herself. She should never have voiced her intention to approach him while in London. She should never have clung to her idiotic hope that he might treat her with respect and kindness. If he could abandon her to seek diversion abroad merely weeks after proposing and declaring undying love, then there could be no chance of courteous indulgence now, after seven years. He had forgotten their youthful friendship and had made that much perfectly clear two months ago at Hartfield. She almost laughed hysterically; it had been her intention to come and appeal to his good nature!

She knew bored, wealthy gentlemen mixed with all levels of society in their quest for diversion, but for this viscount to mingle with these vagabonds… And, worse still, to seem quite at ease and accepted by them. She recalled the painted-faced vulgar women who had verbally abused her. She also recalled her aunt's genuine shock and disgust when recounting details of his debauchery. Surely not with such as were hereabouts…? It was too much! With a choked, woeful sob, she shoved fists against his solid torso, desperate to escape.

Firm, gentle fingers slid into her hair, holding her close, as he wordlessly allayed her alarm and anger. And, despite all her misgivings, her face instinctively sought the familiar muscled nook below his shoulder as though it were only yesterday when last she'd found comfort there.

'I have to go back to my aunt. Please let me go back. I'm worried some ill might have befallen her and my maid…'

Shielding her slender body with the solid strength of his, David began shouldering a path through the throng. Even in her agitated state she realised people were deferentially clearing a path for him to move through. One woman bobbed a curtsey and several men dipped heads or tugged forelocks as he approached.

A press of people milling on all sides forced them to a halt and David's arms circled her protectively. Victoria darted anxious glances this way and that and spied Toby; with him was a woman whose neat, fashionable attire made her seem oddly out of place. At that precise moment the woman's blonde head turned and almond eyes glanced idly about then swept back to her. They narrowed to slits and Victoria was horrified to read not only recognition but cold hatred there too. Those feline eyes shifted to David, lingering covetously on him.

Victoria stared, mesmerised, as the woman spoke to Toby. He looked startled and stared over at them before dropping his dark, wiry head close to his companion's elegant coiffure. The woman began hurriedly moving away from him. They were arguing, Victoria realised, and quite violently, judging by the way people close by were turning to laughingly watch. Then the couple were disappearing into the bobbing, seething throng.

Feeling unaccountably alarmed, Victoria nestled instinctively into David. Her disquiet took on a keener edge as long, controlling fingers urged her body into even closer contact with his. Her senses were chafed raw by the heat of him warming her, a muscled thigh melding against her hip, a hypnotic gaze drawing grey eyes to blue. Slowly, inexorably, her ebony head was angling back. She sensed him inclining towards her, his mouth a mere sigh away.

Cherished, buried memories surfaced immediately. She had loved it when he kissed her. Leisurely, drugging assaults inflicted with narrow, sensual lips that looked so selfish, so savage…yet had often been unbearably attentive and kind. Her thick, lush lashes unmeshed; she glimpsed what she yearned to touch her as her eyes swept upwards to his face…and through a break in the crowd she spied her coach.

Drenching guilt that she had momentarily forgotten it and relief that it hadn't, after all, been misappropriated vied for supremacy. She prayed her aunt and Beryl were still safely within.

They weren't! Victoria ripped free of David's grip. Dodging the last few folk weaving about, she skipped over the filth on the cobbles and ran lightly to her travelling companions.

'You are a most stupid man!' met Victoria's ears as she

came close to her indomitable aunt. 'Anyone knows this is not Cheapside. Look about you! Gin houses—flash houses too, I'll warrant. Rogues and doxies everywhere…' Matilda halted mid-flow, catching sight of Victoria and then of David walking behind her.

'We'll all be murdered in our beds…deaded by morn…' Beryl wailed, enfolding herself tightly into her cloak and jamming her bonnet hard down over her pretty fair hair to conceal it.

'Foolish girl! We'll be lucky to get to our beds tonight, let alone be murdered in them. Cease that shrieking and moaning. You'll draw every wretch's attention to us with your caterwauling.'

Victoria wrapped her arms about her rigid-backed aunt and then drew Beryl's shivering form into her embrace. 'Quick…get back into the coach…please. Don't fret… I'm sure these people will let us leave unchallenged. They are far too busy with their entertainment to bother with us,' she encouraged. She addressed George Prescott sharply. 'Let us be moving on immediately…'

He nodded his sparse grey head knowledgeably at her. 'Well, I reckons, if we keep the Thames to the left and the moon to the right…'

'You'll end up back here in about ten minutes,' David Hardinge remarked drily, nonchalantly leaning his immaculate figure against the battered coach.

Matilda beamed at him then sent her niece such a look of explicit congratulation that Victoria felt mortification and anger heat her face. She glanced at the focus of her aunt's appreciation, hoping he had not noticed the woman's tacit approval. A cynical smile told her he had, as did the very blue eyes watching her. And all at once an awful realisation struck her: he had not seemed as surprised as he ought to on learning that she was seeking him!

'Mr Hardinge was by lucky chance here with some

friends.' Victoria quickly put both of them right, sure he quite believed she had somehow managed to engineer the whole incident to waylay him.

'How fortunate,' her aunt said in a tone which only served to endorse this theory.

'Get in the coach now, Aunt, and you, Beryl. We must leave here immediately.' Beryl needed no further prompting. She scrambled aboard with Aunt Matilda quickly following.

'No doubt you'll want to thank and take your leave of the Viscount.' Matilda reminded Victoria of his status through the window she had forced open then jammed shut again.

Her aunt was, of course, right. He was most certainly owed her gratitude. She didn't dare guess what might have befallen her at these scoundrels' hands. 'Thank you for your protection, my lord...' she dutifully said.

'You're very welcome to it, Mrs Hart.'

The insinuation in his immediate, husky reply made Victoria blush although she was unsure why such innocuous words should make her feel so uncomfortable. Or why he should look at her in that sleepy yet intent way.

'If you're hoping to arrive at your destination some time this evening, Mrs Hart, perhaps I ought to accompany you. Your coachman still seems confused.' David indicatively raised his eyes to George Prescott, now perched on the driver's seat but swivelling about on his posterior muttering to himself about left and right and moon and stars.

It was a sensible and welcome offer. Victoria was aware that they could indeed end up returning to this unsavoury stew, or find a worse London slum, should George Prescott again come upon his quandary. 'You're very kind,' she said, inclining her head in acceptance and allowing him to hand her into the coach.

Ten minutes later, almost at the same minute that their

tired greys clopped into Cheapside, Margaret Worthington appeared silhouetted in her open doorway with a glow of honey light at her elegant back. The elderly mares whinnied to a grateful halt by black railings fronting a neat, red-brick mansion.

David Hardinge alighted nimbly from the seat he had shared with George Prescott. Ensuring the man stayed alert and travelling west as they negotiated the maze of dim city streets had necessitated him sitting close by his side to give explicit instructions. So exasperated had he become with his colleague's failing faculties at one point that he'd nearly snatched the reins to drive himself.

He held the carriage door and had helped each of the three women alight before old George Prescott's rickety joints had allowed him to gain the cobbles.

'So kind of you…' Matilda beamed up at David, reluctant to relinquish his long fingers. She turned triumphantly to her old friend, to find her squinting through the dusk at her.

Margaret Worthington shook her greying ringlets. No…it couldn't be. It was a trick of the light…or rather the lack of it. She had seen Lord Courtenay before, several times at a distance, and it did indeed look like him. But then it was almost nine of the clock. Apart from milky moonbeams and the flickering coach lamps there was only the muted glow spilling from her open front door. All was patchy and shadowy.

But then again, she had heard that he and his friends indulged in some quite outrageous pranks. But to act as a footman… No, it couldn't be. But then she also knew that young men today wagered on the most bizarre events and dares. And, to top it all, she had never seen a groom quite so sartorially splendid…or handsome…

'Lord Courtenay has been kind enough to show our man directions to Cheapside…' Matilda gladly put the woman's confusion to rest, with every intention of making her seethe with envy.

She did not need to wait long. Margaret Worthington grasped at a speared railing and her crushed handkerchief went to her mouth. She almost ate it in sheer frustration.

More than a dozen times she had invited this viscount to her soirées; never had he once deigned to grace her doorstep. Now he did…late in the evening, unexpectedly, and with Emma's hair needing a wash and curl to it. It was beyond bearing.

'How wonderful to see you, Matilda,' Margaret Worthington enthused. 'I was so worried when you didn't arrive by six of the clock. I have been stationed by my windows these past three hours. Please…let us all remove inside for warmth and refreshment.' This was directed to the party as a whole yet her sugary smile was for his lordship. She daintily tripped down the steps and got behind him somehow, cutting off his retreat.

Once they had reached the drawing room and Matilda and Victoria were seated, David announced his intention to leave. Mrs Worthington immediately demurred. 'Oh, come, my lord, you must at least take a sip of wine with us. I know gentlemen are not great tea drinkers. Indeed, my own Mr Worthington is not. He is a port and brandy man. Had he known you were to visit he would never have retired so early. He is usually up and about till well past midnight. I'll just send Rawlings to fetch him. I know you gentlemen like another such to talk to. No interest in ladies' chatter, naturally.' Margaret Worthington paused for breath and started for the door.

David immediately put out a hand to detain her and insist she did not needlessly disturb her sleeping husband; he was most definitely ready to depart. Margaret, spying a chance, grabbed it, in the shape of an empty crystal goblet on a side table. She immediately stuck it in his hand. 'There.

Just hold that while Rawlings fetches some wine.' The middle-aged woman sped to the door and began hissing something to someone outside with much flapping of the chewed
handkerchief in her hand.

Victoria avoided her aunt's eye. She knew that the harder
Margaret Worthington endeavoured to detain David, the
better Matilda liked it and was not above showing it. He
had so far declined beverages, cinnamon cake, alcohol, a
male companion, a tour of the conservatory stocked with
exotic blooms—which Emma would be delighted to show
him, Margaret had sweetly assured him, ignoring her
daughter's whiplash look.

As she sipped at her weak, warm tea, Victoria's grey
gaze roved the over-furnished drawing room of Rosemary
House. She replaced her wafer-thin cup and saucer on a
table close by the comfortable fireside chair she sat in and
glanced across at Emma. The young woman's honey-brown
head was inclined towards the book she read as though for
all the world she had little interest in any guest who had
joined them this evening.

Despite the fact that Emma seemed a little meek and
unassuming, Victoria now knew she was not. On their arrival, Margaret Worthington had attempted to shut her
daughter away in a side room as they entered the house. It
had looked almost comical. Emma had been about to
emerge into the hallway and had just avoided having herself
squashed in the door.

But Emma had refused to be pushed out of sight until
primped in readiness to receive their unexpected, but exceedingly welcome, male guest. Angrily side-stepping her
mother, she had snapped shut the book she held in her
hand, serenely walked into the drawing room and welcomed everyone with an odd detached warmth. Having dutifully taken care of the expected niceties, she had then sat
quietly reading. She now appeared oblivious to her

mother's staring, glaring and hissing words through the lacy scrap she clutched.

Exasperated by the muttered asides, Emma finally looked up from her tome and met Victoria's watching grey eyes. The two young women exchanged a small, exclusive smile…one of instinctive empathy and friendship. Victoria relaxed into her chair. She was going to like Emma.

Margaret cautiously shook her handkerchief at her daughter to gain her attention and then began mouthing through it. Most of the undercover comments issued so far, as Margaret skimmed back and forth close to her daughter, had concerned Emma removing herself and reappearing in her purple gown.

Politely looking at her agitated parent, Emma loudly enquired, 'I beg your pardon, Mama? What was that you said? I didn't quite catch it.'

Margaret coughed daintily into her hankie. 'Nothing…nothing, Emma. Just wondering why your papa's not down,' she snarled, shooting a glance Lord Courtenay's way. Matilda choked a gleeful laugh and then grunted as her china cup caught against her teeth in her haste to smother it. She also looked at his lordship.

Victoria found her own eyes wandering his way too. He had that effect on people, she realised. His physical stature, dark good looks and louche sophistication would always draw eyes.

David was unaware that he was the focus of quite so much female attention. He was studying the goblet, spinning its slender stem between his long fingers as though confused as to how to rid himself of it. He glanced about, sapphire eyes flicking from ledge to ledge for a suitable repository. Then he caught Victoria's eyes on him and his restless gaze stilled. She smiled, unable to disguise her amusement at his discomfort. Rogues and ruffians he could deal with. Scheming mamas were obviously another matter entirely.

He smiled back, wryly acknowledging the fact that she was relishing his predicament. Then he strolled towards her and quite unselfconsciously hunkered down by her chair and looked straight at her fatigued, wan face. He leisurely positioned his empty glass by her cup and saucer on the small wine table close to her chair.

'So… We never got around to finishing our conversation in Hounsditch, Mrs Hart. As I recall, you've come to London looking for me,' he softly reminded her, just for her hearing. Very blue eyes roved her tense face and immediately dropped to her mouth as she began nervously chewing her full lower lip.

'If you were to visit me tomorrow afternoon at Beauchamp Place, you could explain why you want to see me. Will you do that? But just you and your aunt. Please don't bring your hostess,' he added as a dry afterthought.

Victoria hastily reached for her cup and sipped, unable to answer or credit that he would pay her such obvious, intimate attention. Her eyes skipped to Margaret Worthington but that woman was fanning herself with her shredded scrap of lace and peering out of the door, obviously awaiting Rawlings.

'Shall I bring her daughter instead?' Victoria nervously, softly taunted, wondering how he liked the fact that Emma was patently unmoved by his illustrious, eligible self.

'Well, you might have to drag her screaming away from her literary pursuits. She might not thank you for it.'

Victoria touched her lower lip to her cup but slowly raised her dusky thick lashes and damson-grey eyes merged with blue. She was exhausted, she was anxious, she was uncertain how to deal with this man and yet she was flirting with him, she realised. It seemed the most natural thing in the world, and so familiar. She could even remember his usual reaction to her coquetry. He would close his eyes, throw back his head and give a small defeated laugh. For whenever they had crossed swords and she'd employed feminine wiles she had invariably got her way—whether which park to drive in, which dance to dance together, which tea shop…theatre…friends…

She watched him intently, barely breathing as she waited. Blue eyes rose above her head, lengthy lashes swept down to shield them and a throaty laugh was just audible to her…followed by a hard muttered curse. That she didn't remember!

She hadn't been expecting Margaret Worthington to come bearing down on them either. The reed-thin woman whispered towards them, clutching a decanter. Her astute brown eyes fixed on the handsome man and the beautiful, unwanted female visitor, their dark heads close, and her aspirations plummeted. The last person she had expected…hoped her sister-in-law would bring as companion was a lovely young widowed relation who made her own homely Emma look dull as ditch-water. An unseen glare arrowed to her uncaring daughter as she sat, unkempt head bowed towards her Jane Austen novel.

'Do have a little brandy, my lord,' Margaret insisted, splashing the fine cognac into his wine goblet abandoned on the table.

David stood slowly, bestowing on Margaret a charismatic smile. Raising the glass to his lips, he downed the considerable quantity in two swallows and replaced his glass. 'I really have to be going now, Mrs Worthington. Thank you for your hospitality.'

Having bowed politely to all the ladies, David made for the door, Margaret hot on his heels.

'We are having a birthday celebration for Emma this Saturday evening,' she breathed at his back, thinking she might as well try as not. 'You may remember my invitation to it. I know you have declined with a prior engagement…but I do so hope you might find a spare hour to honour us with your presence.' Margaret's crafty brain whirred on. They were lacking gentlemen of any consequence at the weekend. 'And do bring along that charming friend of yours…Mr Du Quesne…too. I can assure you of delicious food and fine wines, wonderful music and entertainment, and, of course, most beautiful dancing partners…'

David glanced back thoughtfully at Victoria. Margaret Worthington intercepted the look. Nevertheless, she sweetly lured through gritted teeth, 'Of course, Mrs Hart and my dear sister-in-law, Matilda Sweeting, have journeyed from Hertfordshire especially for the event.'

David mused idly back over his invitations. He couldn't recall this card; but then Jacob now knew him so well and was so efficient at sorting his correspondence into accept and reject that he barely glanced at the latter. To be fair to his clerk, yesterday he would never have dreamed of attending. 'I shall be delighted to come along for an hour or so, if I find it is at all possible, Mrs Worthington.' David dipped his head politely, in thanks. 'I shall convey your invitation to Mr Du Quesne, also. I'm sure his sentiments will be as mine,' he told an ecstatic Margaret, and with another courteous bow to the assembled company he was gone.

Once outside, David swore aloud as he glanced up at the lighted window but strolled on past. He owned the house, paid handsomely for the services of the woman who occupied it and yet found himself unwilling to enter.

Annabelle was probably expecting him; not only that, she would make perfectly apparent her delight at seeing him. She was a city draper's daughter and both she and her parents were extremely appreciative of his attention and protection. Annabelle had no coy inhibitions about proving that to him in any way she could. She was fresh, pretty enough, curvaceous and tonight he needed a woman…and yet he knew she was the wrong woman.

The fact that the woman he did want was probably even now retiring for the night at Rosemary House, barely a minute's walk away, made things worse. He cursed the fact she was so close. He felt, ridiculously, as though visiting his auburn-haired mistress tonight would somehow be tantamount to infidelity. Yet nothing between him and Victoria was even agreed. But he was confident enough that tomorrow it would be. A smile just quirked his thin mouth. Fidelity? What was that? And why had it reared its unwanted, meddlesome head?

He deliberately turned his thoughts elsewhere. He'd been saved a trip to Hertfordshire this weekend after all. Not only that, the fact that Victoria's situation was dire enough to bring her out seeking him meant he could easily dictate terms. Not that he was about to be parsimonious. Far from it. But he was well aware she had dependents and that she would allow them prior claim on her time, given half a chance.

He halted close to a street lamp, took a cheroot from his pocket and lit it. He drew deeply on it and arrowed a look back towards number ten Gracechurch Street wherein he had every damned right to spend a few hours in sensual pleasure and comfort.

But, however much he tried to force himself to dwell on the erotic welcome Annabelle would provide for him, she couldn't sustain his interest for more than a few minutes.

Pitching the virtually unsmoked cheroot into the gutter and shoving his hands deep into his pockets, he walked on, towards Hounsditch and his carriage home to Mayfair.

'Will you look at that?' Matilda expostulated, aiming the peak of her bonnet at a barouche just turning into Hyde Park. 'Hood down and barely a stitch to cover their shoulders. No wonder these young females end up lying abed half the day asniffling and asnuffling. What you have to bear in mind in spring is that the climate is unpredictable. Sunny it may be now, but by three of the clock today it could blow a gale or sleet or rain in stair-rods...' Aware that Victoria was not impressed by her seasonal knowledge, nor had even bothered to glance at the open-topped carriage bowling away into the park conveying two improperly attired young ladies, Matilda pressed together puckered lips.

She was well aware of the reason for Victoria's apprehensive quiet and, as they drew ever closer to Beauchamp Place, again endeavoured to introduce a little lightness to the atmosphere. 'Thank goodness Margaret allowed us to use her carriage. Now where do you imagine we might have landed had George Prescott had the reins this afternoon? The docks? The Thames? I hear from Margaret that parts are only lately thawed. There was a frost fair, you know. People skating on the river... Only think...with that fool George Prescott, it could have been us...'

Victoria managed a weak smile for her aunt. She knew she was trying to engage her attention and take her mind off the purpose of this outing but it was impossible to simply chat. Her head had started to pulse with tension and her mouth was so parched her tongue felt glued to the roof of her mouth. She wished now she had taken breakfast this morning; it might have settled the churning of her stomach.

Matilda leaned towards her, determined to draw her niece into bland conversation. 'Margaret thinks we are to visit my old schoolfriend Felicity Walsh. I knew I had only to mention her name to keep Margaret indoors this afternoon. They detest one another, you know. Have done so since Felicity stole Desmond Walsh from under Margaret's nose. All three of us were but sixteen then. Felicity was the first to marry at seventeen and I was the last, when I wed your uncle Harry ten years later...'

Victoria suddenly sat forward, blurting, 'It's no use, I can't go through with this.' A hand rose to rap for the driver to halt, but Matilda grabbed at it.

'You can and you must!' She looked fiercely at Victoria. 'All he can say is no. And if that is what he does, then we shall know him for a fool and that you have had a lucky escape.'

Victoria closed her eyes, praying for the confidence that had forced her from Rosemary House at one of the clock this afternoon. In the quiet, pretty bedroom she and her aunt shared at the Worthingtons', it was easy to forget just how dismal a situation she had left behind at Hartfield.

She had but a week in London and during that time she needed to do her utmost to find a husband. It was humiliating, it was degrading but it was a realistic plan. And one which women through the centuries had employed to keep them from penury. She was hardly unique in husband-hunting, she consoled herself. A great many females throughout the land, of every age and class, were engaged in it with her. But most genteel ladies had a good deal more to offer, she acknowledged miserably, and might not set their sights so high. Neither might they set convention on its head by seeking to marry so soon…before a husband was cold in his grave… Society's scandalised matrons would doubtless be whispering behind their jewelled fingers as they calculated the months since Daniel's demise.

But her debts deprived her of the year's mourning that etiquette demanded, and if she returned to Hartfield next Tuesday unengaged Alexander Beresford was her only hope. And her father and aunt had none. And Hartfield would be lost for ever. That was not what Daniel would have wanted!

David Hardinge was still her best bet, she reminded herself again and again. He was wealthy, she was sure he had once cared for her a little and she still… She put the next thought from her mind. Emotions need play no part.

He was a businessman…a very successful financier, so she had learned from Margaret Worthington last evening after he had left. Well, she had a business proposition to lay before him. That was all it was, she stressed to herself. He would either show interest in the deal or decline it. In which case she would have to pray that Emma's ball at the weekend provided other opportunities for her to meet wealthy men in need of a wife and a cash-eating country estate to upkeep but never own. The absurd futility of it made a small choke of laughter escape her before her head dropped forward into her hands.

'There.' Matilda patted her bowed head encouragingly. 'I knew you'd cheer up and see the sense of it. Your papa will be jolly proud of you…'

Hollow cheeks and a gaunt frame filled Victoria's mind. Dr Gibson had told her with barely concealed pity that, although mentally frail, Charles Lorrimer's constitution was strong and he might expect to survive for years. Neither she nor Dr Gibson had said more but she knew their troubled musings were the same: Charles Lorrimer would remain a burden on his daughter for quite some while yet. Victoria immediately felt guilty. She had barely spared her father a thought since departing Hertfordshire early yesterday. She prayed he was behaving himself and not giving Samuel too many problems… So lost was she in her anxious musing on her cantankerous papa and Hartfield that it was a moment before Victoria realised Matilda was hissing words at her.

'Oh, my. Look, Victoria. Did you ever see anything quite so magnificent?'

Victoria did look then. Her grey eyes took in first the bewigged footmen standing impassively by their motionless carriage; they then slowly climbed the cream stucco of the most palatial double-fronted town house she had ever seen. Its sumptuous splendour, and that of neighbouring properties, made her immediately sink back into the cushioned squabs and close her eyes. What on earth have I done? ran screaming through her mind. This man doesn't want an impoverished widow; he could have a duke's daughter. He probably already does have one…as a neighbour.

Matilda fell back against the cushions opposite, mirroring Victoria's pose. 'Oh, my!' she breathed, awestruck, her small pale eyes wide and apprehensive.

'Aunt Matty?' Victoria prompted with a shaky laugh, while garnering every ounce of courage and pride she possessed, for it was most certainly too late to turn about now. A phlegmatic footman resplendent in blue and gold livery held the door for them.

Noting that her aunt still lay back against the squabs as though she was going nowhere, Victoria slid forward on the seat, ready to alight. She clutched at one of her aunt's thin hands and gave it a fond shake. 'I would certainly prefer not to enter alone, you know. I have my reputation to think of,' she weakly joked. 'Come, what can he do to us? What can he say? Only no.' She echoed Matilda's recent assurances with a rueful smile.

Chapter Five

'You're making a mistake, David.'

Dickie Du Quesne had guessed his cautiously tendered opinion might be ignored. His tall, dark-haired comrade carefully adjusted his cornflower silk cravat then shrugged into a superbly cut charcoal tail-coat. Straightening snowy linen cuffs, David turned from the mirror.

'You think so?' he finally said, bored, his attention on his diamond shirt studs. A lazy blue gaze rose to meet Dickie's watchful eyes. 'What makes you say so?'

'I remember Victoria well,' Dickie quietly explained. 'She is…she is…oh, I don't know,' he dismissed, with a laugh and an idle gesture. 'I suppose I mean that unless her character is drastically changed she is no man's mistress, of that I'm sure.'

'Good,' David said with studied irony. 'That makes having her as mine simpler.'

Dickie gazed out over Beauchamp Place, his eyes skimming the carriage that had recently deposited David's female guests. He wasn't sure why he was championing a woman he had neither seen nor spoken to for seven years. But he did remember her well…and not just because of her unique black and white beauty. He could recall her sweetness, her simplicity, her innocence. Mostly he recollected being astonished at how easily and quickly she had gentled this man.

David had fallen so hard that practically overnight the wildest reprobate of Dickie's acquaintance was tamed, and by an elfin, slender-bodied virgin, barely eighteen years old. He glanced sideways at his friend. And there of course lay the crux of the matter. Despite all David's vigilance and territorial prowling—and several prospective suitors had nervously withdrawn on learning David Hardinge was laying claim to Victoria Lorrimer—another man had, after all, got to her first. And he'd never got over it, no matter how insouciant he liked to appear.

He had known David since their schooldays. Even as a youth David had permitted very little to disturb him. Because of his mother's scandalous history, his friend had once been the butt of cruel jokes and abuse. As a youngster David had fought for the honour of the 'Courtenay Courtesan', as Maria Hardinge, née Poole, was sneeringly styled. Later, on realising she had none, he'd fought for the hell of it. Any foolish enough to think of bullying or tormenting him about his family had soon regretted it. David Hardinge could and did defend himself with a skill that would not have shamed a street fighter.

Yet following Victoria's marriage to an elderly widower Dickie had witnessed his hard, ruthless comrade in black, inconsolable despair. And the fact that this private man had allowed him to see it was a measure of just how distraught David had been in that first month. Yet he had disciplined himself out of it and into becoming one of the finest financial successes Dickie was ever likely to know in his lifetime. *Gentlemen didn't sully their hands with commerce…*the beau monde loved to sneer. Well, this one did, and his wealth and investments were now the envy of many of his aristocratic peers.

Jeremiah Clavering put his stately, steel-grey head about the study door. 'I have showed Mrs Hart and Mrs Sweeting into the blue salon, my lord.'

David nodded. 'Have refreshments sent there in ten minutes,' he directed at his phlegmatic butler. 'Well, let's not keep the ladies waiting,' he said to his reflective friend.

'I hope you've been brushing up on topics likely to engage the interest of a genteel lady of advanced years,' David remarked as the clack of their heels resounded against polished mahogany, echoing away to the vast ceiling.

'My knowledge of embroidery is second to none,' Dickie responded, deadpan, as they halted before a pair of gilt-scrolled doors. 'I am well versed in all the scandalous *on dits*, probably because most concern you and me, and as for the latest Paris fashions...'

'You're well aware of how much they cost,' David chipped in, recalling Dickie moaning about his current *amour's* tendency to greatly overspend her allowance.

'Mrs Hart...Mrs Sweeting...how nice of you to call,' was David's suave welcome on entering his spacious blue salon. He walked towards the two seated women with an easy, confident stride.

Victoria jerked to her feet. She automatically dipped a curtsey to the two elegant gentlemen approaching even though she could barely rally a coherent thought, her heart was racing so frantically.

During the ten minutes or so that she and her aunt had sat in almost total silence in this sumptuous room she had striven desperately for courage and composure and was sure she had achieved both. The cause of her turmoil had now arrived and, with a charming greeting, destroyed it all. Her wide grey eyes clung to his handsome, imposing figure before skittering to Dickie Du Quesne. She recognised him at once.

He had retained his boyish blond looks although his

overall bearing held a mature sophistication. She remembered she had rather liked him. Dickie's friendly smile elicited a hesitant one from her in return.

A swift, imploring glance at her aunt went unheeded; the woman was still huddled, mesmerised, in her chair, unable to take in the extent of the grandeur all around. Victoria swallowed a hysterical laugh. If there was one thing she had been sure she could draw comfort from this afternoon it was her aunt's solid, unflappable strength. To discover her mainstay reduced to a dumbfounded, gawking wreck and herself suddenly abandoned…

'I'm not sure if you remember Mr Du Quesne, Mrs Hart.' David's cool, level tone sliced through her mental agitation.

'Yes, of course,' Victoria forced out lightly, steadying her smile. 'How are you, Mr Du Quesne?'

'I'm very well, Mrs Hart,' Dickie said gently. 'How are you? And your aunt, I believe, has accompanied you?' Dickie couldn't take his eyes off her: her raven-haired beauty was still stunning, if anything enhanced by the passage of time, but the demure vivacity he remembered was gone. There was an air of wistful fragility cloaking her, as though the cares of the world burdened her slender shoulders.

Victoria flushed unhappily. 'Oh, I'm so sorry. Yes, indeed. Please let me introduce you to Mrs Sweeting. Aunt Matilda, this is Mr Du Quesne, a friend of Lord Courtenay's. Do you remember we were acquainted some years ago when we lived in London? I believe you met once or twice then.'

Matilda smiled and nodded then made as though to rise belatedly to dip a curtsey.

David lifted a languid hand. Please don't disturb yourself, Mrs Sweeting. Ah, here's tea.'

Two female staff attired in smart blue and gold uniforms filed in bearing laden trays. They efficiently, discreetly rustled between the room's silent occupants, offering refreshments. Victoria graciously accepted both tea and cake simply for the respite of fully occupying her attention. Such conspicuous wealth and power bombarding her senses was oppressive; it made her dejectedly sure only an arrogant fool would ever dream this man might agree to marry a poor widow.

A quiet tension hummed in the sedate room and Victoria fiddled nervously with positioning her gilt-edged plate on a polished rosewood side table.

Dickie Du Quesne, bearing his teacup, noiselessly strolled across the plush carpeting to her aunt. Pulling an ebonised chair close to Matilda, he sat down and began casually chatting about the beneficial effects of countryside air and the rigours of highway travelling. Victoria overheard Matilda's brief, awkward responses and winced inwardly for her; she was still overwhelmed.

With Dickie's patient persistence Matilda slowly regained a little of her normal gregariousness. A pithy opinion of the imprudence of patronising the King and Tinker over the Bell Inn at Enfield had Victoria slowly relaxing, and Dickie politely promising to store away that useful titbit for future reference.

The light conversation to one side of her was soothing and inspiriting. At some time she would have to look at him…she would have to speak to him. She could either pretend that she and her aunt were simply paying a brief social call, and hope he would gallantly not mention her odd declaration yesterday evening that she was in London seeking him, or she could persevere with the futile aim that had really propelled her to Mayfair.

She glanced at her aunt, dwarfed by a regal velvet armchair, then raised her lashes slowly, finally meeting deep blue eyes she knew were quite openly studying her.

He didn't smile; he didn't do anything. He simply held

her gaze as though he knew exactly what she wanted and it gave him an amount of private amusement.

Victoria hastily looked away, her flimsy valour disintegrating, and wished herself miles away in Hertfordshire.

Oh, why *had* she come? She was sure she had never in her life felt more mortified than she did right now. And so far she had asked for nothing.

'You have a beautiful home, Mr Hardinge…I…I'm sorry, Lord Courtenay. I forget…' The words tumbled out in a breathy rush.

'That's quite all right, Mrs Hart. At times, I forget myself. Call me David, if it's easier,' he challenged softly. After a brief pause in which her lack of response occasioned a wry smile at the immaculate arm lounging against the marble mantel, he added, 'I'm pleased you like my house. Would you care to see more of it?'

The offer was casually made but Victoria knew its purpose. She had come to speak to him on a matter of some delicacy and he was introducing the opportunity for privacy.

'Yes. Thank you,' she agreed, in little above a whisper. He believed she had come to plead for charity, was the thought that suddenly, awfully, penetrated her mind. She was an impoverished widow of one of his relations and he thought she had come abegging. Had he already decided to refuse? Was that what amused him? That they were bothering with pointless civilities?

He walked away from the magnificent marble chimneypiece and held out a hand to her.

With a fleeting glance at her chatting aunt, Victoria took David's arm and allowed him to lead her into the corridor. She sensed the hard muscle beneath her shaking fingers and attempted to lighten their already faint contact with his sleeve. They proceeded silently, Victoria banishing thoughts of their closeness yesterday in that noisome marketplace. But memories of long fingers soothing her face, in her hair, his mouth close to her cheek…her certainty that he had been on the point of kissing her…

He halted abruptly by a door, swung it open and indicated she should enter. 'The study, where I spend most of my time. Do sit down, Mrs Hart.'

Victoria did so, choosing a corner chair by the large casement window which offered a view of the quiet, majestic square below. She glanced down at the Worthingtons' carriage, idle in front of the house.

'This…this is also a very nicely proportioned room.' She shattered the tension, with an encompassing flitting of her grey eyes about mellow polished panelling. They settled on the leaping flames in the ornate grate. Her tongue lightly moistened her parched lips. Why on earth was she bothering with the sham that they were on a tour of the house?

'Indeed it is,' he agreed, so wryly that she knew his thoughts were identical.

Nervous palms smoothed along the pearl-grey silk of her mourning dress as Victoria took stock. She would not be intimidated. He was as keen to know exactly what had brought her here as she was reluctant to let it out. He obviously knew of her financial difficulties and had guessed she was about to petition for aid, but she sensed he was very curious as to how she would go about it. He had invited her to visit; she was not here on sufferance. Not yet. They could at least make an attempt at polite conversation. They had once been close friends, after all. Then, when she finally set out her proposal…

'How is your mother, Lord Courtenay? I hope she is well and…' She could think of nothing to add, belatedly remembering that David had only ever mentioned his parents with sarcasm or subdued bitterness. He would always avoid meeting them when out. 'I hope she is well,' she finally resorted to repeating softly.

'I can't answer with any certainty, Mrs Hart. When last I saw her she seemed healthy enough, but that was a year or more ago. I imagine she goes on tolerably well or I should have been informed of how much I owe the physician,' was his curt summary.

Mesmerised by his emotionless face, Victoria sensed her heart squeezing at his chilling callousness. One of his parents was still alive yet he never visited, and spoke of her with such open indifference. How could she even imagine he would treat her otherwise? She should excuse herself now, flee this graceful, soulless house, and seek the sanctuary of rustic Hertfordshire and Alexander Beresford's placid presence. 'And your sister, Clarissa?' Victoria whispered, desperate to establish some scrap of rapport between them.

She recalled he had little fondness for her either. But Clarissa had been a newly married woman when Victoria had first met David. Perhaps she now had children; perhaps he held them in affection. 'Have you nephews or nieces?' she asked, sweetly optimistic.

'One of each.' His terseness made Victoria's incipient smile fade away.

David thought of his blonde sister and his mouth curled unpleasantly. She was most definitely her mother's daughter. Her father's identity was open to conjecture. Most had guessed at the flaxen-haired head groom at Hawkesmere at the time of her birth. It certainly would give credence to Clarissa's proclivity for the stables and rolling about in hay with, quite literally, any man who would have her. He hadn't seen her or the elderly fop she'd married since July of last year when she had inveigled to use his house and position to enjoy the London season for a month before returning to Shropshire where she now resided.

David strolled to the window close to Victoria's chair and looked out and just for a moment he allowed himself to dwell on his family, if one could call it that…for he knew that of the three children of his parents' marriage only his brother Michael had been a product of their union. He and his sister were merely flyblows. A travesty of a smile twisted his lips, for despite technically being a bastard he could claim the most august sire.

He put it all from his mind, acutely conscious of the uneasy silence to one side of him. He glanced down at a bowed ebony head, his blue gaze caressing her alabaster profile. He could quite clearly see the tremor in slender white fingers gripped together in an effort to disguise it.

Her nervousness soothed him. He had instinctively known that she'd had no illicit lovers during her marriage and would be inexperienced in opening negotiations. As he had more expertise in amorous exchanges than he cared now to bring to mind, he really ought to make things easier for her and take over. His jaw gritted. Seven years ago she hadn't made it at all easy for him. He'd risked his life for her; she'd not even risked waiting a few more crucial days. The recalled anguish on learning she'd wed could still tumble his insides and clench his face into an aching mask. It did so now with sickening virulence; nevertheless, his hand moved spontaneously, seeking to touch her…reassure her. At the last moment it skimmed past instead and gripped the back of the chair she sat in.

'How is your father? Is his health at all improved?' He relented a little and indulged her need for small-talk.

A sweet, grateful smile as she looked up nearly melted his vengeful resolve to make her do all the running in this cat-and-mouse game. 'He…he is very well, thank you,' Victoria said, so quickly, so appreciatively, she stumbled over the words. 'He has days…weeks when he is completely lucid. Then at other times he can barely remember any of us. Or where he lives. He believes himself still in Hammersmith…and my mama still alive.' Mention of her mother brought a painful lump to her throat. She huskily soldiered on. 'But his physical health is robust. He has a hearty appetite…' The words faded, her face aglow beneath fiery sapphire eyes roving her features.

He was not really interested in anything she told him regarding her papa. But he was interested in her: a solid, expectant tension was building between them. He wanted to touch her. White knuckles gripping her chair-back were on the edge of her vision and powerful, muscular thighs encased in soft buff material were close to her cheek. 'I think…I think perhaps we ought to open the door,' she choked out in a rush. 'My aunt will wonder where I am. She might search for me…'

'Are you fretting about your reputation, Mrs Hart?' David asked on a grunt of hard laughter.

'One of us has to worry about our reputations, Lord Courtenay,' Victoria shot back.

'Are you including mine in that statement?'

'Yes.'

'You believe it worth the saving?'

'Yes,' Victoria said simply.

David looked down at her solemn, beautiful face. He remembered that sweet, guileless expression so well. Long fingers unclenched from her chair-back and just one trailed the smooth satin of her jaw. 'Tell me why,' he softly demanded.

No better opening was likely to present itself, Victoria realised. 'Because a husband should have his wife's respect,' she slowly said. She watched his face minutely— saw disbelief and uncertainty narrowing his eyes and slanting his sensual mouth. And she knew there was no going back.

'I must first beg your pardon for speaking so plainly. I'm sure you understand how dire my situation is to force me to humiliate myself in such a way. It is not yet three months since my husband's funeral and I know it will be deemed scandalously unseemly for me to so soon socialise or think of remarrying. So I must apologise in advance for any embarrassment I might cause you. But my circumstances are such that I cannot afford niceties or to dissemble. I have just one week in London and must try to resolve my difficulties before I return to Hartfield on Tuesday.' She couldn't bear to read his expression. Whether amusement or disgust or interest was there, she couldn't yet summon courage to find out. 'I shall not try to make out that my debts are less than they are,' she rushed on. 'My late husband's attorney tells me they are extremely worrying…'

'Approaching forty thousand pounds,' David Hardinge supplied coolly over his shoulder as he walked to the study door and opened it a little.

'Forty thousand pounds…?' Victoria repeated in a horrified whisper at his back, the shock of the sum obscuring the question of how he could possibly know.

David strolled to his desk and rested his weight against it. His face was inscrutable as he moved a hand in an explicit gesture for her to continue.

'I…I would like you to marry me.' The words scattered like small pebbles into stony silence. 'I'm sure…most certainly sure you must be wondering what on earth you would gain from such a marriage of convenience…'

'Marriage of convenience…?' whipped into her speech. 'Explain that.'

'Well…I realise that we no longer…there is no affection between us. We are virtually strangers with our own lives. I know you are…that you have a life in London that you would not wish me to share. You have your own friends and…social circle, whereas I have Hartfield and my relatives to care for. A marriage in name only, a marriage of convenience, would inconvenience neither of us.'

'So…I marry you, pay off your debts, maintain the estate

left to you by another man——a freehold which I believe will nonetheless never be mine—provide for you and, I imagine, your dependants, and in return I get....' His sardonic summary tailed off. 'What *do* I get, Mrs Hart?' he asked with soft irony.

Victoria felt blood surge into her face, her chagrin uncontrollable. Stated so baldly, it did, indeed, seem an outrageous arrogance on her part that he would ever entertain such a one-sided proposal.

'Hartfield is a very beautiful estate,' she hastily explained. 'When you attended Daniel's funeral you would have seen very little of what it has to offer.' She stole a fleeting glance at his closed expression. 'I know when your father died you lost your family seat at Hawkesmere. I was very sad to learn at your brother's funeral that it had been seized by the bank because of your family's misfortune. Most gentlemen like to hunt and shoot and fish when the London season is come to an end. I know you have the means to lease an estate for such pursuits, if you wish. Perhaps you do so. But if we were married you could have Hartfield as your own. It has extensive parkland and woods. It is a fine riding estate. It has much to recommend it. You could come and see for yourself...' She gazed beseechingly up at him. 'Because no gentlemen have hunted there for so long the wildlife proliferates. The lake and streams are teeming with tench and bream and pike,' she enthused. 'My manservant tells me that even with the poachers he pursues we are still overrun with deer and hare, and pheasant and fowl of every description. You and your friends would be most welcome to spend as much time as you will at Hartfield. The house is comfortable and large enough to accommodate guests. If you would only just come and see what Hartfield has to offer...'

David pushed abruptly away from the desk and seemed about to speak, but at that moment Matilda Sweeting's voice became audible. Her silver-grey figure swept into the room followed by Dickie Du Quesne's long stride.

There was an awkward silence for no more than a second as four people looked startled. Then David bit out, 'Why don't you show Mrs Sweeting some of the other apartments, Dickie?'

'I believe this is the last room we have to see, Lord Courtenay,' Matilda said, with a brief, calculating look at the furnishings and then a longer one at her niece seated by the window. She could detect nothing encouraging in her solemn mien. 'It is the most opulent house I believe I have ever entered,' Matilda stated while rotating on the spot to inspect the walnut-panelled study. Once her back was presented to the gentlemen she began mouthing encouragement and making eye signals at Victoria. 'You must need armies of domestics. I expect the kitchens must be huge…'

'Take a look,' David ordered bluntly.

'At the kitchens?' Dickie interjected, swiping a horrified sideways glance at his friend.

'At the kitchens. They're huge. It should take some while,' David said with straining patience as he paced to the window and stared out, grim-faced.

'I imagine the cooking ranges must be huge as well…' Matilda added, glancing over her shoulder at her silent niece. With a covert, unintelligible aside for Victoria, she exited the room on Dickie Du Quesne's stiff arm.

In the taut silence following their departure Victoria reflected on all her pleas so far. Stinging humiliation in smoky grey eyes was swiftly shuttered by pearly translucent lids. There had been an opportunity for her and her aunt to take their leave. And she had allowed it to slip. She could, even now, have been travelling back to Rosemary House. She had said all there was to say. She had set out all she had to offer…almost all she had to offer.

'So,' David said quietly, splintering her regret, 'you get

my money and I get your estate to use for sport in season. Is that it?' He gazed sideways down at the top of her glossy, raven head.

The mocking disbelief in his tone made her face snap up and she proudly met his eyes. 'You also benefit from the respectability conferred by marriage and get a wife who will make no other demands on you…who will never interfere. She will simply be grateful if you exercise a little discretion and restraint in all your…in the way you go on. You might find that your reputation does indeed repair under such an arrangement.'

David gave a hard choke of laughter and abruptly sat in a chair opposite. He leaned towards her, his long fingers loosely clasped together. 'And you believe that's an inducement? Why would I care to improve something of so little consequence, Mrs Hart? My reputation has long been lost to me. In fact I was born without one to my name. But it's to no real detriment. I have a title and more money than I know what to do with; those things ensure I can act with impunity and still be welcomed everywhere.'

Victoria moistened her lips. All that was left was her trump card. If this failed, there really was nothing else. 'I realise you might want heirs and your wife to be…to come to you…that you were the first to…to be chaste,' she finally stammered out.

'No…' David softly soothed her embarrassment. 'Perhaps at one time it might have mattered but not any more. In fact, if there's anything I've definitely no desire for, it's righteous virgins. But then from what you've implied so far I imagine you're well aware of tales of my debauchery. I won't insult your intelligence by denying them. As for heirs, I've no intention of inflicting on society any more dissolute Hardinges. In short, experienced women like you interest me, children and continuing my line don't.'

Victoria stared, unblinking, at him. His brazen immor-

ality was frightening. He had no interest in virgins. Not any
more. And only desired sophisticated women. And that was
what he thought her. What she had naïvely believed to be
her most precious asset had unknowingly been tossed back
at her as valueless.

'Did you and your late husband not want children?' he
asked abruptly.

This unexpected interrogation left Victoria floundering.
'I…we…I don't know. We just…we just never had children,' she finished lamely.

'Ah,' David said softly, sardonically. 'Such an exem-
plary husband…' he murmured. 'Well, as we're being painfully honest this afternoon, Mrs Hart, I'll tell you that your
proposition is the third I've received this week. And I'll
admit that the others were more…persuasively executed
and of less cost and greater personal benefit. I should also
add that I am a confirmed bachelor and have no intention
of ever marrying.'

Victoria froze as though summarily doused in icy water.
Then just as swiftly anger burned white-hot. He had let
her…no, helped her make an utter fool of herself and no
doubt enjoyed every minute watching her squirm. Now he
casually let her know she had abased herself in vain. Not
only that, she was just another petitioner and inept, too.

She had always known there was very little chance of a
successful outcome but he had deliberately toyed with her,
ruthlessly prevaricated to prolong her agony. She had set
out her proposal quickly and honestly, yet he had withheld
vital information until sure she had nothing further to divulge.

She had been manipulated, encouraged to talk. She had
told him private things…things that a prospective husband
should know: of her father's mental frailty, of her beloved
Hartfield. She had been on the point of confiding her own
intimate secret too. How he would have relished that! She

was well aware of his mordant amusement at any mention of Daniel or their marriage. His scorn would now target her too…for she was not at all what he happily assumed…

She quickly got to her feet and he, too, slowly unwound from his chair. They faced each other, storm-grey and gentian-blue eyes inextricable.

'Had you said so sooner, Mr Hardinge, I would have removed myself and saved us both a wasted afternoon. As I have said, I am in London for just one week and need to make expeditious use of my time. If you will excuse me for troubling you, I shall seek my aunt and leave, for I have other visits to make…' Victoria approached the door while speaking, desperate to escape him before her fragile veneer of composure cracked. Humiliation would then get the better of the smarting fury that clenched her fists and her insides and it might send her scuttling meekly away.

Her pace increased as she drew level and she attempted to sweep swiftly past but long fingers fastened about the tops of her slender arms. She shook herself in his grasp, striving to break free, but he jerked her against him and blue-black eyes stared down into her white, set face.

'Other visits? What do you intend? To tout yourself about London seeking someone with forty thousand pounds?'

'Of course,' Victoria lied glibly, hugely gratified at inciting such disapproval that for a second he neglected to camouflage it. 'That's *exactly* what I intend to do, Mr Hardinge,' she lightly stressed. 'I simply came here first because yesterday you invited me to.'

Lean fingers tightened painfully about her soft flesh. 'You won't find anyone willing to match what I offer you,' he emphasised slowly, with a return to control and narrow-eyed mockery. 'You've set out your terms; now I'll let you know mine. In return for settling your debts, I'll expect you to move to London. I'll provide you with a fully maintained

house of your choosing, a staff of your choosing, a generous allowance and…' he looked at her, his expression
hard and unsmiling '…and anything else you care to stipulate. In fact, at the outset, you can have carte blanche, Mrs
Hart.'

As the significance of his brusque words was absorbed,
Victoria bit down ferociously on her soft lower lip, stilling
its tremor. Her eyes focussed on the blue silk cravat close
to her face; she concentrated on the slub in the weave, the
extraordinary brilliance of the diamond nestling in its
sheeny folds. But the awful realisation would not be denied
and wormed back into her mind: he'd not thought her here
abegging, after all, just awhoring.

'I see,' she finally whispered at his throat.

'Good,' he said.

She wrenched free of him and proceeded towards the
door.

David intercepted her with one pace and she stepped
back a little to avoid touching him. She raised glacial grey
eyes to his handsome, angular face. 'I should like to find
my aunt now. It is time we left.'

'Is that all you have to say while we still have some
privacy, Mrs Hart?'

His wry, amused confidence was not lost on Victoria and
made her seethe. 'Oh, of course, you're right,' she dulcetly
concurred. 'Perhaps I should discreetly let you know that
your arrogance and vile lechery make me sincerely regret
ever having renewed our acquaintance.' A cool, disdainful
look swept his sardonic features then settled on a delicate
oriental jar to one side of him. 'And I must agree with you
on one other point, Mr Hardinge: I, also, do not expect any
gentleman to match your offer to me. I'm sure some will
exceed it. In fact, one already has. Before I came to London, I received a proposal of marriage from a kind and
decent man.'

'Kind and decent…but short on cash, I take it,' David dismissed, with a shrewd, cynical look. He laughed unpleasantly as she blushed. 'So who will you go for? The decent man or the rich one? But we both already know, Mrs Hart, don't we? Or you wouldn't be here.'

She was unable to control her humiliated gasp or a slender hand from flying impulsively towards his face. His reflexes were so impossibly swift she barely saw him move. Her wrist was arrested mid-arc and imprisoned in a grip of steel.

'I should be grateful if you would now allow me to leave,' Victoria said, breathing hard, with an explicit, contemptuous look at his custodial fingers.

'Do I receive an answer before you go?'

'If you require one,' Victoria murmured. 'Although I would have thought it quite obvious I would sooner entertain the poorhouse than you, Mr Hardinge. You might revel in your own disgrace, I have no intention of letting you revel in mine.'

A slow smile met this speech. 'From that I deduce, then, you are declining my protection and my forty thousand pounds?'

Victoria's small, savaging teeth drew blood from her lip this time as she steeled herself against the urge to wrestle free of his clasp. 'I have said so. Let me go. I wish to find my aunt and leave.'

'When you come back at the end of the week, and beg me to reinstate this derisory offer, I wouldn't be able to call myself a successful businessman if I didn't renegotiate terms in my favour. At the moment I will agree to whatever you want. If you want me to provide for your father, your aunt, maintain this estate…Hartfield, isn't it?… I will do it.'

'You would provide me with a house in London and

maintain Hartfield too?' Victoria whispered, frowning disbelief at the fiery jewel below his shadowy square chin.

'I have said so.' He mimicked her earlier response and inclined his head a little in emphasis. Thoughtfully narrowed eyes studied her reaction. 'Oh, I expect you to actually reside in the house in London. Disappearing to Hertfordshire seven nights a week would not be acceptable.' His ironic smile deepened as Victoria's ivory complexion flushed rose. 'You can have a day to ponder on it. Think carefully before you definitely refuse me, Mrs Hart. For when you next approach me, your father and your aunt… and this Hartfield that seems to mean so much…you will no longer be in a position to plead for them.'

Victoria's lush ebony lashes lifted then, revealing stormy eyes glossy with hatred and tears. 'I need no thinking time and I will never again seek you, Mr Hardinge. I beg your pardon, *Lord Courtenay*. But I am grateful to have finally come to know you better. You will laugh when I tell you that when younger I actually rejected gossip and believed you an honourable man.'

A movement beyond the door drew her attention. Her lids lowered in utter thankfulness as she glimpsed her aunt's peculiarly mottled face peering in.

'Aunt Matilda,' Victoria greeted her huskily, deliberately letting her captor know they were no longer alone.

David immediately released her wrist and walked away from her before turning to the new arrivals.

Dickie Du Quesne, his face pink and his blond hair lank with perspiration, entered the room. Matilda, feverishly fanning herself, followed, clutching his elbow with a moist palm. Dickie thrust two fingers between his stiff collar and his sticky neck. He glanced uneasily from David to Victoria. 'Er, the kitchens and cooking ranges are indeed huge,' he dropped lightly into the thick atmosphere.

'Hot too…' David drily observed, jamming his hands

into his pockets. He jerked his head back and stared up at the lofty, ornate ceiling, his mouth thrust consideringly. A muscle started to pull in his cheek. He arrowed a searing, determined look at Victoria.

He was aiming to rid them of company yet again, she fearfully realised. The thought of once more being alone with him, once more being baited with his calm, callous contract, was beyond bearing. The more so because she knew herself susceptible to the lure. And so did he. Oh, so did he! No doubt he was well practised in such heartless strategies. She hastily addressed her aunt with a constrained little smile. 'I hope you have finished your tour, for we really must leave now.'

Without awaiting a response, Victoria turned her attention to Dickie Du Quesne. She politely took her leave and had gained the door within a few moments and stood waiting until her aunt joined her.

'Thank you for your time and hospitality, Lord Courtenay,' Victoria tonelessly said into the mellow, fire-flickering room.

'Thank you for your visit, Mrs Hart,' David returned in the same impassive way.

'Well?' Dickie interrogated impatiently once the women had gone, yanking off his cravat and blotting his damp brow. The material was then waved about in front of his warm face.

'Shut…up,' David bit out irritably as he strode to the window and stared down at the carriage and the two women in the process of boarding it.

'Well?' Matilda asked as soon as the coach door closed and she and her niece were settling into the squabs.

Victoria feigned frowning interest in the noble portal through which she had just escaped. Unsteady white fingers guarded her face from her aunt's astute gaze while pushing stray tendrils of ebony hair into place. She shook her head and murmured a simple, husky, 'No.'

David watched the gesture, watched her dark sheeny head bow into a slender hand before she turned away from the window.

The carriage had turned out of the square before his eyes rose, his back teeth unclenched and he swore savagely.

Dickie strolled to the door. 'I told you...' he muttered inaudibly with a smug shake of the head. 'I need a drink,' he amiably sent back over his shoulder. 'I'll find us something. Don't worry, it won't be tea!'

Chapter Six

'Purple isn't really my shade, is it?' Emma asked, with a frown at her reflection in the pier-glass.

'The amber silk is perhaps better suited to your colouring,' Victoria suggested tactfully.

'It's Mama's favourite, but only because it's the most expensive. I hate it,' Emma groaned, tossing the heavy purple gown onto the bed to join some others, similarly discarded. 'It makes me look like a dowager in mourning.' She bit her lip, her peachy complexion pinking in embarrassment. 'Oh, I'm so sorry. I didn't mean…'

'Please don't worry. I'm not offended. I honestly had not realised I am a dowager. It sounds so ancient.' Victoria brushed her fingers along her lavender silk. 'Luckily I like the colours grey and lavender.'

'They suit you so well too. I expect most shades suit you. You're so very pretty, Victoria.'

Happy with the change of subject, Emma said, 'You probably don't remember me from when you lived in London. I wasn't out then. When shopping with Mama, I recall seeing you with your aunt several times and thinking how much I would like to be like you…so pretty and popular. Lord Courtenay was always close by…although he would not have been a viscount then, of course.' Emma sighed wistfully. 'I was but sixteen and you seemed so poised and sophisticated. I would dearly have liked you as my friend—'

A bitter choke of laughter interrupted Emma. She blushed again, a trifle indignantly now. 'I didn't mean to be over-familiar…I just…'

'I'm so sorry, Emma; I didn't mean to imply you were. I'm laughing…no, not really laughing…' Victoria offered quietly, staring at her hands. 'It is just a little ironic: when I was eighteen, and living in Hammersmith with my aunt Matilda and my father, the last thing I actually achieved was a sensible sophistication. I have only recently discovered just how immature and foolish I was then.' A small wry smile emphasised the point. 'But thank you for your compliments. It's comforting to know I didn't actually look as stupid and credulous as I was. And I'm very glad we are now friends. You must promise to come and visit me at Hartfield…' Her happy invitation faded away. Soon Hartfield would be hers no more. Once back in Ashdowne next week the sale of the estate would need to be pursued.

Forcing a lightness into her tone, Victoria mock-chided, 'We are not so fusty and dull in the country as we are made out. 'Tis not all tilling and turnips. We have some fine assembly rooms and soirées and balls amongst friends and neighbours.

'I have a good friend close by,' Victoria continued, clearing herself a space next to Emma on the bed strewn with gowns. 'Laura is married to Sir Peter Grayson and they live near the village of Ashdowne at Willowthorpe. Before Daniel's illness, we used to have some fine entertainments, sometimes at Willowthorpe, sometimes at Hartfield. Many a dull winter evening has been brightened with gay music and good company.' She paused. 'Then in the summer months the countryside is incredibly beautiful, the meadow greens spotted with every shade of wildflower: buttercups, cornflowers, poppies… Oh, the list is endless. The woods are a cool Eden on hot days. Often, at luncheon or teatimes, we picnic by the lake…on the wooded side…and watch the swallows soar and swoop low to skim its shimmering surface. The bees and blooms and larks all contribute to the scent and music all around…a mesmerising hum that makes one want to rest back into the long grass and drowse…' She trailed off, her eyes distant. 'So you must come and visit. Your mama too…'

Emma grimaced at the idea of her mother's company but murmured dreamily, 'It sounds wonderful. I wish I could go there right now.' Picking idly at the dresses, she casually remarked, 'When Lord Courtenay was here the other evening, he seemed to pay you a lot of attention. Mama says he is one of the most eligible men around at present. She is desperate for him to come to my ball at the weekend. It's all foolishness in any case. Eligible he is, I'm sure, and very content to stay that way. But because you are here I believe he might actually attend.'

'I…he is one of my late husband's cousins,' Victoria hastily explained, conscious of her friend's astute observation. 'We recently met again after many years, when he attended Daniel's funeral. He and his sister are, in fact, Daniel's only surviving kin. Although they were not close cousins, Lord Courtenay was good enough to pay his last respects,' Victoria truthfully told her. She gave Emma a small smile. 'I imagine you know of his objectionable reputation. I noticed you were very sensibly unimpressed by him.'

Victoria busied herself sorting through the gowns. Lifting a plain empire-line amber silk, she handed it to Emma. 'This would set off your lovely tawny eyes remarkably well. Look in the mirror; the colour is perfect.'

'It is a favourite of mine. But Mama would disapprove.

Not nearly elaborate enough for her taste. But I shall wear it...with my amber drop earrings. Mama says they make me look like a heathen,' she confided with a grin. 'Would your maid, Beryl, dress my hair, do you think? Yours always looks so elegant.'

'Of course,' Victoria readily agreed.

'You will come to the Blairs' tonight, won't you? I simply can't endure an evening of cards and out-of-tune warbling with no one interesting to talk to.' A crafty little smile quirked Emma's lips. 'Yes, please do come. The Blair girls will hate it! The eldest daughter, Moira, rather thinks herself an incomparable beauty. Just wait till she spies you! I swear those big blue eyes might just pop out of her head.'

Victoria grimaced disgust at the picture. 'I'm not sure Aunt Matilda and I have received an invitation. Besides, I've no wish to set tongues wagging by socialising too frequently.'

'Your late husband must have been a very kind, selfless man to insist you waste none of your youth on mourning him.'

'Indeed he was. He was truly a fine gentleman,' Victoria said softly, but her thoughts involuntarily turned to the man she now knew to be the opposite.

Since leaving Beauchamp Place two afternoons ago she had shut David Hardinge and his mercenary offer from her mind. But she had not been able to exclude an uneasiness that other men she met might view her as he did. And, worse, that they might believe, as he had, that she would be amenable to their lecherous schemes.

Never in her life had she been a suspicious cynic. The fact that he had managed to affect her attitude so fundamentally infuriated her and made her the more determined not to hide herself away like a pariah.

Her troubled thoughts returned to the blonde woman who had stared at her with such malevolence in her slanted eyes.

Victoria didn't want to recall the noise and odours and the ghastly fear experienced on that first evening in one of London's most unwholesome stews. But banishing it all from her mind was impossible. So was ignoring the reason for the woman's antipathy: David had been holding her in his arms at the time and now Victoria recognised that green-eyed spite for what it was: rivalry and jealousy. The woman was obviously one of the Viscount's mistresses. Perhaps one he had no further use for. She had certainly had a possessive hunger in her slitted, angry stare.

Victoria swung her head miserably to sightlessly frown out of the window. Had her own desperation been so patently obvious when she looked at David? Was it already being whispered that she was prowling society so soon after her husband's death, eager to attract male attention? But then wasn't that the truth? She was... The conflict raged on in her battleground mind until logic was defeated and all she yearned for was Hartfield. Yet even that haven was soon to be snatched from her...and her sick father and vulnerable aunt. For, as proud and outspoken as her aunt might seem, Victoria knew Matilda would have no answer for real poverty.

'It's not that I was unimpressed by your Lord Courtenay.' Emma's voice scattered Victoria's tortured thoughts. 'I do understand why he is so popular with the ladies. He is the most roguishly attractive man I have ever seen,' Emma continued. 'It's just that I'm still carrying a torch for someone else...and Mama despises him because he's a widower with children.' She stared at her reflection, her honey-brown head to one side as she viewed the amber silk against her skin. 'Oh, and unforgivably for Mama, he's poor too. And, unforgivably for me, he is still carrying a torch...beacon, I should say...for his late wife. He simply wants someone to care for his brood and quite tactlessly told me so when he asked me to marry him.' Catching sight of Victoria's stunned expression in the glass prompted Emma to smile wryly. 'I get the distinct impression I have astonished you, Vicky. I also believe you would love to be back at your Hartfield.'

Emma swished about and dropped the amber silk gown onto the bed. 'I would gladly bolt there with you. I'm not sure I can endure Mama's unsubtle matchmaking this weekend. Or the sight of Papa sprawling drunk in a chair. Mama makes excuses for him all the time. He was intoxicated by eight of the clock the evening you arrived. He usually is every evening when he shambles home from his club. Thank goodness Lord Courtenay was gentleman enough to dissuade Mama from disturbing him.'

Yes, when he wanted, he could be so charming, was Victoria's acid thought. So charming and so very, seducingly generous. If she could punish him for treating her with such hateful disrespect by allowing him to settle her debts before she absconded to Hartfield and Alexander Beresford's care, she would be sorely tempted to do it. If she could summon courage enough, she hysterically inwardly laughed. She was quite sure that David Hardinge would not take such ill usage lightly or philosophically.

He was a ruthless degenerate. She recalled her papa hissing that at her seven years ago. Despite the fact that her poor papa had even then been displaying the first signs of dementia, he had been perfectly reasonable in his opinion of the man she had once idiotically idolised.

'Did that come from the top of the pack?'

The whining query was followed by an odd, eerie stillness in the gaming room.

Piercing blue eyes pinned down the weak brown gaze of the man opposite him. 'What did you say?' David Hardinge asked in a level tone as he fanned out his winning hand in front of him and leaned back in his chair.

Scenting blood, groups of men abandoned gaming tables in Watier's and silently sauntered over to watch and wait. Glasses froze by lips. No one dared to speak or swallow lest something be missed.

Frederick Worthington attempted to lower his eyes from those of his opponent but found he couldn't. He couldn't even rake his gaze to the appalling sight of all his money clustered in the centre of the table. Even a last, yearning glance before it disappeared into another's pockets was beyond him. He vainly attempted to dampen his fleshy mouth with a dry tongue. He was desperate for a drink and was furious not even to have enough left for a tot from some cheap, seedy gin house on his trek home through the suburbs. The possibility of purchasing other tempting pleasures likely to waylay his progress back to Rosemary House was definitely gone. No matter; the urge had expired along with his credit at Watier's. His membership of this exclusive gentleman's club might too unless he was exceedingly careful.

He wasn't sure whether David Hardinge had been cheating or not. Probably he had not. The man had the devil's own luck in every single thing he turned his hand to. Whether women, cards or commerce, he invariably came out on top. The unguarded accusation had simply slipped out as he resentfully saw his last chance of recouping some gin money finally drain away.

'Sorry, old man. Just a joke,' Frederick Worthington rasped, his Adam's apple jerking fitfully, his hands apologetically gesturing. 'You won fair and square, I know that.' He attempted a hoarse laugh and took refuge in what he knew best: acting the fool. 'Mustn't upset you, in any case. The dear lady wife is expecting your presence at Emma's little ball at the weekend. I'd sooner crawl home, tongue hanging out and on me uppers, than face her wrath by offending you, y'know.' This self-mocking titbit indeed

gained an appreciative chuckle from several of the spectators and caused a quirk to soften David Hardinge's mouth.
But he neither confirmed nor denied his plans for the weekend.

Frederick visibly relaxed. His tongue lizarded about his
mouth before a shaky hand wiped across it. Perhaps it
would be worth performing again; there was the possibility
of a drink in it for him.

'A snippet of inside information, Courtenay, just for you,
as I've allowed me mouth to run away with me this afternoon. We've got a tasty little widow as house guest at
present. Very pretty little piece. I'd attend the ball if I was
you. You'll be straight up her street, if y'know what I
mean…Cheapside.' A crêpey eyelid drooped in a conspir-
atorial wink and he paused for laughter.

It indeed came, uproariously and immediately, and many
a hand clapped his chubby back in tribute to his wit. Then
just as quickly it died away.

David Hardinge's reaction to this punning flattery about
his prowess and the mistresses he installed in Cheapside
was not as expected. And those that knew him were aware
he could easily take a joke about his popularity with the
petticoat set. He had once held court, in this very room,
giving advice on seduction to some green young blades
keen to learn tips prior to their first foray into Vauxhall
Gardens.

'You've allowed your mouth to run away with you again,
Worthington,' David quietly told him, shattering the tension. 'I believe you are referring to Victoria Hart, my late
cousin's widow. I do have a very special interest in her
welfare, actually, and am happy to let it be known.'

David suppressed a smile. Oddly enough the buffoon had
just done him a great favour. Frederick Worthington had
conveniently provided him with a prime opportunity to
warn off any prospective suitors interested in wedding…or

bedding…her, while letting them assume his own atten-
tiveness arose from duty to his late kinsman. He really
owed the fool a drink.

Frederick looked stricken. His wine-bloated face puffed
further. He yanked at his cravat, loosening it from his
blotchy neck, unable to credit what he'd done. He had just
unwittingly insulted a relative of the man who held an un-
paralleled sparring and duelling record. 'So sorry, Courtenay. No offence meant, a'course. Had I known of your
family's connection…' he croaked.

David smiled at his long fingers idly tapping against the
cards that had cleaned Frederick out. The other hand moved
in a patronising, dismissing gesture.

The spectating men started to wander disappointedly
away, pitying, disgusted glances and muttered asides directed at Frederick.

Humiliation and relief vied for dominance as Frederick
scraped back his chair, about to scurry away.

'Buy you a drink, Worthington?'

Frederick sat down again immediately, as David had
known he would.

'Just the one, old man,' Frederick gratefully accepted.
'Got to be home on time this evening. Lady wife's dragging
me off to the Blairs' soirée. Promised this time I'd not be
late.'

Better and better, David smiled to himself. The man had
just proved useful again. He signalled to the steward for
drinks. 'Simon and Petra Blair?' he probed casually.

'Yes. Dashed boring lot. Comely daughters, though. Especially the eldest, Moira. Not so tedious when one's got
a decent poppet to eye, eh?'

Frederick gulped greedily at his drink as soon as it arrived. He smacked his lips appreciatively. 'Nice to see that
homebody daughter of mine with a companion, y'know.
Victoria Hart and she seem firm friends. They've been

shopping 'n all sorts together. Sweet-natured young lady, your cousin's widow.' He smiled nervously but was sure this time he'd said nothing offensive.

'Another?' David asked, indicating Frederick's empty tumbler and watching the man lick his lips.

Frederick pushed the glass away in irritation. 'Damned if I wouldn't like one, but best be off now. As I say, all the ladies will be waiting on me.'

Dickie Du Quesne sat in the chair Frederick had just vacated. He stared across the table at his friend, noting the satisfied thrust to his moulded mouth. Deep blue eyes met Dickie's over the rim of a whisky tumbler.

'Wainwright says he's been charged to issue us with an invitation to Mrs Crawford's…er…bacchanalian extravaganza this evening.'

'Has he, now?' David said, his eyes on the pile of money still heaped on the table.

'I take it we're not going,' Dickie muttered. 'Did you get an invitation to the Blairs' at home?' He didn't expect a reply and answered himself drily. 'Yes, so did I. I have to say I've been looking forward to it all week.'

David smiled, leaned back in his chair with a sigh and stretched his long legs out under the baize-topped table. 'You'll be bored stiff. You needn't come.'

'I wouldn't miss it for the world, Davey,' the blond man grinned. 'I need a little tutoring in dignified remorse. I'll be watching closely.'

David's eyes narrowed on his friend's back as Dickie sauntered, whistling, towards the door. Thin lips compressed before an expletive blew through them, then, shoving his chair back, he followed his friend into the six o'clock dusk.

'Well, I think it's scandalous…'

Despite her resolution that she would not react, Victoria

felt her cheeks heating under the middle-aged woman's continuing sibilant censure.

Emma caught her eye and smiled encouragingly. She then turned innocently to the two matrons ensconced in a settee, their fat, satin bodies rolled together in the soft cushions. 'I beg your pardon, Mrs Porter? Did you say something?'

Victoria pressed her lips to disguise her smile. Emma had no qualms about confrontational discourse; that much was apparent.

'No...no, my dear Emma. I was not addressing you. I was just commiserating with Mrs Plumb, here beside me, about how sad it is for your new companion to be widowed so young. How grief-stricken she must be...' she studiedly hinted, her eyes boring into Victoria's radiant profile.

'I thank you for your concern on my behalf, Mrs Porter,' Victoria said quietly, twisting to face them. 'My husband was a fine man and I am indeed sorely missing him.'

'Yes...we can see...' the woman simpered, eliciting a muted snigger from her sly-eyed companion. 'In the normal way, of course...in polite society...one would not venture out so soon. But I know you're from the country. Standards differ so much. And, indeed, I'm sensible of that...'

'I beg to disagree, Mrs Porter,' Victoria said coolly, drawing a smothered snort of approval from Emma. 'We can be polite in Hertfordshire too, and dedicated to cherishing the memory of people we care about. My husband decreed I neither wear black nor shut myself indoors after his funeral. By complying with those fond wishes, I seek to honour him rather than strangers' notions of etiquette.'

Mrs Porter's jowls wobbled, her companion's pinched mouth slackened and Emma gurgled a laugh before gulping from her teacup.

'No doubt Viscount Courtenay was being apprised of your lofty ideals, Mrs Hart, when you called on him the other afternoon,' Mrs Porter sneered, purposely drawing attention and her fat, shiny shoulders up about her ears. 'Mrs Plumb noticed the Worthingtons' carriage stopped by his door in Mayfair. Margaret recalls loaning it to you and your aunt that afternoon.'

Victoria's face blanched with fury and disgust at this malicious woman's aim to publicly humiliate her. 'You are entirely correct in your assumption, Mrs Porter,' she quietly said, and almost laughed at the absurd truth of it. Oh, yes, indeed! She had set out her lofty ideals for his lordship and had never rued anything more. How these spiteful women would love to know the details of that afternoon's negotiations. What sport they would then have, shredding her character and reputation. She swallowed pride and anger, eager to defuse this verbal duel before it became a full-blown battle. 'As you seem keen to know the nature of our connection, my late husband and Lord Courtenay were blood relations.'

Mrs Porter looked startled by this revelation but forged a smile for the spectators. 'Kinsmen…indeed?'

'Indeed they were,' Emma chipped in innocently. 'Perhaps Lord Courtenay might confirm it. Why do you not ask him, dear Mrs Porter, for a list of his cousins?' Emma's steady gaze past the harridans had them eyeing each other warily. Then turbanned heads turned slowly inwards, feathers colliding as they peered over the sofa-back.

Victoria's glossy, dark head spun that way too.

Moira Blair was dangling prettily on one midnight-blue arm while her younger sister Daphne clutched at the other. Both had their blonde heads angled up to his handsome, laughing face as they proceeded further into the drawing room.

'It is him. Indeed it is…' Mrs Porter breathed at Mrs Plumb. Both simultaneously struggled to free their broad hips from the snuggling confines of the sofa. They beat a path across the carpet towards him. A good deal of the other guests appeared to be heading the same way. Some even abandoned their card games to rise and greet him.

He certainly wasn't expected, Victoria hysterically realised from glancing at awed expressions and the impromptu stampede. And she understood why: a prosperous merchant banker and his wife were hardly likely to tempt a jaded peer of the realm away from his sophisticated pleasures with an evening of hazard and whist and unaccomplished music. Had she herself ever believed they might, she would never have ventured out of Rosemary House this evening.

Her heartbeat was so fast and irregular, she felt quite light-headed. She had hoped never to see him again. Despite what Emma had said about expecting him at her birthday ball, she had been sure he would avoid attending. There was nothing polite left for them to say to each other.

Blue eyes were raised from Daphne's upturned face and slanted across the room at her.

Victoria immediately swung her face away, furious with herself for staring just that second too long.

'The Blairs must be wondering what brings them such exalted company tonight,' Emma remarked softly. 'I feel most inclined to tell them.'

Victoria was again made aware of just how perceptive her friend could be. 'Is there a terrace, Emma, do you know? Or a cool corridor to refresh oneself in? I feel quite hot and thirsty…'

'Yes…come on, let's escape,' Emma whispered conspiratorially, giving one of Victoria's hands a comforting squeeze. 'Let's leave these simpering females to waste their time with the infamous Viscount and his equally rakish friend. I believe the Blairs have a small conservatory, rather like ours. Mama is always denigrating the size of their plants.'

Victoria gave a wry smile. 'Let's go and ridicule their blooms to our hearts' content, then.'

Brilliant blue eyes, heavy-lidded with mingling desire and irritation, tracked glossy raven hair and lavender silk slipping by unobtrusively on the perimeter of the people milling about him. David barely recognised the Worthingtons' daughter, looking attractive in a dark gold gown, until she raised her topaz eyes challengingly to his while passing.

'Please do partner me at cards, Lord Courtenay,' Moira Blair petitioned, a fluttering fan shielding rosebud lips, fluttering eyelashes screening ice-blue eyes.

'Please do let my girls lead you to some refreshment in the dining room before you play, Lord Courtenay,' her mother insisted.

'First things first, m'dear,' her husband jovially countermanded. 'What will you have to drink, Courtenay?' he solicitiously asked their honoured guest.

'Is there a chance I might win some of me money back tonight, old man?' Frederick Worthington slurred drunkenly over the crowd, raising a chuckle from the men who had heard tell of his afternoon antics at Watier's.

'Is there a chance you might be regretting this already?' Dickie needled in an undertone as he sauntered past David, allowing Daphne Blair to triumphantly steer him towards some inharmonious noise issuing forth from the music room.

Victoria held the cool crystal tumbler against her flushed face and then sipped a little of the bitter-sweet lemonade. 'This is very good,' she said to Emma, sitting next to her on the iron bench nestling amid the foliage in the conservatory.

Emma nodded in agreement and broke in half the piece of madeira cake she had snatched from the dining table when the pair of them had subtly withdrawn.

'This isn't so good.' Emma voiced Victoria's thoughts. Glancing about for somewhere to deposit the cake and finding nowhere, she dipped a little of it into her glass of lemonade to soften it then persevered with chewing it.

The sweet, exotic perfume of foreign flowers and the cool quiet were welcomingly soothing. 'I believe I can detect the scent of jasmine,' Victoria murmured, resting back into the seat.

Emma pointed to a climber some feet away.

'Shall we share a headache and return to Cheapside?' Victoria wrinkled her nose appealingly. 'I don't think I can endure any more of that ill-toned soprano. Or the ill-mannered Mrs Porter, Mrs Plumb or Misses Blair.'

'Or the ill-reputed Viscount…?' Emma suggested with a sideways smile.

Victoria returned her a defeated one. 'Yes…especially not him.'

'I'll find Mama and discreetly say we are poorly. It will make her determined to pack us off home, lest I am still ailing at the weekend. We can send the carriage back for her and Papa and your aunt. Two grooms are in attendance tonight so we'll be perfectly safe and respectable.'

Once Emma had disappeared, Victoria became aware of a sound which their muted chatting had covered. She rose and idly strolled along the cool avenue of greenery, her fingers lightly slipping over large, glossy leaves, until she found the little fountain playing. She had arrived at the Blairs' most pleasing musical offering, she wryly realised as she allowed the crystal-clear water to splash her fingers. And then she noticed the gilt cage suspended above it.

'I don't believe we've been introduced.'

Emma slowed her speedy pace at the unexpected greeting and twisted towards the tall blond man who had stepped from a doorway to block her entrance to the conservatory.

She gave him a cool smile. 'Your reputation precedes you, Mr Du Quesne. I know perfectly well who you are and I'm sure you have little real interest in who I am.'

Dickie choked an admiring laugh at her unfazed composure and candour. 'Well, don't beat about the bush, Miss Worthington. Please say what you really mean,' he wryly retaliated.

Now Emma suppressed a smile. 'Very well, Mr Du Quesne, I will do so. I really mean…that I am aware I am being waylaid for a purpose. I shall allow your friend no more than a few minutes with Mrs Hart. If it should ever become necessary, I shall swear I never left her alone with him for one second. And if I hear one sound that makes me think she wishes not to be alone with him I shall scream blue murder and accuse you both of behaviour most unbecoming to…er…gentlemen.' She looked thoughtful. 'And, before you tell me, I am aware that our reputations will suffer irreparable damage as a consequence, whereas yours will not. But scream I shall, nonetheless. And have a fit of the vapours while you and the Viscount explain.'

Dickie's eyes narrowed on her serene golden gaze. 'Where have you been all my life?' he drily muttered.

Emma was aware of the reluctant compliment in his sarcasm. 'Oh, I rarely mix in polite society,' she mellifluously told him. 'But then, of course, neither do you.' With that parting shot she walked away a little and began an interested perusal of the portraits lining the corridor walls.

Victoria gazed up at the tiny silent creature and the linnet inclined its head to put a beady eye on her. It made no sound. A song bird but it simply bobbed jerkily on its perch and then grew still. A slender white finger was stretched out to rest against its golden prison. 'I'd set you free if I could,' she whispered. 'Do they let you out to fly? Do you remember how to fly?'

'Shall we find out?'

Victoria spun about and immediately froze before taking two careful steps back.

David Hardinge seemed unbelievably tall and dark in the narrow, leaf-fringed walkway, and far too close. Glittering eyes rose from her startled face to the linnet. 'You're not hoping to fly away too, Mrs Hart, are you?' he deliberately challenged her.

Victoria fought to control the thundering of her heart, grasping her fountain-wet fingers behind her back. 'Why…why should I do that?' she asked haughtily, completely meeting his expectations. 'I was here first. I believe it is you who should leave. I would be grateful if you would do so right now—before we are discovered and the malicious tabbies are entitled to their outrage.'

David lifted the cage from its golden hook and looked at the bird. Even thus disturbed it made no protest, simply dipping and cocking its head this way and that. He placed it on a high ledge close to a tilted fanlight and opened the cage door.

'I…I don't think you should do that, Mr Hardinge,' Victoria said nervously, but her doubt was disproved by a small, sweetly admiring smile for the linnet's liberator.

'There are lots of things I shouldn't do,' he said softly. 'Lots of things I regret… But this isn't one of them.'

Victoria felt her throat tighten, and her limpid eyes rose to his. Just for a moment she was sure those words were a prelude to an apology. The hope was doused on glimpsing an unmistakable lust smouldering between his lashes. Despite her determination not to seem intimidated she was: she was so terribly afraid that he was simply preparing to barter with her again. 'I should be grateful if you would leave, Mr Hardinge…' Her voice shook with the strength of plea in it.

'Why won't you call me David?' he asked quietly, his eyes dark, brilliant stars in his shadowy face.

'For the same reason you won't call me Victoria,' she answered, striving for calm and logic. 'It would imply a friendship we no longer have. Please leave…'

'I want back what we had, Victoria. I want us to be close…'

A choke of sour laughter interrupted him. 'I'm sure you do, Mr Hardinge. Unfortunately, I want the reverse.' Her unsteady fingers gripped behind her back. 'As you won't go away, would you allow me to pass? I should like to find Emma. We are ready to depart…' She trailed off, realising Emma had had ample time to return. She guessed at once who might be detaining her and why. 'Have you sent your friend to intercept her…?'

David smiled. 'Dickie does as he pleases. If he wants to talk to a pretty girl, no doubt he will. Emma does look very attractive tonight… And you look quite beautiful…as usual.' David watched his compliment fire glossy gunmetal eyes into seeking escape routes.

'Which malicious tabbies?' he asked obliquely, confusing her.

After a moment of collecting her thoughts, Victoria laughed shortly. 'Oh, those who are scandalised by my presence here tonight, Mr Hardinge.'

'Scandalised?' As the possibility dawned, he frowned. 'Because you and your aunt visited me at home?'

'Partly. But it seems respecting my late husband's wish that I should not shut myself indoors shrouded in black is the greater sin.'

'You've been insulted?' David asked in a tight, toneless voice.

'Why so surprised, Mr Hardinge?' was Victoria's bittersweet response. 'Did you believe that to be solely your prerogative?'

'You think offering you anything you want and forty thousand pounds is an insult?'

Victoria's eyes flew to the bird cage while her heart raced. She had been desperate to avoid any mention of that afternoon's mortification yet had stupidly led to it herself.

She watched the linnet. It was still there, facing freedom, yet too timid to go.

'Do you?' David persisted softly.

'I should return to the assembled company if I were you, Mr Hardinge.' Victoria breathlessly changed the subject. 'I'm sure you're already missed. Immoral you may be, but still very welcome—as, indeed, you said you would be. Whereas I, having the effrontery to come here this evening and share a conversation and a sofa with Emma, am completely beyond the pale and will be gladly despatched home.'

'I find their hypocrisy as distasteful as you do. When you leave, I leave. And they can make of that what they will.'

'Are you trying to ruin me?' Victoria gasped. 'By making your attention so obvious?'

'Forty thousand pounds' worth of debts is ruination, Victoria. But it needn't be. I could make sure it isn't,' David reasoned softly. 'You're an impoverished widow, not a child. You're not being sensible or mature in this and you know it.'

'Yes, I do know it,' Victoria agreed in an acrid whisper. 'Even moments ago I was naïve and foolish. You see, I thought you might include your odious proposition to be amongst the things you regretted.' She swung sideways, examining the closest petals as the truth in it brought a stinging heat to her eyes and a thickening to her throat. She forced through it, 'I shall marry when I return to Hertfordshire and very much hope never to see or speak to you ever again.'

'And your father and your aunt? Are you happy never to see or speak to them again either? Beresford can't support you all. He certainly can't maintain your estate on what he earns.'

Victoria twisted back to face him, her complexion heating with temper. 'How did you know? Who told you that? You've been checking on my affairs!' she choked furiously.

'Naturally, I take an interest in my late cousin's widow...and her misfortunes,' David remarked mildly, amused by her ire.

'And that fake concern can cover a multitude of sins, I suppose. But only yours. Never mine,' Victoria lashed at him, revelling in this white-hot rage that was decimating her anxiety.

'So, what is it you have regretted, Mr Hardinge, in your shameless, selfish life? Perhaps paying so obscenely for your pleasures. Or behaving in such a disgusting manner that my aunt tells me the details would shock the devil himself. Or perhaps that you travelled in the snow to attend Daniel's funeral and discovered something truly diverting...something you couldn't have. No? None of that?' She sarcastically read from his face. A wild exhilaration emboldened her as his sardonic features set into granite. 'How strange, for I swear I believed the last must count. I know I have never regretted any day more in my life. But I don't think I can be bothered to guess further what it is you rue. Please allow me to pass or I shall call for assistance and...'

She was hauled unceremoniously against his rigid body and long, hard fingers were laid against her softly quivering mouth. His dark head dipped close to hers. 'I shouldn't do that, Victoria. If you thought these genteel ladies a trifle cruel to you before, you'll never survive them clawing into you over this.' Cool fingers slid against her trembling lips, expertly parting them before abruptly moving so his warm mouth could take their place.

It was unbearable. She had expected her insolence would make it a kiss full of lechery and revenge. But there was no pain, no revulsion. It was exactly the same as the last proper kiss she had received...seven long years ago. A kiss of tender, restrained passion, with stroking lips and fingers soothing her face and spearing into her hair.

She drifted into the caress, languid, swirling, the years effortlessly peeling away. Even the cool greenery surrounding them, the dusky shadows, the faint echoes of music and gaiety conspired to rejuvenate the memory.

It was a summer evening and she was being loved in a walkway in Vauxhall Gardens; loving back; matching him kiss for shy kiss, returning endearments as she received them, listening to plans for their future whispered against her upturned face in between those tender, sensual assaults. Listening to his husky promise that tomorrow he would speak to her father.

The tableau was so clear, so bitter-sweet, so much at odds with her mood and expectation that inexorable stinging tears flooded her eyes, spilling before she had sense or will to stop them.

She knew the moment he realised she wept. He deepened the kiss and his arms tightened, soothingly rocked her, as though he could woo away her sorrow...her anger...as he always had. Knowing he was sharing her reminiscence caused a juddering sob to escape and mingle with his breath. That was the final time she had seen or heard from him until Daniel's funeral.

David's mouth slid slowly away across her wet cheek, large hands cradling her silken head against his shoulder.

'I'll tell you what I regret most in my life, Victoria,' he finally, hoarsely said against her hair. 'I regret waiting until I had twenty thousand pounds, seven years ago, when ten might have been sufficient.'

'You had no money seven years ago…' Victoria sobbed into his shoulder.

'No. I had no money. So I borrowed some from my father. And because I felt ashamed of begging money from a man I had never acknowledged, a man I had always slapped away when he extended friendship, I waited until I'd doubled it for I wanted some self-respect when I returned to Hammersmith to offer for you again. Tried to buy you, your father would have called it. I had twenty thousand pounds two days after you married Daniel Hart.'

Victoria trembled in his arms at the awful significance of these quiet, harsh words. Her mind raced back, scrambling for information. 'You said your father was without funds…that he was verging on bankruptcy. How could he have loaned you so much?' Victoria whispered into his shoulder.

David grunted an unpleasant laugh. 'Not him. Not the man who gave me his name. The man who gave me life. The Duke of Hawthorne.'

Chapter Seven

'The jasmine is quite remarkable and this variety is particularly worth obtaining for its perfume.'

Alarmed by the dialogue, and the knowledge that they were no longer alone, Victoria tugged free of David's embrace. Emma was bearing down on them at some speed. An explicit, warning look from her friend had Victoria's blood freezing. Sweeping past, Emma grabbed at David's arm, urging him towards the foliage. She pointed up towards a pale flower, while hissing, 'Please do look interested, Lord Courtenay; I believe it is the very least you can do.'

Her small fingers were picked from the crook of his arm, his expression thunderous as he tried to jerk away, but Emma hung on. Then David saw Dickie talking urgently to Victoria; she was listening earnestly. A hum of female voices became audible and he understood.

'Ah, Mama,' Emma called brightly. 'Do hurry, I need your advice. Now I am quite sure this might be an orchid but Lord Courtenay believes it to be a lily. What's your opinion?'

Margaret Worthington gawped at the astonishing sight of the Blairs' sought-after guests being advised on horticulture by her own daughter and Matilda's pretty widowed niece. She hurried forward, while craning an anxious look behind at her hostess and her chattering daughters. They had been tracking these gentlemen for some while. 'Well, my dear Emma.' She gulped. 'On closer inspection, it seems his lordship is correct.'

Petra Blair sliced a steely look at the two young women usurping her own girls' privileges. A millionaire viscount and the heir to a rich baronetcy were actually attending one of her soirées! After such a monumental achievement, the last thing she was prepared to countenance was said gentlemen spending precious time in the greenery with young ladies who were not her daughters.

'Moira!' she summoned. 'You are quite an expert on the flowers. Please show Lord Courtenay all the largest specimens. Daphne...' she barked. 'Perhaps Mr Du Quesne might like to see the fountain...' The two blonde girls rallied at once, poisoning their rivals with darting glances while homing in on their quarry.

Victoria and Emma exchanged private looks. Emma even managed a small, relieved smile until she noticed a suspicious wetness sheening her friend's long, sooty lashes. She then glared at David Hardinge as he stood woodenly with his newly acquired female companion.

'Ah, there you are,' Aunt Matilda called out, tripping along the pathway towards them. 'Victoria, are you unwell? Emma tells me the two of you have the headache...' Spying the two gentlemen, her pale eyes targeted David Hardinge and she sniffed disdainfully. No one, in Matilda Sweeting's eyes, had the right to reject her beautiful, worthy niece when she offered herself as a wife. Certainly not this man, who wasn't good enough for her in any case, however rich and regal he might now think himself. Having examined her niece's strained face, she joined Emma in hating the hard, handsome profile presented to them.

Dickie strolled towards Emma with Daphne attached to his arm. 'Well, Miss Worthington, thank you for introducing me to the delights of...er...an unusual flower. I should like to know more. In fact, I'm keen to invest a little time in becoming familiar with such a rarity.'

'Oh, but it would require a great deal of time, Mr Du Quesne. And patience. Not a pastime for the faint-hearted, I fear. Perhaps you should dedicate that "little time" to a more common species...much as you do now. They are better suited to a novice.' Emma smiled sweetly but something in Dickie's expression made her lose no time in slipping past them.

Victoria smothered the hysterical laugh that threatened. She followed Emma a few paces and then swung about. She felt utterly confused. Thirty minutes ago all she had wanted was to feign illness and escape to Rosemary House with Emma. Now, despite a genuine headache, she was reluctant to leave: she so wanted some more time alone with David. There was so much more she needed to know. But it was hopeless. No chance of further privacy was likely to present itself.

Her mind sifted through melancholy memories. Had he really been on the point of offering for her again seven years ago? She knew when David had initially approached her father he had endured such insult and vilification, she had panicked he might never venture back. After lengthy, solitary debate, she had convinced herself that mere odium would never deter the strong man she knew and loved, despite the prospect of such a hateful father-in-law.

Her father had unashamedly recounted to her his slanderous abuse, and with a mean triumph that had made her forcefully renew her championship of the man he so maligned. Her unshakeable faith and temerity had re-stoked her father's apopletic rage and henceforth it had been directed at her.

A slanting, soulful glance sought David and the yearning to return to those intimate moments they had just shared, to talk further, was like a physical ache. Had her faith been justified after all? Had he then not consoled himself with pleasure-seeking abroad following her father's invective? Had he actually been in London making money for their future when she'd wed Daniel? Or had she somehow misunderstood his meaning moments ago? She sighed. If only she'd had time to confide her own heartfelt sorrow at how abruptly and sourly it had all ended. But perhaps bitterness might have overtaken her, making her rail openly at him as, long ago, she had done privately. For, ultimately, what excuse was there, other than cowardice or apathy, for ignoring both her letters and abandoning her to her father's sick acrimony?

She pushed thoughts of recrimination away; it was all now far too late. Besides, she was sure they had been on the threshold of a new understanding and warmth. Destroying it needlessly would be foolish.

She focussed on him properly, watching him as everyone else seemed to be doing. His head was angled back as though he was indeed admiring the exotic blooms. But his stillness and the rigidity in his jaw consoled her; he was as intensely aware of her as she was of him.

As if attuned to her need, his dark head slowly turned and for a fleeting, unnoticed moment their eyes were inextricable. The longing was in him too. So was smoky desire and such raw exasperation that Victoria was terrified he might not control it but vent his temper.

One side of his mouth pulled in a wry smile as though he read her fears and wanted to allay them. His eyes lifted to the gilded bird cage and Victoria's followed. She smiled too. The linnet was gone.

* * *

'Tonight I received the greatest set-down of my entire life…twice.'

Having just returned in mutual thoughtful silence from the Blairs' to Beauchamp Place, both Dickie and David now poured drinks in the study. Dickie strode towards the blazing fire carrying his and jabbed an irritated kick at the ornate fender.

'Are you going to call him out?' David asked, mildly interested, as he stretched his considerable length out on the brocade sofa, resting his dark head back, with a weary sigh, into the scrolled arm.

'She called me a novice,' Dickie thundered. 'Me! A novice! The little…' His teeth gritted and he was unsure why the insult battering at them wouldn't force past.

A soundless laugh softened David's chiselled features as his fingers felt for the table and retrieved the cheroot from the ashtray. He stuck it between even white teeth and spoke past it. 'I told you not to come to the Blairs' tonight. I warned you you'd be bored and regret it.'

'*Bored? Regret it?* I was insulted twice by a…a slip of a girl with extraordinary golden eyes. You didn't warn me about that.'

'How was I to know she'd like you?' David enigmatically excused himself, still laughing. He pulled his heavy gold hunter into his line of vision. 'It's not yet midnight. Mrs Crawford will be glad to unruffle your feathers at her salon, you know. Even happier now you'll be determined to impress her with your mastery.'

Dickie strode towards the door. 'Coming?' was flung back over his shoulder.

David swung his feet off the sofa and had pushed himself upright in a lithe, fluid second. A lean hand went to the nape of his neck, massaging the tension beneath his thick mahogany hair. Stubbing the cigar out, he downed the remaining inch of cognac in his tumbler, stood up…and remained motionless. His long fingers massaged at his nape again. His eyes closed and he cursed beneath his breath.

Dickie walked slowly back towards him, biting his lip and looking sympathetic. 'You might just as well marry her. She's got you acting like a husband...an unusual husband,' he amended drily, 'but a husband nonetheless.'

David paced the room restlessly before halting by the window. He gazed moodily up at the full moon then down into the quiet street.

'You go,' he ordered Dickie.

'You really think she likes me?' Dickie demanded disbelievingly.

'Undoubtedly,' David confirmed with a lop-sided grin through the window.

The quiet click of the door let him know Dickie was receptive to his wish for solitude. But then Dickie knew him well. Better, probably, than anyone else. Better than his family who had never understood him at all. But then from his mid-teens he had never wanted them to. He had learned young to be secretive...to guard his character and feelings. It was less painful that way. He could still remember as a young child wanting...needing his parents' attention and affection. He had never received either meaningfully.

Paul and Maria Hardinge had, at times, ostentatiously paraded their three children for friends' and visitors' compliments; for all three were handsome of face and figure, although not alike. Unsurprisingly considering each had been differently sired. But Maria Hardinge had been a beauty and each child had inherited her perfect facial bone-structure, if not her petite frame and fair colouring. His own sire, the Duke of Hawthorne, had also been a tall, handsome man.

But once their offspring had been admired and picked over they had been dismissed again, banished back to the nursery or the schoolroom, their usefulness complete, parental duty, as they saw it, accomplished.

The adults would then commence carousing. And heaven knew some of what he and Michael had witnessed as children from between the banisters as their parents had entertained their guests…or the servants…or, rarely, each other would have shocked the devil himself. He smiled, his spare features silvered by milky moonbeams slanting across his face. Now why had that particular phrase sprung to mind? he drily wondered. And which incident was it that Victoria's aunt had heard about?

He didn't want Victoria hearing any embellished tales. He'd rather recount it all honestly himself. Most of his exploits had been wildly exaggerated by the time they circulated back. He should have told her that he regretted his former way of life: since Daniel Hart's funeral pangs of guilt had been niggling. Had they not been interrupted in the conservatory tonight, no doubt he would have.

He swung away from the window with an exasperated oath. *Former way of life?* What about it was over? He had no intention of explaining or modifying his behaviour for anyone. Or apologising for it.

Dickie was right. He was moping about like a besotted fool. Much as he had seven years ago, he damningly reminded himself. And he was never hurting like that again.

Then, she had professed to love him and had seemed so sincere. Within a month of her father sending her to Hertfordshire, she'd married another man. So much for his arrogant certainty that she would have faith in him. That she would remain constant until he came back with enough money to claim her. He would have sworn he knew her, yet she had effortlessly transferred that sweet, loyal affection from a penniless, adoring suitor, willing to die rather than see them parted, to a landowner old enough to be her father.

He wouldn't go to this damned ball of Emma's. He
wished now he'd never gone to the Blairs' this evening.
Kissing her had been foolish, as had being moved by her
tears. He had promised himself that she wouldn't sway him
with feminine wiles. And she could, he wryly recalled. She
certainly could. He'd vowed he wouldn't touch…not until
she was installed in one of his London properties and he
was entitled to do so whenever…however he pleased. But
he had yielded to temptation and the scent and taste and
feel of her had stirred him as overwhelmingly at a jaded
thirty years old as it had when he had been a comparatively
fresh youth falling in love for the first…the only…time in
his life.

He wandered to the decanter and refilled his glass and
downed half in one swallow. She would agree to his terms
before she returned to Hertfordshire; he was sure of it.
There was no dispossessed woman, whatever her station in
life, who would hold out against such ridiculous generosity.
Most women forced to improve their prospects were exceedingly grateful for his interest and protection and very
keen to prove that to him.

Victoria had her relations to think of and this damned
estate she was so proud of. He was confident those things
would make her sensible.

He wouldn't go the Worthingtons' at the weekend, he
decided, stretching out on the sofa again. He'd let her ponder…and wonder… There was no way she would return to
Hartfield without again seeking him out. He was certain of
that.

'Well, he's regretting it already; that much is perfectly
clear. And don't you go accepting too soon. He deserves
to suffer.'

Victoria swivelled on her dressing stool and looked at
her aunt as she rustled into the bedroom in her voluminous

nightrobe. 'What *are* you talking about, Aunt Matty?' Noting that Beryl also seemed quite intrigued by her aunt's odd outburst and was gawping at Matilda, Victoria took the tortoiseshell hairbrush from her slack fingers and commenced brushing her own hair. 'That will be all, thank you, Beryl. You may retire for the night now.'

Beryl closed her mouth, bobbed dutifully and quit the bedroom Victoria and Matilda shared in Rosemary House.

'That girl has too much to say for herself,' Matilda sniffed.

'Hardly fair, Aunt,' Victoria reproved on a gurgling laugh. 'She said nothing. In fact she rarely says anything. Can't you see, she's still sulking for being deprived of Hartfield…and Samuel? But she is not deaf and she understands a great deal,' Victoria subtly warned. 'Now, what mustn't I accept?'

'Viscount Courtenay's proposal,' her aunt explained with much accentuation. 'Let him stew while you pretend to consider… You may accept his apology.'

Victoria continued drawing the brush through her long, sleek hair. 'There is nothing to accept, Aunt. Neither proposal nor apology, and there never will be. I've told you, he considers himself a confirmed bachelor,' Victoria huskily reminded her, 'and he is hardly likely to deem it necessary to apologise for that.'

'Margaret has told me he rarely socialises in such conventional circles as he has these past days. He is obviously out seeking you. He has let it be known at his club that he has a *special interest* in your welfare.'

'Has he, indeed?' Victoria gasped, shaking ebony tresses back from her shocked face.

'The gentlemen at Watier's looked suitably put in their places, according to Frederick,' Matilda said smugly. 'You see, he is letting them all know he has first claim on you.' She flapped a dismissing hand. 'I have no sympathy for

him. In fact, that Mr Du Quesne is rather a handsome sort
of chap and very rich too…'

Oh, he had let it be known he had first claim on her, had
he? Victoria fumed. He had no wish to marry her himself
but neither did he want anyone else to: it would spoil his
sport. By publicising his intentions he had cleverly deprived
her of any respectable offers that might have come her way.
His confirmed-bachelor status coupled with his dissolute
womanising ensured all and sundry knew exactly what was
meant by his *special interest*.

She pressed her cool fingers to her heating face. She
would be pored over by gentlemen in every London club…
laughed at…ogled… And when their wives heard the whispered gossip they would despise and shun her.

And her dear aunt Matty, in her innocence and ignorance—for she had kept from her David Hardinge's terms
for saving Hartfield—believed that he harboured honourable intentions towards her!

What a fool she had been again. She knew he was an
habitual philanderer yet, merely hours ago at the Blairs',
she had been ready to seek another quiet place to be alone
with him. She had practically allowed herself to be seduced
right there and then by some clever reminiscing and an
expert kiss. No doubt he meant none of it. And no doubt
all his prospective mistresses were bamboozled with a little
contrived wooing at the outset.

'When he proposes—'

'He is not going to propose, Aunt,' Victoria interrupted
fiercely, her grey eyes stormy purple in her chalky face. 'It
is not what he intends at all.' She drew a deep, shaky
breath. 'Do you remember once refusing to tell me a scandalous anecdote of his friends who were not ladies? Well,
I had hoped never to tell *you* this: he has invited me to join
their ranks. That is the only reason he pays me attention.

He has no other role for me in his life and you must stop thinking he has.'

'He wants you to serve him at table naked?' Matilda shrieked, astonished.

'*What?*' Victoria gasped, equally amazed.

Matilda sank onto the edge of her bed and a veined hand went to her wrinkled brow.

'*What* did you say, Aunt Matty?' Victoria demanded in a querulous whisper. 'You had better tell me the details of what would shock the devil himself. It might, after all, be what he had planned for me.'

'It's probably not true,' Matilda hastily dismissed. 'At the very least, it's grossly meddled with…' Her pink cheeks displayed her embarrassment and reluctance to divulge more.

'You said, "serve him at table naked". You heard that one of his mistresses did that?'

'Not one…three. And they were not his mistresses but had every ambition of becoming so,' Matilda recounted falteringly. 'These trollops were vying for his attention at a dubious private salon. One aspirant was a countess, so the story goes. Each woman believed her figure more comely than her rivals' and was keen to prove it to him…much to the amusement of all the men present.' Matilda paused and darted an anxious glance at Victoria's stunned expression. 'I suppose you cannot really censure him for 'twas not his stipulation. The harlots devised between them this contest…'

'And whom did he choose?' Victoria gritted, unable to discipline the trembling hurt from her voice. 'Did the countess win? Did all of them win?'

'None, I believe. He left with a young woman new to the…er…the profession,' Matilda finished uneasily. 'I'd rather you hadn't found out, Victoria…'

'Why?' Victoria choked, veering between fury and hysteria. 'Because had he been willing to marry me this would all be acceptable? Is that not as shameful in its own way as what you've just recounted?' She flung her hairbrush onto the bed. 'Oh, I wish I'd never come here! It was foolish to ever believe a solution to our problems could be found this way.'

Matilda enclosed her trembling shoulders in a hesitant hug. 'As soon as Emma's ball is over we will depart the following morning. I'm so sorry I ever persuaded you to accompany me,' she said tearfully. 'To think you've been so insulted…'

Victoria laid slender, tapering fingers over her aunt's bumpy, mottled hand. 'Well, it is all an experience, Aunt Matty,' she managed on a woeful laugh. 'We shall hereafter be on our guard against such…such men.' She soldiered on brightly. 'And it has been good to see you enjoy yourself with Margaret and all your old acquaintances. And how wonderful to find a new friend in Emma! Our time in London has been enjoyable. We will not let such people ruin it for us.'

She gently put her aunt from her and stood up. 'Mr Beresford is a kind man…if not wealthy. Hartfield must be sold but I'm sure there will be something to put by to provide a modest home for us all. If so, no marriage at all will be necessary and we can make do and mend much as we do now.' She sighed. 'It will be sad to see Samuel and Sally and the others put off. But they are all young and strong and with references I'm quite sure they will find work.' She walked to the window and gazed up at the full moon and suddenly wondered how the linnet fared: whether it would survive its liberty or whether, perhaps, captivity would have been kinder, after all.

'I thought I wouldn't be at all bothered about tonight but I feel terribly excited. How do I look?' Emma demanded as she pirouetted in front of Victoria. She put a hand up to check her glossy ringlets and the elegant fall of peach velvet ribbon Beryl had artfully twined into her hair.

'You look lovely, Emma. Absolutely radiant. And that shade of pastel apricot suits you.' Victoria lightly flicked an amber eardrop. 'And these suit the colour remarkably well too.' She raised enquiring dark brows and whispered, 'I take it your mama had no hand in your attire tonight.'

A gay chuckle bubbled from Emma and she shook her head. 'A successful shopping expedition I made alone some months ago.' She cocked her head to one side. 'And you look just as stunning in lilac silk as you do in grey and lavender…and every other shade you wear…'

'Well, now we have complimented each other very prettily, perhaps we ought to go down,' Victoria warned. 'If we do not, your mama is sure to be up the stairs again shortly, looking for you. Your guests have been arriving this past half-hour.'

With faultless timing, Margaret Worthington burst into the room. 'Emma, come along! The Blairs are here and the Watsons and Sophie Greig, who I swear is wearing exactly the same shade of orange as you. I told you it would be a common colour. Purple is more outstanding…more unique…'

Victoria and Emma exchanged looks and the appalling description 'orange' could be read on both their lips. They widened their eyes simultaneously.

Victoria gave her friend a sympathetic smile, politely commented on the fineness of Margaret Worthington's ensemble, then swished past and down the sweeping stairwell of Rosemary House in search of her aunt Matilda.

'Well, I have to own that Margaret has excelled herself.' Matilda proudly praised her sister-in-law.

Standing next to her in the drawing-room doorway, Victoria could only murmur wholehearted agreement. Her eyes rose to admire rainbows sparking from the chandelier's crystal droplets as candle flames danced upon them. The carpets had been removed to reveal a marquetry floor for dancing, and already many of the chairs lining both sides of the long room were occupied by fashionably dressed guests. A cosy hum of conversation and laughter amongst the assembly lent a warmth to the atmosphere that blended nicely with the blaze in the hearth.

Victoria and her aunt had already feasted their eyes upon the variety of delicacies laid out for supper in the dining room. Margaret had certainly not overstated the luxury of her daughter's twenty-fourth-birthday celebration.

'Shall we find a seat now, Aunt Matty, before they are all taken? I see Mrs Plumb and Mrs Porter are heading this way,' Victoria warned on a grimace. 'Shall we beat them to the last comfortable sofa?'

'Indeed we shall not,' Matilda decided with a hand-flap. Let them have it. We shall circulate and meet new people…not sit with your beauty concealed in the cushions.'

Victoria bit her lip, a wry expression twisting her full, soft mouth and making her grey eyes smoky. For, despite her aunt's assurances that she was finally resigned to the fact that Hartfield must be sold and they must all take their chances with fate, Victoria knew the woman was unable to relinquish her dream that this ball would educe a rich, honourable hero bent on rescuing them.

In undoubted confirmation of this, Matilda ran her pale blue eyes the length of her niece's slender lilac-silk figure. She assessed from sheeny raven head to satin-slippered toe, before nodding contentedly. 'You look exceedingly pretty in that new gown. The scoop in the neckline shows your fine white skin and shoulders to perfection.'

Victoria immediately shielded the delicate contours of exposed collarbone with a slender hand, aware the spiteful harridans were almost upon them. 'Does it need a fichu, do you think?' she asked anxiously, unable to countenance any verbal assault from the hateful women on the subject of her *décolletage*. Not that she minded battling on her own behalf, but she would let nothing spoil Emma's birthday ball.

'Indeed it does not.' Matilda picked her niece's white fingers from her throat. 'You've the shapeliest bosom of any young lady here, if not the fullest,' she declared. 'Some of the wanton displays I've seen here tonight—' Matilda sniffed, glancing disdainfully about at naked cleavages '—make your gown look exceedingly demure and your neat figure a joy to behold.'

'Dear Aunt Matty,' Victoria said with a laugh. 'What would I do without you to constantly flatter me?'

'It's truth, not flattery,' Matilda returned huffily, straightening her head on her crêpey neck as Victoria gave her bony arm an affectionate squeeze.

Loud conversation and laughter in the corridor drew their attention. They watched as a large birthday cake was carried carefully between the butler and cook towards the dining room.

'Indeed, Margaret has done Emma proud,' Matilda stated with an emphatic nod as her eyes followed the progress of the magnificent confection. 'If the girl can't attract a man after all this expense and finery, then Margaret might just as well pack her off to a nunnery...'

Her niece's blanching complexion and involuntary shudder made Matilda gasp and hide her mouth with freckled fingers. The other gripped hard at one of Victoria's arms in comfort and remorse. 'Oh, I'm so sorry, Vicky, my dear. What a thoughtless, stupid thing to say. I'm so very sorry,' she stressed, her voice and pale eyes replete with shame.

'It's all right, Aunt,' Victoria soothed with a wobbly smile. 'I know you meant nothing ill by it. It was all such a long time ago. It is time we all forgot...' Victoria cast about for something bland to say, to take her aunt's mind off her gaffe and restore her previous jollity. Distraction came in the shape of a distinguished, fair-haired man just entering the drawing room. He saw them and smiled.

'Look, Aunt, Mr Du Quesne is arrived, and is coming our way,' Victoria said huskily, her eyes immediately skimming past him to locate the man she was sure must follow. But he seemed to be alone.

'Mrs Hart…Mrs Sweeting. How nice to see you again. I trust you are both well?' Dickie charmingly greeted them.

'Indeed we are, sir,' Victoria replied with a smile and a small bob.

'May I book a dance with you early, Mrs Hart, before your card is full?' Dickie gallantly asked.

'I shan't be dancing this evening, Mr Du Quesne,' Victoria told him apologetically, unconsciously smoothing her lilac mourning dress. 'But thank you anyway.'

'Of course,' Dickie murmured, dipping his head a little in understanding and regret.

'Ah, there you are, Mr Du Quesne,' Margaret beamed as she swept up with a hand fixed on Emma's elbow, propelling her along too. 'And where is your good friend this evening? Did Viscount Courtenay accompany you, or is he coming along later?'

'Ah, I believe he was unable to break his prior engagement, Mrs Worthington,' Dickie smoothly explained, his eyes seeking Victoria's grey ones which immediately glided away. 'He was, of course, extremely disappointed…'

'Oh, well…' Margaret murmured dejectedly. She had naturally hoped that the wealthy Viscount would attend but had known it a vain ambition. But, she thought philosophically, she had acquired the presence of the next best thing. Sir Richard Du Quesne, as she already thought of him, was also very rich and would be richer still on gaining his title and birthright.

'Emma…do show Mr Du Quesne your birthday cake,'

Margaret suggested with a meaningful nod. 'The decoration is quite a work of art and the gentlemen rarely take time to appreciate these things.' Realising that might be construed as criticism, she hastily added, 'I beg pardon, sir; I only mean gentlemen prefer to physically enjoy rather than simply admire delicious treats…'

'You're absolutely right, Mrs Worthington,' Dickie admitted with an ironic smile and a long look at the woman's daughter. 'I'd be the first to admit that, in the matter of cake icing, I am a complete novice.' He turned to Emma, offered her a suave arm and waited.

Victoria and Emma slanted each other private glances before Emma finally slipped a hand onto his sleeve. They disappeared into the hallway.

'Can I not tempt you to partner me, Mrs Hart? Not just one quadrille?' the short, squat man cajoled, sidling closer.

'Thank you, Mr Villiers, but no. I am not dancing tonight…as I told you earlier.'

He half closed his bloodshot eyes and eyed her through sandy lashes. 'So, I hear tell that you and Viscount Courtenay are almost related?'

Victoria looked about in irritation, hoping that soon either Emma or her aunt would reappear and rescue her from this unpleasant man's attention. He had been mercilessly tracking her from room to room for more than half an hour and her straining civility was close to snapping. 'My late husband and Viscount Courtenay were cousins, Mr Villiers.'

'He's a lucky man to have such a lovely young woman to care for…'

Victoria faced him, infuriated by his sly looks and probing innuendo. 'Lord Courtenay does not *care* for me in any way at all, Mr Villiers. We are not close acquaintances. Please excuse me; my aunt is beckoning.'

Victoria sped away from him and out into the quiet hallway. She positioned herself behind a cool marble pillar and leaned her hot forehead against it. She knew exactly what the odious man was implying and why he looked at her with such disrespect and lust in his piggy eyes.

An unsteady hand tidied silken ebony tendrils into their pins. She was tempted to escape to her bedroom, for she was acquainted with few people here tonight. Those who had approached her to talk were more inquisitive than friendly. Several ladies had merely run assessing eyes over her clothes and figure, then quizzed her over her connection to Lord Courtenay and whether she was expecting him to attend.

With a resigned sigh, she moved out from behind the pillar then stepped speedily back behind it. Frederick Worthington was shuffling unsteadily towards her in one direction and Gerald Villiers was craning his neck about and approaching from the other. He was obviously seeking someone and Victoria was unhappily sure she knew who.

'Frederick!' she heard Villiers call. 'Not seen Courtenay's uppity widow, have you? Can understand why the Viscount's being so damned territorial. I'd like a taste of that sweet madam myself. Soon drive some of the starch from her, I can tell you.'

'Best keep those thoughts to y'self, Villiers,' Frederick slurred, 'lest you want to find y'self on the sharp end of the man's rapier…or the blunt end of his fist.' Frederick chuckled drunkenly. 'Heard he floored Wainwright the other day…and that was just for trying to renege on his measly vowels.'

'Damn Wainwright…and the Viscount,' Villiers blustered. 'I've got a hot itch for this Hart woman…where's she got to? D'you think he'll give me the nod when he's done with her? I reckon he might tip me the wink with Suzanna Phillips, y'know, now she's spare. He damn well ought to. I've offered him me best chestnut gelding. I know the man drives a damned hard bargain so she'd better be damned worth it. Need a reference on her too…' he snorted, and muttered something vilely salacious about his preferences to Frederick. 'Where is he, anyhow? Thought the vaunted Viscount was due in Cheapside this evening.'

'And so he is…so he is…is my guess,' Frederick drawled. 'He's probably just around the corner in Gracechurch Street giving that red-headed hussy of his a little of his precious time. The divine Annabelle has finally lured him to her side, I suspect. For I hear tell he's been neglecting her of late.' An inebriated wink preceded his next words, 'The man's no fool. I'd sooner be entertained by her than this confounded racket any day.' They both roared lustily before ambling towards the first melodious strains of the orchestra just starting up.

Two minutes after they had gone, Victoria still stood rigidly, barely able to breathe. Her head was tipped forward against the marble pillar for support. So now she knew exactly what the gentlemen of the *haut ton* thought of her. She also knew which prior engagement David had refused to break. He was with one of his mistresses, just around the corner. She and Emma had walked through Gracechurch Street only yesterday. She strained to recall the people they had passed, to bring to mind a woman with red hair.

She swirled about in anguish so her back pressed into the pillar and her black satin hair cushioned creamy marble. She would not even think of her…of any of them. But her tortured mind refused to let go. Would that woman be passed on to the likes of Villiers? Had she herself yielded to David's coercion would she, in turn, have been auctioned once he had finished with her? It was a detail that had never once occurred to her…that at some point she would be cast adrift or sold on for the price of prime horseflesh.

She battled to suppress the humiliation and anger threatening to engulf her. And a grinding sorrow. For she was indeed learning something new of David Hardinge and his sordid life every day. Yet still she wanted to refuse to believe any of it and find excuses, despite incontrovertible proof.

But it was stupid and futile, she impressed on herself, her slender fingers automatically smearing the wet from her cheeks even though she hadn't realised she was crying. He would have destroyed her and Hartfield too. For her home would have been lost when her time was up and he withdrew his money. Had she acquiesced to his terms, it would have merely postponed the inevitable.

Retribution was suddenly, blindingly crucial. He had kissed her. He had spoken gently of their past and she had cried…mourned what they had lost…what might have been. Yet she was nothing to him now. Nothing other than another female body to be used and discarded.

Well, as that was so, she was entitled to play by the same mercenary rules and take everything she could and give nothing in return. She recalled thinking how satisfying it would be to dupe the infamous Viscount into paying her debts before absconding back to the safe haven of her beloved Hartfield. It now seemed condign to put that into practice.

Chapter Eight

Victoria swung open the door of the small library and sighed thankful relief on finding the room unused but with a small lamp casting eerie, elongated shadows onto a lofty ceiling.

Emma and she spent a great deal of daylight hours enjoying the tomes in this sunny library. Its atmosphere seemed friendless and gloomy now. She hurried towards the glow illuminating the writing desk. Having selected paper and quill, she sat down and began writing.

The flame leaping in the hearth gilded her tense, pale features as she wrote quickly with barely a pause for reflection. The words seemed to flow effortlessly from the quill and even pausing to dip for ink seemed a nuisance.

She sat back and reread the finished note twice before blotting and then sealing it. Her weary head leaned back into the leather chair and tear-weighty eyelids drooped.

She had never indulged in trickery before…never before believed she would ever have the necessity or courage to do so. Because of that, she knew she should immediately give this note to a servant to post before cowardice or conscience made her instead relinquish it to the fire in the grate.

For in it she had deceitfully agreed to abide by his terms. She would move to London, she would accept his protection, his house, his money and let him know of any other requirements once established. All she expected before she took up residence was written confirmation from the bank that her debts were paid. And all this she stipulated in her letter to David.

Yet it was all falsehood. She had no intention of ever again leaving Hertfordshire once she returned home next week. And why should she? For he had already made it clear he wouldn't want her: she was, after all, a righteous virgin…one of those despised *ingénues* he had no desire for. At some point she hoped to have the sweet satisfaction of telling him so. How that would gall when he realised all his time and attention and money had been spent for nothing!

But it was imperative that she avoid meeting him between now and learning her plotting had been successful; she lied badly and could never conceal the most trivial misdemeanours. Years ago, David had fondly told her so! He had once understood her so well. And if he was to become at all suspicious…she didn't dare imagine how he might react.

Doubt and panic were bubbling beneath the fury that had fired her so quickly into action. She stood up immediately, instilling courage by clenching her small fists and concentrating on Gerald Villiers' nauseating ambition to be next in line when David finished with her. A faceless red-haired woman figured in her torment too. Would this Annabelle have been her predecessor? Or would David have spread his time and attention thinly?

Victoria made determinedly for the door, the note clutched tightly in one hand, her intention to find Rawlings, the Worthingtons' butler, uppermost in her mind. She was adamant the letter be despatched first thing in the morning.

'Victoria?'

A small shriek was startled from her at horrified recognition of the voice that had quietly summoned her.

She spun about to lean back against the library door. Her breathing was so laboured, milky globes of satin skin thrust seductively above her lilac bodice.

David walked slowly towards her in the deserted hallway.

'What…what are you doing here?' Victoria blurted, guilt and astonishment making her stutter the first words that entered her head.

He looked quite magnificent. His long, dark hair glinted a rich mahogany beneath the glittering chandelier and his midnight-blue tail-coat exactly matched the deep sapphire of his eyes. A thick screen of jet lashes half shielded their shrewd assessment as they scanned her white face.

Victoria strove to determine what to do next…what to say. And all the time she was obliquely aware of the serene melody issuing forth from the heart of the house.

'What's the matter?' sliced calmly, imperatively through her panic.

'Nothing.' She immediately rejected his concern. She shook her head back and met his eyes squarely. If he recalled her agitation tomorrow when reading her note, it might stir suspicions. 'Nothing at all, Mr Hardinge,' she lightly stressed. 'I…I was simply surprised to see you, that's all. I heard you had a prior engagement…in Gracechurch Street.' She inwardly winced, railing at herself for letting spite make her careless.

An immediate knowing gleam between dark lashes and the twist to his lips mesmerised her to such a degree that she wasn't aware he'd moved until she suddenly stumbled backwards. Firm fingers prevented her falling while manoeuvring her safely back inside the library.

He turned immediately, closing the door and imprisoning her against it with arms barring each side of her shoulders.

'What…what are you doing? My aunt's looking for me, Mr Hardinge…I have to go,' Victoria said breathlessly, one small hand yanking at solid muscle to remove it, the other shielding the letter in the folds of her skirt.

'No, she's not,' David rebuffed easily.

'Well, no doubt everyone here will be scouring the building for you…as usual…' Victoria sniped in desperation as she tried to dodge beneath his braced arm.

'No, they won't. I've only just arrived. I told the servant not to announce me. I've seen no one apart from you.'

Victoria flung her head back, the violent movement dislodging ebony tendrils to drape about her white face. She glared up at him, roiling hurt at all she'd overheard earlier making her want to spit venom at him…physically attack him.

Smouldering logs in the grate highlighted the side of his lean face, his hewn, angular features and the snowy linen of his shirt taking on a devilish hue. She struggled for composure; concentrating on the reason for his delayed arrival helped her immediately achieve it. 'I didn't expect you to attend, Lord Courtenay, it is now so late,' she mentioned icily.

'I didn't expect to come either, Victoria,' he wryly admitted. 'And if you call me Mr Hardinge or Lord Courtenay once more I'll feel inclined to go straight home again. I'm a little late, it's true. But that's not what's upset you.'

'Nothing's *upset* me,' she forced out on a brittle laugh. 'Apart from the fact that we might be discovered here alone.'

'I'll concede that's partly bothering you. What else?'

Into the pulsing silence he said, 'You think I'm late because I've been first to Gracechurch Street to visit a woman.'

Victoria choked and sought again to escape him. Unable to do so and wary of meeting those intelligent dark eyes, she turned about between his arms so she faced the door. Slender fingers crept to the doorhandle and gave it a subtle tug. It infuriatingly didn't budge an inch.

As long fingers tenderly trailed the side of her neck, her eyelids drooped. As a warm mouth skimmed a path along her smooth, pearly nape, she instinctively swayed against him, her head angling to allow his tantalising lips better access to those wonderfully sensitive places. She couldn't help it: it had been so long since her starved body had been touched like this. Firm hands relinquished the door to slide about her tiny waist and draw her back against his hard, muscular body.

'You've been listening to gossip tonight, Victoria, haven't you?' he murmured against her ear. A smile and fond fingers moving consolingly acknowledged her involuntary whimper as his mouth withdrew from her deliciously shivering skin. 'Ask me,' he said gently into the silence. 'I'll tell you what's true and what's false, if you want to know.'

The pumping of her heart seemed to jerk them both with its violent rhythm and a vice-like arm banded her soothingly tighter to him. 'What have you heard?' he enquired conversationally.

'Nothing of any moment,' Victoria snapped tremulously, furious with him and also with herself, for the hurt was impossible to deny and so was the seduction. 'What else is there for the *haut ton* but gossip of Viscount Courtenay? His money and his morals occupy them all. No doubt they're diverted by the inequality…too much of one and not enough of the other.' She slapped at his hand as his thumb extended upwards, brushing across her pounding ribcage and mounting the curve of a tingling breast. She strained against her captivity, reaching for the door handle.

He held her easily away from it. 'Well, that's all about

to remedy, isn't it, Victoria? Settling your debts is going to deplete my finances and you always have a remarkably rejuvenating effect on my morals,' he mocked himself.

'Let me go now,' Victoria demanded, and both slender hands covered his larger ones to try and prise them away. It was a thoughtless move, for he did indeed partly release her, simply to relieve her of the letter gripped at the back of his hand.

'I take it this is for me?'

Victoria swivelled about in his arms and spontaneously made to snatch back the note but he held it out of reach. Having read his name and direction on it, he then offered it to her. She simply stared at it while hectically deciding what to do next.

'Shall I keep it?'

'Why not? After all, it will save me the cost of the post,' she agreed, blasé. 'Please don't read it now,' she nervously rattled off as he made to break the seal.

'I'm not sure I can withstand the suspense of waiting longer,' he returned drily as probing eyes scanned her face.

Every scrap of courage and guile was desperately raked together. Now he knew of its existence, it might be as well to recount its content. 'There's no reason for you to open it,' she pouted, sliding a glance at him from beneath dusky lashes. 'I can tell you briefly…if you have not already guessed.' Another coy look fluttered his way. 'I have seen the sense in your proposition…as you knew I would. And I should like you to…to provide me with a communication from the bank that Daniel's debts are cleared before I take up residence in London. That is all the note contains. Oh, and that the sooner the matter is attended to, the better it will be for you, for I recall Alexander Beresford telling me that the interest accrues at a ridiculous rate.'

Watchful eyes were slowly raised to his. She could read nothing in his face at all…no triumph, no suspicion, no pleasure. He was simply returning her gaze, steadily and unsmilingly, but with an air of sardonic amusement about him. He had looked that way in his elegant blue salon at Beauchamp Place on the day she'd visited him to propose they marry. Shortly afterwards, in his cosy, firelit study, he had demolished all her hopes with deliberate callousness. She quickly looked away.

'Well, I'm pleased you're concerned to save me money, Victoria. Not so pleased you need the bank to confirm that I've kept my part of our bargain. Don't you trust me?' The silky challenge sent an icy shiver racing through her and she was sure he must feel it. She stepped away from him and this time he allowed her to go.

'It is not a question of trust, Mr Hardinge. Business partners do not trust. They have terms and contracts and each is entitled to be certain the other will honour their part.' Her voice faded into a whisper at the rank hypocrisy of what she espoused.

'That's right, Victoria,' David endorsed quietly. 'Each has that right. Are you certain you want me to have this?' The letter was briefly indicated.

'Yes, of course. Why should I not?'

He smiled at the wall before choking out a hard laugh. His eyes lowered to her face and, with deliberate leisure, he extended long fingers towards her. 'There is a pleasanter way to seal an agreement than through officials, Victoria.'

Purposely misunderstanding him, Victoria caught at one of his hands and quickly, briefly shook it before gliding surreptitiously backwards. She'd managed two paces before she was tugged back close to his statuesque body.

'I think you know I didn't mean that, Victoria,' he murmured. His narrow, sensual mouth lowered tormentingly slowly and, unable to meet the test, her face twisted away at the last moment, so his mouth grazed the ebony silk of her hair.

He tutted disapproval close to her ear. 'That's not a very auspicious start for an auditioning mistress,' he chided with a thread of threat. 'Shall we try it again?'

'No. I have to go,' Victoria excused herself in panic. 'I have been gone for some while…I will have been missed.' The memory of Villiers' lascivious mutterings and his repulsive interest in her made her again negligent…and vengeful. 'Besides, so far you have paid for nothing, Mr Hardinge. Why *should* I kiss you?'

'For forty thousand pounds and counting, I think I'm entitled to a small sample, don't you?' he said sweetly, but his eyes were black and slitted as he jerked her face up to his.

Her soft, tremulous mouth was immediately bruised beneath a savage, punishing kiss, nothing like that wonderful caress she'd received in the Blairs' conservatory, or any other she had ever known. Never before had he kissed her with such force and selfishness. She thrust her hands between them, trying to break his hold, but it was impossible and she yielded with a defeated sob.

He wooed her then, with the same tender cunning and patience as he had before, until her mouth clung helplessly to his. A warm, soothing tonguetip traced her swollen lips before he eventually let her go. Within a second he was halfway to the door. 'Last week I did have a mistress in Gracechurch Street. This week I haven't…I've come directly from Mayfair tonight,' was thrown carelessly back at her. 'I just thought you might like to know that. Whether you believe it or not is up to you,' was added with crisp indifference.

His demeanour was woundingly cool and controlled and incited her to senselessly provoke him. 'Dear me! Did she displease you in some way, Lord Courtenay? Not display enough charm at table perhaps? And pray…do tell…what have you done with her? Was she traded in for a phaeton?

A hand of brag? What will you get for me, I wonder? A chestnut gelding…?' Her audacious sarcasm came to an abrupt halt as she was belatedly conscious he was no longer by the door but walking back towards her.

'What did you say?'

Victoria froze at his calm, clipped query for no more than a moment before retreating in time with his advance. When would she learn to guard her unruly tongue? And why was it that only this man could drive her to such impetuous aggression and recklessness?

There was no option but apology; she had been incredibly rude. Parched, pulsing lips were moistened with a tongue-flick. 'Please forgive me. I should not have…'

'That's right, you should not have… But then I did tell you if you wanted to know, ask me,' he ruefully admitted. 'I take it this is partly to do with what would have… shocked the devil himself…and almost did, Victoria. I certainly wasn't expecting the food *and* the service to come *au naturel*. And as to the rest of your impudence…'

Victoria's wide grey eyes were held by the narrowed thoughtfulness of his. Just as he backed her against the desk where she had sat to write his letter, he said evenly, 'So, Villiers is here, is he? He didn't actually speak directly to you of any of this, I take it?'

Victoria remained tight-lipped, simply staring wide-eyed up at his granite-like features. A long blunt finger gently traced her jaw. 'Did he?' he interrogated far too quietly.

'I don't know what you mean…' White knuckles gripped at the desk behind her. If she was not now extremely subtle, the plan to save Hartfield by her duplicity would be doomed before it started.

'Oh, I think you do. Even Villiers wouldn't risk such indelicate talk in front of ladies at this sort of polite gathering. You must have been eavesdropping. Is that it?'

'I never eavesdrop!' she hotly asserted. And it was true.

Had she in any way been able to escape unseen from those gossiping men, she would assuredly have done so.

There was nothing for it, she realised, but to somehow sidetrack him, for if this altercation ran to its logical conclusion she would eventually reveal all her hurt and anger at what she'd unintentionally overheard. Thereafter guessing the true motive behind her letter might be easy. She could recall only one sure way to divert and gentle him.

For the first time in seven years her slender, ivory-skinned arms slid up about his neck. Unable to meet his eyes, she rested her forehead against his shady, abrasive chin and whispered, 'I'm sorry...please forgive me for being so impertinent. I'm...I'm more tired...overwrought than I thought. And I would like to kiss you...' While she spoke, her fingers combed instinctively into long soft hair and a strand was wound round and round a slender finger in an old familiar way. But there was nothing familiar in his reaction to her flirtation. He seemed to have turned to stone.

'I'm not nearly so easily swayed...or pleasured as I once was, Victoria,' he said with cool amusement. 'Consequently, I'm hoping your upstanding husband has tutored you well in loving arts.'

Victoria's arms fled from his neck and small hands flattened against his shoulders and pushed. 'Daniel was a fine gentleman and I will not listen to such as you mock him.'

He didn't budge and she was still trapped between his muscular strength and the desk behind.

'That's not mockery, Victoria, it's genuine concern that I get satisfaction from you...and value. Which makes trading you in for a one-hundred-guinea horse a little unlikely. Come,' he jibed softly, 'you wanted to kiss me a moment ago...a sensible course of action now conflict is out of the question. It's no longer an option, is it, if you're to receive the bank's written assurances on Monday that a reprobate has taken care of your blameless husband's debts?'

Well, if that was how he wanted it, Victoria fumed, see if she cared! She irritatedly pushed her arms back about his neck and angled her face to receive a kiss. Nothing happened. Pearly eyelids flicked up and met narrowed, large-pupilled eyes.

'What's my name?' he breathed against her soft, trembling lips. She slammed her mouth angrily against his, more to stop his taunts than anything else. It was almost the reluctant kiss of an angry child humouring a nuisance adult. She exasperatedly ground her lips on his, but still he remained unresponsive and she flounced her face away.

'Oh, I can't be bothered with this. If you don't really want a kiss—'

Further petulance was cut off as his lips fitted expertly over her pouting mouth and his hand subtly manoeuvred her jaw apart.

The kiss deepened immediately without any seductive preliminaries. His tongue merely probed at her sensitive inner lips to widen them before plunging hard and fast, with determined erotic assault, into the warm velvet interior. Then just as quickly it was over, leaving her dazed, wobbly on her feet and gazing at him with glazed eyes.

'I...I didn't like that...' she finally whispered, feeling utterly betrayed by his selfish disregard.

'You'll get used to it,' he stated callously.

She stared at him, soulful eyes shining with tears. *And more besides*, he could have added, and she knew it.

Pushing past him blindly, she was out in the hallway in a few seconds and rushing towards the lilting harmony issuing from the ball.

David closed his eyes and his teeth ground, jerking the lean muscle in his jaw. He slowly approached the door and was about to quit the library when he changed his mind. A flick of a hand crashed the door shut and, pivoting on his heel, he walked to the desk and helped himself to Frederick's brandy decanter. The letter in his hand was tapped against a thumbnail for a moment, then he placed his glass on the desk and broke the seal. He read it twice before grunting an unamused laugh and shaking his head. He folded it exceedingly carefully, then slipped it into a pocket with one hand while retrieving his glass with the other. He walked to the fire, sipping brandy, and stared sightlessly into the leaping flames. He twirled the empty glass by the stem, watching firelight sparking through crystal, then abruptly placed the glass on the mantel and made for the door. It was closed quietly before he strolled in the direction of the music.

The drawing room was crowded with people dancing or chatting in groups. Victoria noticed Emma, standing thankfully close by the entrance with two young ladies. They were sipping lemonade and watching the set.

Victoria quickly joined her. 'The music is wonderful, Emma. The whole evening has been such a success for you,' she softly greeted her with a strained smile.

'Where *have* you been hiding?' Emma demanded of her friend as she immediately took her arm and urged her aside for privacy. 'I've been searching everywhere for you…so has your aunt Matilda.'

'Oh, Mr Villiers was intent on paying me his attention so I thought it best to disappear for a while,' Victoria wryly explained.

Emma grimaced with sympathy and revulsion. 'He really is a weasel of a man, isn't he? Why Mama invited him, I'll never know…' Her voice tailed off and her tawny eyes widened in astonishment. 'You'll never guess who has just appeared, Vicky,' Emma hissed, *sotto voce*.

'Oh, I think I might,' Victoria murmured without turning

although she noticed several people close by craning their necks towards the door.

Emma looked shrewdly at her and raised her glass of lemonade. 'Ah…' she murmured knowingly before she sipped. 'One can't blame just Gerald Villiers for your absence, then. It seems the sophisticated Viscount couldn't manage to stay away tonight after all.'

Victoria felt the hair at her nape prickle and knew David had located her in the crowded room. She linked her arm through Emma's and they proceeded to stroll away, following the line of chairs against the wall, towards the dining room. 'Well, what has happened to Mr Du Quesne? Was he impressed by your cake?'

'I'm not sure. We…er…had words before we got to it, actually. He asked me why I took such delight in insulting him and I…' Emma looked uncomfortable and frowned. 'And I said because it was so easily achieved.' Avoiding Victoria's eye, she shrugged her bemusement. 'I don't know why I do it. I just wanted to escape. He makes me nervous…frightens me almost. And that's ridiculous for he is always perfectly civil. He even paid me a sort of compliment by saying how surprised he was I was unwed at twenty-four. So I told him…I don't know why…I told him my mama was expecting an offer to be made very shortly.' An uneasy giggle escaped. 'Well, it is the truth, Vicky. She is always utterly optimistic. Anyway, Daphne Blair had by then tracked him down. She and her sister have kept him in their clutches since. He has not looked my way again.' There was a brief pause. 'Which is good…a relief, of course.'

As they exited through the double doors into the dining area, two excited young females, fanning themselves furiously, hurried in the opposite direction. 'Our popular guest has been spotted, I believe,' Emma drily observed.

Emma carefully piled some delicacies onto a plate for

Victoria before attending to her own supper. Settling at a small, damask-clothed table, they dined in amicable quiet for a few moments, making small sounds of approval and delight as they sampled various unusual hors d'oeuvres.

'So, what do you intend to do?' Emma explicitly, gently asked, brushing crumbs from her gown.

Victoria finished chewing a savoury titbit before she raised her eyes to her friend's sympathetic gaze. She had sensed for some while that Emma had guessed the true nature of David Hardinge's interest in her. 'I shall manipulate him as selfishly and disrespectfully as he does me,' she told her slowly, vehemently, while picking agitatedly at the pastry on her plate. 'I hate dishonesty but sometimes there is no other way and sometimes it is condign.' She glanced at the remnants of vol-au-vent now crushed to powder beneath her fingers and carefully wiped her hands on a napkin. 'If I can just allow my papa to see out his remaining days at Hartfield, thereafter, selling up will not be such a wrench, although I should hate to move away. But I am still young. I shall perhaps find employment…or a decent man to take me on…and Aunt Matty, of course.' She gave a wry smile. 'I cannot expect a gentleman of moderate means to board and lodge us all; I know that. So while my papa is alive—and I pray daily for his good health—we shall have to muddle on.'

'Well, where on earth have you been, Vicky, my dear?' Matilda demanded on sweeping up to their table, pulling out a chair and sinking into it. 'I was beginning to think you must have retired for the evening, you had been gone so long. Well, what a to-do.' She changed subject without pausing for breath. 'Poor Mr Villiers…well, not exactly poor, for he is a rather unpleasant specimen…he's had an accident. Quite a bruise forming beneath his eye. He slipped on the marble floor in the hallway, so I learned, and quite a mess he looks too. Apparently, Lord Courtenay kindly helped him up from the flags and Mr Villiers has thanked him profusely for his aid.'

All three of them turned towards Margaret Worthington as she solicitously led the object of Matilda's sympathy into the dining room. A male servant hurried after them, keen to be of use.

Gerald Villiers was indeed puce-faced but strangely subdued. In fact he meekly allowed Margaret to steer him towards the frozen confections without any sign of exasperation. The bump beneath his gingery eyebrow, however, looked extremely angry.

'Fill that napkin with ice,' Margaret directed her servant, and the footman dutifully plunged into the bucket and withdrew handfuls of melting fragments.

Matilda scraped back her chair and bustled over to them. 'What you have to bear in mind, Mr Villiers, is that the best thing for a swelling is a cold compress. Here, allow me.' She elbowed aside the servant and helped herself to ice. She squashed it into the napkin and directed the heavily breathing invalid in which way to lay it on his contusion.

Contrastingly, Victoria had almost ceased exhaling. Grey and tawny eyes collided and Victoria stifled a smile as she read her own suspicions and horrified amusement mirrored in her friend's expression. They simultaneously rose from the table and started slowly back towards the music.

'Surely not…!' Emma squealed, horrified, beneath shielding fingers. 'Well, the Viscount can't be all bad, Vicky,' she decided with wry humour. 'In fact I believe I'm warming to him.'

He was deliberately ignoring her, Victoria realised. Not only that, he was cruelly demonstrating just how advantageous a match he could make, should he ever decide to rescind his confirmed-bachelor status.

Three heiresses were encircling him and competing very seriously to be noticed. Judging by the frequency with which delicate fans were rapped against his arms to gain his attention, horrible bruises would be forming. Victoria acidly desired them to equal that about Mr Villiers' eye.

At that moment, the man passed by the sofa, forlornly taking his muted leave of various people. Victoria now found herself feeling a little sorry for the invalid, as her gaze rested on his injury. She had convinced herself it must be the result of a genuine accident. Had it been any sort of altercation between him and David there would surely have been an almighty commotion. Gerald Villiers didn't seem the kind of character to surrender so quietly and gracefully.

It was no use: Victoria could not avoid her beady eye for ever. Seated on the other side of her aunt on the sofa was Mrs Plumb. For the past ten minutes or so the middle-aged woman had been inclining and signalling with her feathered turban, ostensibly to draw attention. Victoria finally gave in and looked at her and was rewarded with a twitch of a mean mouth.

'I see your late husband's kinsman has arrived, Mrs Hart.'

Victoria murmured neutrally, returned a firm smile, then immediately looked away so no further discourse was possible. The fact that the eminent guest, who also happened to be her distant cousin-in-law, had made no move to approach her was probably as intriguing and noteworthy as if he had been paying her too much attention. She now found herself torn between hoping he would continue to keep his distance and praying that he would simply come over and formally greet her to stop the stares and whispers. But what did he care of her reputation? Or her peace of mind?

Undeniable pique was stirring again and she furiously bit her lip and then winced. A punishing kiss returned to haunt her, making her tonguetip instinctively soothe tender, swollen lips. She sank back into the cushions, vowing that her plot to save Hartfield would definitely succeed and that henceforth tonight she would equally ignore him.

In seeking Emma and her dancing partner, grey eyes skimmed across broad, sartorially splendid shoulders. They skittered determinedly on then slid defeatedly back to deny just how imposing and elegant he appeared.

Long dark hair curling over a midnight-blue collar and a hand thrust carelessly into a trouser pocket should, indeed, have marred the impact of his tall, athletic figure. But didn't, she begrudgingly realised. He was undoubtedly the most impressive man in the room.

He threw his head back a little, laughing at something one of his clinging, doting admirers had whispered, while simultaneously flexing the fingers of his right hand. It was an unconscious easing, as though they were stiff…or sore. He turned sideways on his heel at that precise moment and glanced idly about before looking slowly her way.

For the first time since they'd left the library, their eyes tangled. Before she could have the satisfaction of disdainfully snapping her head away, he was walking over.

The excited squealing on the other side of her aunt let her know the gossiping matrons were also aware of his approach.

'Mrs Hart…and Mrs Sweeting…I trust I find you well this evening?'

Matilda patently snubbed him and turned with a sniff and a stiff shoulder to Mrs Plumb. Matilda was overlooked by that woman who was more concerned with scrutinising Victoria's reaction to this distinction.

'We are very well, Lord Courtenay, thank you,' Victoria quickly replied in a toneless voice. After a brief, pulsing pause in which she found she could not look at anyone at all but gazed off into the middle distance, she blurted, 'And we hope you are well, too, sir.'

'Very well, Mrs Hart, thank you,' he enunciated, so politely that she knew he was laughing at her.

She glanced at him then and her lips compressed to contain her dangerously building indignation. So he found it all amusing, did he?

Fighting the need to provoke him was a lost cause. Her sparking eyes were drawn to a fresh abrasion on his hand. 'I'm surprised to hear that, sir. I thought perhaps you might have had an accident...' She stared pointedly at the knuckles wrapped about a crystal tumbler. 'You seem to have a nasty graze.'

As though just made aware of the damage, he glanced idly at his fingers, slowly stretching and flexing them. 'It's kind of you to concern yourself, Mrs Hart. But I assure you it's nothing. They must have tapped against something inconsequential for I hadn't realised I'd scraped them.'

Blue eyes locked onto hers. He was coolly challenging her to say more, she realised. He was inviting her to give voice to her suspicions that he had hit a man here tonight for gossiping about his private affairs so recklessly that details had been overheard. But she couldn't. For, as he had so rightly pointed out in the library, she could no longer afford to antagonise him...not if she expected to receive a letter from the bank on Monday morning.

As the silence awkwardly stretched and she was aware of probing, prying eyes pouncing on every nuance of reaction, Victoria felt light-headed with a maelstrom of sapping emotion.

'I believe I recall how it occurred.' David gently came to her rescue. 'It was the incident with the chestnut gelding...'

'Those horses!' Mrs Porter interjected, glad to slip into the conversation. She gave David a coy smile. 'You gentlemen and your love of the stables. My dear late Mr Porter,

God rest him, was always losing the flesh from his body to the hunters or the saddle…'

'Splinters like spills up under the fingernails from those stalls…' Mrs Plumb endorsed with a nod. 'Mr Plumb has become quite an expert with the tweezers…'

'These are the malicious tabbies you were telling me about at the Blairs'?' David murmured interestedly as he inclined close to Victoria. She looked him straight in the eye, but could only manage to nod slowly, feeling completely enervated. Luckily the matrons still seemed intent on discussing equestrian hazards.

'Broke his neck at the third fence in Pickett's field…' Victoria obliquely heard, and was thankful that David's close attention was largely unnoticed.

His narrowed blue eyes slipped over her face, lingering on her battered lips. As he slowly straightened, a thumb idly, softly skimmed her mouth, and Victoria was almost sure she heard him murmur, 'Sorry.' Then he was nodding politely to the ladies and strolling on.

Mrs Porter was looking at her oddly. She couldn't be sure of what she'd heard, or observed, either, Victoria realised.

Chapter Nine

Concentrating on passing scenery and the astonishing difference a little over a week had made to the weather was infinitely preferable to pondering on the letter in her pocket.

Victoria squinted up at sunlight dappling between the trees as they bowled along towards Hertfordshire. Frost-rimed skeleton branches passed on their way into London were now fleshed with mild green. It augured well…she was sure.

Sinking back with a contented sigh into the battered upholstery, she glanced across at her two companions. But there was no change there. She smiled to herself. They had journeyed to London in chilly silence or oblivion and travelled back to Hartfield in exactly the same manner.

Matilda and Beryl were still at loggerheads and both had snoozed away the best part of the morning.

Having bid a tearful farewell to Margaret and Emma in Cheapside at nine of the clock, the trio had set out on the road. Leaving Emma had been so hard—almost a literal wrench as Matilda had finally prised the two of them apart. They had become such firm friends that they could have been confidantes for several years instead of just one week.

She so hoped Emma would soon take up her offer to visit Hertfordshire.

Thankfully, George Prescott, refreshed by his sojourn in the city, had managed to negotiate the London suburbs and located the outskirts of the town with very little trouble.

So far they had turned about just the twice...and then in very pleasant parts of Hyde Park. George hadn't seemed at all put out by irate riders shaking their crops or their fists, and continued his tuneless whistling and interested perusal of the Quality on the move while changing direction. But now they were well along the Cambridge Road and making good speed.

Victoria removed her grey velvet hat and shook damp curls from her brow. It was getting quite hot as noon approached. A moist palm wiping against her skirt encountered the letter in her pocket once more. Now she was aware of it again, the thick parchment lay like a lead weight against her slender hip.

It would no longer be denied... Impulsively delving into her skirt pocket, she slowly withdrew the message that yesterday had been hand-delivered to her by an employee of Coutts' bank. Unsteady fingers unfolded the paper and she reread, for the hundredth-or-so time, the few succinct lines of neat script beneath the formal greeting:

Confirmation is hereby given that today an amount equal to your late husband's debts was received from your benefactor, namely, David Hardinge, Viscount Courtenay of Hawkesmere in the County of Berkshire.

The message was signed by the managing director and bore the seal and address of the bank in the Strand.

It *was* ambiguous! The thought screamed through Victoria's mind, decimating her fragile tranquillity. What she desperately wanted confirmed was that she no longer owed forty thousand pounds. That was what she had longed to read.

She was being ridiculous. She calmed herself, gazing out into the glorious morning, the letter crushed in her fingers. Why on earth would the bank write and tell her they had received such a sum if the intention was not to clear her dues? Probably a clerk had drafted the message and a dignitary had merely signed it. They were not concerned, as she was, with nuances of meaning.

But she was quite sure her benefactor would be. He was important and wealthy enough to dictate how his correspondence should be worded and the bank would act on it.

No further conversation had passed between them at Emma's ball. Within five minutes of walking away from her, David and Dickie Du Quesne had taken their leave. She had been sure they had parted on reasonable terms. Had he not touched her gently on the mouth and apologised for his savage kiss? Or was she just imagining that, too?

On first receiving the bank's letter she had been triumphant. When the euphoria had subsided a little she'd scanned it word for word and doubts had set in. She had then agonised over whether to contact him and make him refute her fears. But she didn't dare! If he confirmed payment and thus his side of their bargain was honoured, he would expect her to reciprocate...perhaps immediately considering the enormity of the sum involved.

She sensed the hot needles at the back of her eyes and a thick, aching blockage in her throat and knew it wasn't only dread of his revenge on discovering she had absconded that caused it. If she closed her eyes she could sense gentle fingers at her face and a warm, stroking kiss...and a cruel, selfish one...and harsh words, she sharply reminded herself. He was a cold, heartless man, a stranger now, and she wouldn't think of him again.

Instead she concentrated on the kindly, plump face of

Alexander Beresford. How was she to explain away the payment of her dues? Kind and decent he might be but she believed he was probably also a man of the world. Her benefactor might be a distant relative of her late husband's but such outlandish generosity was liable to stir speculation of the worst kind. And quite rightly, she miserably allowed.

No doubt, in his professional capacity, Alexander Beresford had before come across incidents of impecunious women clearing their debts by payment in kind.

Shame drained blood from her face but she tilted her chin. She owed no one explanations and would not feel obliged to justify any action she took that kept Hartfield a while longer for her and her relatives. She determinedly closed her eyes and raised her face, warming her ivory complexion with golden sun filtering through the dusty carriage window. A small, wry smile tipped her full mouth as she concentrated on her papa.

'Can you guess what I have brought you back from London, Papa?' Victoria teased from the morning-room doorway.

Charles Lorrimer tetchily swung his bony pate towards her. 'I told you yesterday not to disturb me while I read.' He pulled his spectacles from his nose and flung the book down by the side of his chair. 'Now I shall need to start again,' he peevishly complained. 'Why are you so determined to spoil what little enjoyment there is left to me?'

Victoria walked slowly into the room, holding a small, gaily wrapped gift tied with a crimson ribbon. 'It wasn't yesterday, Papa. You know I have been away visiting for more than a week. Yesterday I was in London…in Cheapside, and I have brought you a present. Something you'll like. The shops are so varied and the wares so tempting… It was difficult to know what to choose.'

He flung his thin face away from her and stared out into

the sun-streaked garden. 'Are you determined never to go away and leave me in peace? Must I seek my chamber to have some silence?' His voice was irritably shrill and Victoria put out a hand to soothe him. He shrugged her off.

'Where is Matilda? Still planning her London outing, I suppose. No one asks *me* if I should like to go to Hammersmith. It is time the house was opened. It will be musty and damp…and your mama will not like that. The lungs suffer in the dust and damp…'

Victoria gently placed the small box of choice sweetmeats on the table close by her father's empty teacup before she backed away from him a few paces. She collected her grey velvet bonnet from the chair where she had minutes before happily discarded it.

'Welcome home, Victoria,' she whispered to herself as she closed the morning-room door.

David flicked open the gold hunter. He studied the intricate chased dial, calculating hours and miles, before he rested his head back into the yielding leather of the wing chair. She'd be home by now.

Because of the patent simplicity of her deceit he'd thought for a while he must have been mistaken…that he was becoming an obsessive sceptic.

But he'd made a point of casually bumping into Frederick Worthington earlier today and discovered that his cynicism was justified…as usual. Frederick had gregariously confirmed what he'd definitely suspected when Victoria had faked affection in that man's library: she was going to try and take his money and run.

Had she proposed a proper marriage, not one that made it clear she didn't want him to touch her, he would have agreed, albeit in shock, to marry her a week ago. But she had made her rejection woundingly apparent. His bruised ego had demanded retaliation, so he'd hurt her back by showing her in the most primitive way that he could easily take what she wouldn't give.

But he had succumbed after all to the need to see her again at Emma's ball. After battening down his pride and battering the plush pile of his drawing-room carpet while he paced away the best part of the evening preparing how to tell her he'd been wrong and he'd never stopped loving her, he'd arrived at the Worthingtons' to find her plotting to fleece him. And what an amateur! His narrow mouth pursed sardonically. It had been so transparent a ruse he'd hardly credited she could believe him taken in by it. She still couldn't lie or deceive convincingly.

He was aware he could…quite expertly. Yet everything he'd said to her so far was perfectly honest. He had considered himself a confirmed bachelor and he wasn't interested in maidenly debutantes or heirs…but strangely he did want Victoria and him to share children.

He wanted everything about her with an intensity that shook him and would no longer be denied…or explained away as simple lust. But she didn't want him. She wanted his money and his protection…just as every woman he selected did. With every other woman that suited him just fine: it was part of their appeal. When they started angling for more, it was time to move on.

Yet the woman he did want to cling to him, as she once had, and talk of the future and commitment, as she once had, no longer wanted him. Victoria had found herself a worthy man to love and cherished his memory in widowhood.

Viscount Courtenay was simply a stranger, an immoral degenerate, and cruel circumstances were compelling her to have dealings with him. He swung the heavy gold watch on its chain and caught it in a broad palm before pushing himself up out of the chair.

Yet something wasn't quite right about it all. She was

too much the same…too much the Victoria he knew years ago. She looked the same; she even kissed in the same sweet, shy way. It was like some unholy torment, as though she'd never emerged from that six months of youthful bliss they'd shared.

Yet he knew it for a lie. She was seven years older…if not more mature. She had been married for seven years. Shared bed and board with a man until he died a few months ago.

He consciously uncurled his fists and flexed his fingers. Dwelling on Daniel Hart was a mistake. He wouldn't think of him. For he accepted quite calmly that, even dead, the man could send him into a senseless, towering rage. Yet he had cared for Victoria, treated her well, as was obvious from her blooming state. And proud, loyal Victoria would not tolerate a word spoken against him. She had obviously loved him exclusively and dearly. And that hurt. It hurt in the way he had vowed he would never again hurt. And because of it he would force her back to him…humble and humiliated. And he would use her in the way she expected him to. He knew she would come…out of duty to her father, her aunt and to keep this damned, beloved Hartfield alive and with it the memory of her dead husband.

'Mr Beresford, how nice to see you…'

'And you, Mrs Hart,' Alexander Beresford said with genuine warmth and a sunny smile.

Victoria laid the flowering rosemary she had just cut in her pannier then stripped off her gloves and waved her slender fingers to cool them. 'It is warm, is it not, Mr Beresford, for so early?' she remarked conversationally, with a glance about at blue sky and a burgeoning, verdant landscape.

'It is indeed, Mrs Hart. Such a change in the climate and it has caught us all on the hop…' He cleared his throat and shifted on the spot. 'I had heard you returned from London earlier in the week and thought it best to let you settle a day or two before again pressing you for your decision…'

Victoria tried to discern from his expression to what he referred. 'Decision?' she repeated quietly. 'Your kind offer of marriage, you mean, Mr Beresford?'

'Hmm…no…Mrs Hart. Actually, the most pressing matter, at present, is the sale of your estate. Hartfield must be sold to meet your debts. I hadn't wished to tell you just how much they amount to but…'

'Forty thousand pounds,' Victoria croaked, her face whitening.

'Indeed…that is correct, Victoria,' he said kindly. 'Has the bank informed you of the amount direct? I wish they had not done that. I am your agent and they should not worry you unnecessarily. But yes, indeed, it is that great amount and it must be settled. The interest accrues…and the sooner settlement is made, the more likely you are to fully cover your dues with the proceeds…'

'And the bank has received no payment…' she whispered to herself, closing her eyes as lead settled in the pit of her stomach. But then she had guessed, had she not? She had known the risks she took. David Hardinge was an astute businessman. How had she ever dreamed he would be taken in by such a flimsy scheme? She hadn't, she suddenly, remotely realised. Not at all. Subconsciously she'd been hoping…relying on him honouring their youthful friendship and thus treating her well. She had wanted to mean as much to him now as she had seven years ago. That was what she had trusted…believed. She was a fool! An utter fool!

'Would you contact the bank on my behalf, Mr Beresford, and enquire whether my benefactor has any intention of clearing his late cousin's debts as he implied he would?'

The lawyer's astonishment made his small brown eyes

bulge. 'You…you mean Viscount Courtenay pledged to pay them?'

Victoria simply, briefly nodded.

A hearty laugh of surprised relief met this news, then Alexander blurted, 'Why on earth would he do that, I wonder? Daniel and the Viscount barely exchanged a word for years and their connection was slight. I know your late husband was quite anxious not to associate with him. The Viscount's…er…um…reputation…' He coughed delicately. 'Was there a stipulation that Lord Courtenay would pay by a certain date?'

Victoria simply shook her head, pressed her bloodless, quivering lips together and frowned at the horizon.

Alexander gazed enquiringly at her and his smile slowly withered to nothing. 'Have you any idea why Viscount Courtenay would be so generous, Mrs Hart?' Into the taut silence, he clipped out, 'There was some sort of… understanding between you, I take it?'

'Indeed there was, Mr Beresford,' Victoria forced out, sweeping her grey eyes to his and tilting her sculpted chin. She slipped trembling hands back into her gloves and swung back to the rosemary bush, snipping away sightlessly at it.

'And he has reneged on the deal, I take it.'

Victoria could hear the sneer in his voice, almost see his thick lip curling.

'I would be grateful if you would do as I ask, Mr Beresford, and contact me as soon as you have a reply from Coutts' Bank.' She spoke briskly and quietly, her attention on decimating the rosemary bush.

An unpleasant, knowing laugh preceded a frosty, terse affirmation that he would indeed do so.

Victoria managed a small dip of her head in acknowledgement but the man was already striding away. From the corner of a glistening eye she saw he had gained the perimeter of the herb garden in a matter of seconds. Within a few minutes more the gravel on the circular drive in front of Hartfield's great doors scrunched as his phaeton pulled away.

Hot eyelids immediately squeezed shut to bank the stream of needling tears but they wouldn't be contained. Victoria moved on dragging feet to the dull russet brickwork of her Hartfield and kept coming until her clothes were grazing against the centuries-old building. She leaned into it, palms clutching at gritty, crumbling mortar, and sobbed until she was again dry-eyed and her grief was no more than a hiccoughing, unsteady breath.

Victoria looked at the letter while swallowing jerkily for it made her mouth parchment-dry. It had been delivered by the express ten minutes ago with the other that was on the mahogany hall table.

She picked up the one she did want to read. She had recognised Emma's neat script and desperately wanted to break the seal and lose herself in her friend's news. But her eyes were re-drawn to the other, addressed in a fast, forward-sloping hand. It looked impatiently written and she was quite certain it was the reply to the letter she had written to David Hardinge last week.

She carried her letters to the sweeping stairwell, intending to read both in her chamber.

Since she now knew she was destitute and there was no option left but to sell up and accept parish relief for her relatives and employment for herself…or acquiesce to David's terms…she felt an odd sense of serene emptiness. There seemed no further point to anger or grief or shame. She glanced at his letter in her hand. She knew what it would say.

The rap at the door had her slowly descending the few

stairs she had climbed and Samuel speeding past, straightening his waistcoat.

He opened the door to Alexander Beresford who walked into the hallway and spied her immediately.

A curt bow preceded, 'Mrs Hart...' by way of greeting.

Victoria smiled at him automatically. 'Please come along to the library, Mr Beresford.'

Once they were seated opposite each other at the library table, Victoria placed her letters close to her and lightly clasped her fingers.

'I said I would let you know directly I heard from the bank, Mrs Hart. I received a reply to my communication this morning.' He proffered a letter and after a tiny hesitation Victoria took it. It was brief and to the point and she had gained the gist of it before the actual words were properly read. It simply confirmed that an amount had been set aside in a holding account and on Viscount Courtenay's further instruction the money would be transferred. More than that they could not comment.

'You don't seem surprised, Mrs Hart,' Alexander commented, scrutinising her face.

She managed a neutral smile although this ultimate confirmation of what she had already suspected wrung her heart dry. She moistened her lips and swallowed, then moistened them again. 'Thank you for bringing this so quickly. Would you like some refreshment...before you leave?' she added pointedly.

He sat back comfortably in the chair and smiled at her. And then at the letters by her hand. 'I see the infamous Viscount has written to you personally. Quite an honour. His clerk, Jacob Robinson, usually deals with all correspondence. Courtenay has an unusual hand...I recognised it from business papers he has authorised over the years that have come my way.'

'Indeed?' Victoria said frigidly. 'The express has only

just come. I have not yet had an opportunity to read my letters but hope to very soon.' She pushed back her chair with frank finality.

He ignored the hint. As he cocked his round head, brown eyes surveyed her thoughtfully. 'Perhaps I was a little hasty in believing the Viscount the…er…reluctant party in the matter of the debt settlement. I now think it was you, Mrs Hart, who reneged on the deal. The Viscount seems to be very tolerantly…very unusually…allowing you time to see sense.'

Victoria felt her face burning beneath his shrewd, bold stare. She raised storm-grey eyes. 'I imagine that your marriage proposal has been withdrawn, Mr Beresford, as you appear to be procuring on the Viscount's behalf.'

He was unperturbed, his meaty hands gesturing his careless change of heart. 'Naturally, marriage would now be out of the question, Mrs Hart. Besides, why would you want it? I could never match what Lord Courtenay seems prepared to offer. He is one of the richest men in the country.' A significant pause preceded, 'However, there might be a time…a time when you will return to Hertfordshire and we could enjoy a less formal relationship…' His eyes lowered to creep over her bodice with blatant disrespect.

Victoria swallowed the furious retort which threatened. 'You will need to be a patient man, Mr Beresford, for it would be quite some time hence.' She steadied her trembling lower lip with small white teeth. 'I am aware that a queue is already forming amongst gentlemen in London for the Viscount's cast-offs. You shall just have to wait your turn.' Grabbing at the letters on the table, she swished to the window and sightlessly stared out. 'Good day, Mr Beresford,' was aimed coolly back over her shoulder. It wasn't until she heard the door close that she ripped his letter into four pieces and threw them as far as she could.

* * *

The fragments of paper on her dressing table stirred in the light breeze as her bedroom curtain billowed gently over them. Victoria slowly slid the scraps back into formation. In length and style it exactly matched the terse note she had sent to him last week. That had been two sentences which enquired if he intended to settle his kinsman's debts. She stared at the tatters in front of her and slowly read:

> *The matter will be finalised when you return to London.*

There was nothing else…no greeting, no signature, no request that she go back.

She ran her palm across the pieces, collecting them, and carried them to the fire before she quit the room to seek her father.

'Will you bring me a present again?' her father asked, sliding a glance at her from a pale, crafty eye.

Victoria perched on his bed and took his clawed fingers into hers. 'Of course,' she promised with a wavering smile. 'Were they nice sweetmeats? Would you like the same… something different?'

He wriggled his fingers from hers. 'Just more this time. There were very few, Victoria. I believe Matilda must have eaten some. I swear I only got one or two…then they were gone…' he moaned, plucking at the blanket on his bed. 'Where is Samuel with my milk? Fetch him, will you?'

Victoria glanced at the cup on his bedside table. 'Lie comfortably, then, Papa,' she soothed him as she stood. 'Lie down… Samuel never forgets your milk.'

'I shall have to return to London, Aunt Matty,' Victoria said to the woman's back a few minutes later, as Matilda pulled a brush through her thin, greying hair.

Matilda swivelled on her stool and stared at her niece in silence for a moment. She then smiled and vigorously brushed and brushed. ''Twill be nice for you to see Emma again. You and she became quite famous friends, didn't you?'

'Yes...' Victoria said quietly. 'But I don't think I will be seeing Emma.'

'London is a gay place. I should have liked to spend more time there but your papa needs me and someone has to run the rule over the servants while you are away.'

Victoria swallowed the jumble of emotions clogging her throat. Hurt, humiliation, disappointment... Her aunt Matty had finally chosen which side of thrift suited her and was dealing with her niece's disgrace in her own way...by refusing to talk of it.

Matilda turned towards her and Victoria saw her weak blue eyes were pink and shining. 'What...what you have to bear in mind, Victoria,' she choked out, 'is that...is that I shall always love you...always...no matter what...'

Victoria closed the door quietly behind her and leaned against it for no more than a second before she returned to her room to write her letter.

Slender fingers slid over the fine hide upholstery. It was the most sumptuous carriage she had ever travelled in: deeply stuffed and buttoned and the leather dyed a pale gold...with blue leather blinds at the windows. She recalled his servants at Beauchamp Place were liveried in blue and gold. Yet the coachmen and footman who were bearing her towards London were plainly dressed in ordinary dark clothes. But then he wouldn't want too blatant a show advertising their dealing together. She had noticed that the carriage was uncrested...quite unremarkable from the outside. As it was, she could be a lone young woman travelling on any business at all.

She leaned her head back and wondered how many others had sat here like this. How many blondes...how many brunettes…redheads had been removed from their families and conveyed to strange houses to await their master's pleasure. How many had felt an awful writhing in the pit of their stomach as they drew ever closer to their fate? She twisted her head against soft leather and stared into the gloaming and wondered instead whether she had been right to leave Beryl behind. She should really have travelled with a companion, but since Samuel and Sally had become betrothed Beryl was unbearably moody. More importantly, the fewer people aware of her new situation, the better!

Besides, had she not been promised a house of her choosing? A staff of her choosing? And anything else she cared to stipulate? Maids…housekeepers…French chefs…dressmakers…she could have them all…

She swallowed the ache in her throat and delved into her reticule for Emma's letter. She had reread it dozens of times but did so again now, smiling at her friend's acerbic wit as she described her latest clash with Mesdames Plumb and Porter at the Watsons' musical evening. She even managed to giggle again when she came to the part that told of Mr Villiers' and Moira Blair's betrothal. A deserving pair, Emma had described them, and Victoria was inclined to agree.

She neatly folded the letter and carefully returned it to her reticule. She leaned back into the lush squabs and closed her eyes. And all that she had carefully locked at the back of her mind broke free.

Henceforth no decent woman…no decent man…would have anything to do with her. Emma and her parents, Laura Grayson…all the people she had previously called her friends…none of them would acknowledge her. She would be a demi-rep…she would live a twilight life. She would be shunned when shopping. Would she shop? What for? Surely services would come to her and she knew she would infinitely prefer that at first. For, as much as she fought to retain pride and courage, she knew that until she grew hardened simply a disdainful glance or a sneering whisper could pierce her fragile defences.

She reluctantly brought to mind the hard-faced, spiteful-eyed blonde woman who had stared at her so malevolently in the East London marketplace. Would she herself eventually become so resentful and bitter that it coarsened her features and was quite obvious to perfect strangers? She sighed it all away. What hurt most was losing Emma's friendship so soon.

They were approaching London. The dusk was drawing in and the well-remembered odours and sounds of the city cluttered her senses.

She had no idea where they were bound. The letter she had received from him divulged nothing other than when to expect a carriage to collect her. She had not cared enough to enquire of the phlegmatic servants he sent with it which part of London they were heading for. Unsteady white fingers covered her mouth to stifle a shrill laugh. Perhaps they would mistakenly deliver her to Beauchamp Place. Perhaps Mrs Plumb and Mrs Porter would gleefully witness it. Her eyelids clamped, stemming hysterical tears. She certainly hoped not; she would be grateful for at least a week's grace before her dishonour spread like wildfire, providing the *haut monde* with some choice gossip.

They had stopped! Her fingers relinquished her eyes and clawed into the seat as, barely breathing, she waited. It was possibly just an obstacle in the road. The horses jerked the carriage forward again and, sighing relief, she sank back into soft leather. Thank God! Not yet. She wasn't ready yet.

The carriage slowly turned and the scrunching of driveway gravel beneath hooves and wheels told her that, ready or not, she had arrived.

The carriage door was opened. A kindly faced footman bowed and offered to help her alight.

As soon as she had done so, the vehicle pulled away. Victoria spun about in alarm as it disappeared along the sweeping driveway. She glanced fearfully up at the large, white-stuccoed building and hoarsely demanded of the servant who remained with her, 'Where...where are we? What part of London is this?'

'Hammersmith, ma'am,' he informed her politely, and picked up her travelling bag.

The house was still, muted in every way. The lighting was little more than an auburn glow casting an incongruous cosiness over the polished wood floor and the high, ornate ceiling.

Victoria stood alone just inside the entrance door, her eyes darting into every corner.

'Mrs Hart?'

A small gasp escaped Victoria at the sound of her name, and as the woman approached, smiling at her, she simply managed a curt nod.

'Please come with me, Mrs Hart.' The woman was smartly garbed in housekeeper's black, keys at her waist. She indicated the stairs and then, without further conversation, or introduction, she was briskly ascending them.

Victoria followed, her legs feeling more boneless and her heart more leaden with every wobbly step she took. One hand gripped at the polished banister to steady and aid her and the other lifted a fistful of black crape, keeping her skirts from under her feet. Then they were pacing silently along a thickly carpeted hallway. The woman halted and swung open one side of double doors, standing aside so Victoria could enter.

Victoria remained motionless and the woman waited, smiling neutrally.

It was her last chance to run, was the thought that slipped

remotely through her mind. Once inside…and he was there, she knew it…once inside and the door closed… Was it a bedchamber? What sort of room was it? What did this pleasant-looking woman really think of her? Was she disgusted? Apathetic? How much did he pay her to keep her opinions to herself?

Even as the stream of thoughts shot through her, she realised the housekeeper was patiently, politely waiting and she obligingly stepped within. The door shut quietly immediately behind her.

Chapter Ten

She saw him at once. He was sitting sideways on to the door, close to the fire. He casually turned his head and glanced at her before shifting his attention to the glass on the table by his side. First the glass then a cigar, its glow and aroma discernible, were raised to his lips.

Victoria tensed, barely breathing, her mind frozen.

His empty tumbler found the table and then her unblinking grey gaze was mesmerised by long fingers slowly grinding out the cigar. Those same fingers rose, beckoned.

She took a few hesitant paces into the room.

His dark head angled back in irritation that she hadn't moved closer.

It was a small drawing room, Victoria noted obliquely, with polished wood furniture and cream and burgundy furnishings. It was warm, too, and despite shivering she felt wispy tendrils clinging to her moist forehead.

She started, apprehensive eyes streaking back to him, as he pushed himself out of the chair and strolled towards her.

She wanted to fly at him and lash out, scream at him for his vileness, his ruthlessness...for making her forfeit even her pride and self-respect...but she didn't. It was a feat forcing her eyes up to his.

'I see you're in mourning, Victoria,' was his quiet, ironic greeting as his blue gaze slipped over her black cloak and funeral dress. 'I know it's not for your husband's benefit. I take it it's for mine.'

She said nothing, merely blinked and pressed her lips tighter together. But satisfaction registered: her small gesture of defiance had been understood for what it was. She would never again wear colours or attractive clothes.

'Are you hungry?'

She swayed her head once.

'Do you like the house?'

A curt nod answered him.

'How do you know? You can't have seen enough to decide.'

She stared past him at the fire, ignoring the dry comment.

'Have you been struck dumb or am I not worthy enough to receive conversation?'

Glossy slate eyes slid to his. 'Is it necessary that we speak?' she tonelessly asked.

'Yes, it's necessary,' he said, and she recognised the steely edge to his voice.

'Then I will do so. Tell me what you wish to hear and I will say it. Whatever pleases you, Lord Courtenay,' was gritted out in a fierce whisper. The sheen in her eyes intensified until they were sparking like stormy stars. But she tilted her chin and continued glaring at him.

He smiled…a humourless distortion of thin lips.

'What would I like to hear?' he softly mused. 'Well, Victoria, I should like to hear why you reneged on our deal. I seem to recall you lecturing me that business partners should each honour their side of a contract.'

Despite herself, Victoria felt heat flood her face at her trickery and that well-remembered verbose hypocrisy.

She tensed, unable to exhale, as his hands moved to her chin, each inadvertent light touch singeing her skin as he untied the ribbons of her black bonnet. It, and her cloak, were removed and discarded onto a chair.

'Come and sit down, Victoria.' He held out a hand, inviting her towards the sofa and fire, but she simply sat on the chair-edge closest to her, some way from the hearth and from him.

An exasperated, muted oath escaped him as he retraced his steps and went down by her chair. Firm fingers tilted her face up to his. 'This isn't very sensible, Victoria, is it? Whatever pleases me...right?' He reminded her of her bitter words with a wry smile. 'It pleases me that you sit close to me and tell me what you've gained from your deceit.'

She shook her face free of his grasp as treacherous tears needled in earnest. She would not cry! She threatened herself. She would not! She jerked back quickly into the chair as the sob swelled in her chest.

His bronze-dark head fell forward and through the glaze in her eyes she saw a hand move to his face, his head sway. His patience, she was sure, had expired and that dismaying certainty caused the sob to spontaneously erupt.

In a movement so swift and powerful that it left her defenceless, she was dragged forward. He stood with her wrapped against his solid strength.

Her face buried deep into the hollow beneath his shoulder as she desperately fought for control. She would not be broken! Not so soon...not ever! She would retain her spirit, if nothing else.

'Victoria, listen to me...' The hoarse, pleading words stirred the hair at her brow.

How dared he comfort her or fake concern! She fought free of his embrace and backed away, hands gripped tightly together. His clinging blue gaze followed her and through her own anguish she realised there was an odd hint of sadness about him, too.

Anger...triumph...satisfaction—those she had prepared

for. At the very least she had expected that latent amusement he exuded when he knew he had her backed into a corner.

Then everything was banished from her mind except that chilling, gnawing doubt. For if her innocence didn't deter him and he decided to keep her there was something she had to know.

It had been almost a month since he'd advised her, so very obligingly, to take all he offered immediately, for, if tardy, her bargaining position would become precarious. It had been peculiarly honest advice from an adversary. She was, indeed, no longer in any position to dictate terms. 'Will you provide for my relatives and maintain Hartfield?' burst shakily from her. Her eyes locked onto his, pleading, proud, yet searching for mockery.

He slowly nodded his agreement. But Victoria stared, unconvinced, believing him to be cruelly joking. 'Why?' she demanded in a voice shrill with tears. 'You said before you would renegotiate in your favour. You must be lying…tricking me.'

'I'm feeling generous,' he gently reassured her. 'But while we're talking of lying and tricking…did you think you could fool me with such a simple plot, Victoria?'

'Yes…no. I don't know.' Victoria wretchedly swung her head. 'It was all irrelevant in any case.'

'It was?' A raising of dark brows demanded further explanation.

Victoria remembered her foolish hope that when eventually she told him he would rue spending his money…his time…his attention. Well, he had wisely kept his cash safe. But there was no denying he had wasted time and attention on her. He was doing so now. And that small, sour victory and a shuddering, indrawn breath spurred her on. 'I went home to Hertfordshire, Lord Courtenay, because…because you had made it clear I would be of no interest to you.

There was little point in remaining in London simply to remind you of it.'

David tracked her back a little way then gave up as she put the sofa between them. 'Remind me of it now, Victoria,' he urged drily. 'Come, humour me. Tell me when it was I said you would be of no interest to me.'

'When I visited you at your home in Mayfair.' The information escaped in a barely audible whisper.

She watched intelligent dark eyes narrow thoughtfully and knew he was retracing their conversation that day, as she herself had done many times.

'The only two things I recall having no interest in were debutantes and babies. You're neither…although I'll allow you're childish.'

'I am not childish…neither am I righteous,' she hotly defended herself.

David frowned and then long fingers, idly splayed on the sofa-back, clenched into burgundy brocade. He remembered what he'd said well enough. It played over in his mind daily. Just as he knew what she had said…that he might want heirs, or a wife that came to him chaste…a virgin. And he'd known she wasn't. So he'd told her neither interested him. He could feel blood draining from his skin. It was impossible…but he could see the truth in her face. Her beautiful, proud white face bore her sheer desperate hurt in finally having to tell him. She'd believed their bargain void because, if he'd known her to be inexperienced, he wouldn't want her…a righteous virgin. She'd been prepared, after all, to let him love her properly, to have his children, and he'd misunderstood. They'd both misunderstood when the other started to compromise. She'd wanted a marriage of convenience and had finally offered herself and he'd wanted a true wife and had unwittingly rejected her out of hand.

Victoria pressed her lips together and anxiously watched

and waited. This utter shock that seemed to have petrified him was terrifyingly out of character and she had no idea how to proceed.

'You're a virgin?' he eventually choked out.

A jerky nod immediately answered him.

The intensity in his fixed, blackening gaze and the ashen tinge to his skin made her quickly, desperately seek to justify all her actions. 'I know it was I who brought about our reunion. I sought you out in London to ask you to marry me and I am sorry for it. But after that…after our meeting at your home, when you made it clear it was not to be…I would never have approached you again. I accepted your views and hoped you would accept mine. I…I did truthfully want you to leave me alone. I only ever ventured out to places I was sure you would avoid…' She swallowed painfully. 'But it was wrong of me to try and dupe you into paying my debts. It was not a premeditated plot, I swear. I…I just…I was angry because of what I overheard between Gerald Villiers and Frederick at Emma's ball. My actions were impetuous and ill-considered. Had you not arrived when you did and discovered that stupid letter, I would have destroyed it in the morning when rational. I'm sorry.'

She bit furiously at her lower lip. She couldn't be sure he had heard anything she'd said.

He was utterly still. But coal-black eyes in a paper-white face tracked an erratic, devouring path from burnished jet hair to black crape hem. 'Your marriage was never consummated? You were married seven years yet not once did you lie with your husband?' The words seemed to tear out of him in anguished disbelief.

'Never,' Victoria confirmed in a murmur. 'Daniel was my father's friend. We had an unusual relationship. An unconventional marriage, he called it.'

'But you loved him…'

'He was a kind and decent man. Yes, I loved him. I loved him as the fond father I wanted but never had,' she cried in a raw voice. 'And he loved me as the daughter he lost with his wife in childbed. There was no passion…no desire between us. It was a pure love.' As though regretting revealing so much that was so private, she paused to collect herself. 'Am I to go home now, Lord Courtenay?' she enquired with tremulous dignity.

He walked away from her and towards the mantel. Bracing a hand against it, he stared at the wall with glazed, sightless eyes. 'Don't call me that, Victoria.' It was an absent correction as his eyes closed.

When, after a few moments, he seemed trance-like, Victoria shifted noiselessly towards her cloak and bonnet and gathered them up.

She had no idea where she would go…just away…out of the house. She should have written and told him, she railed at herself inwardly. It would have saved this journey…this humiliation. But it had never seemed appropriate. And besides, she had always cherished the belief that he had not changed. That he would care for her no matter what.

She forced her mind to focus on her perilous predicament. She was contemplating escaping into a city street…alone at night. The rowdies she had met before, when George Prescott had lost his way in London, crowded in on her and she knew there was no sensible option but to stay in the house or grounds till morning.

She had backed to the door by the time he noticed her retreat. Shoving away from the wall, he immediately started towards her.

Anxiously she watched him come, the flickering candle flame overhead tinting fire into his hair and eyes. He reached out as he came close and she was sure he would touch her but the hand leaned into the door as though he was more concerned with preventing her bolting.

'How many people know of your being here with me tonight?'

It was a totally unforeseen interrogation and for a moment she simply stared at him. 'Just…just Matilda…and I told my papa I would be going to London. He has probably already forgot.'

He nodded. 'We'll have to get you home again with just those people knowing.'

'Thank you.' She hadn't expected him to bother about returning her with her reputation intact. 'Your servants know, of course,' she mentioned coolly.

'And have seen and heard nothing. They understand me well enough to be unfailingly discreet.'

'Yes…I'm sure…' Victoria murmured, dropping her eyes level with a shady, cleft chin.

Long fingers did touch then. They slid beneath silken curls and splayed about her nape, comforting and urging her close to him. 'Not tonight, Victoria,' he pleaded huskily against her hair. 'I'll grovel and apologise and make excuses…even lie, I expect…but not tonight.'

Victoria wanted to look at him, to ascertain what had brought about this change, but his arms slid about her so fast and determinedly, she couldn't move. And after a moment she didn't want to. Rejecting comfort now was beyond her; it was too welcome, too needed.

'It's a long journey home; I want you to eat something first.' Taking the cloak and hat from her again, he dropped them on a chair. With her hand gripped in his he was soon leading her into the hallway and towards another set of double doors.

Ushering her inside, he immediately gave instructions to the servants ranged sedately within.

The dining table was already set for two people and Victoria gazed in awe at a magnificent array of cutlery and flatware. Crystal and silver shed sparks in every direction, reflecting the dozen or so wavering flames set in a central, elaborate candelabra.

David retained a controlling grip on her hand while he clipped out orders to the women to serve the first course then leave.

Steaming soup was speedily ladled into fine porcelain before the serving maids dutifully, neatly withdrew.

David put his arms about her, urging her forward to sit down, but she twisted against him, fists full of her stiff black skirts, ready to flee. 'Thank you, but I cannot eat anything,' she said to his chest. 'I should rather set on the road straight away. It is a long journey…'

'I know it is, Victoria. That's why I want us to eat.' His lips soothingly brushed her white brow. 'Come…we must travel through the night as it is. I've no intention of doing so without first eating. I'm suddenly ravenous and I'm sure you must be hungry, having already travelled for several hours this evening.'

Victoria's grey eyes warily searched his face. Far from displaying shock, he now had an air of calm contentment. There was nothing predacious now in his manner. His touch, his smile were gentle, quite reverential.

'Come, sit down,' he urged tenderly. 'Your soup's getting cool.'

He pulled out her chair and this time she allowed him to settle her in it. The savoury aroma wafting up from the plate made her stomach gurgle and she realised she was indeed starving.

David walked to the opposite end of the table and sent his place setting of embossed silverware skidding carelessly along the polished mahogany towards her. He carried his chair and his soup and settled himself close by her side.

He began to eat and encouraged her to do the same. 'It's delicious…try it…'

Victoria picked up her spoon and tasted the soup.

'French chef…' he conversationally explained, pleased by her unconscious murmur of approval.

'How is your father? And your aunt? Did you leave them well?'

Victoria sipped from her silver spoon while regarding him with wide, watchful eyes. 'Yes…thank you.'

David poured wine into a crystal goblet and slid it towards her. 'Drink it…please. It will warm you. It's a cold night.' He poured a glass for himself and downed a considerable amount of the pale gold liquid in one swallow.

He watched her finish her soup then went to the bell-pull and within a moment the servants were back with them, clearing the dishes. David waved away the fish and ordered the main entrée be served. They scurried to obey, nodding and whispering explicitly to each other to hurry and take care as dishes and cutlery were whipped away then replaced with new.

Aware of Victoria's eyes following the scuttling servants, he said, 'My apologies for the haste. I intended a leisurely supper for us tonight.'

Victoria found herself, incredibly, saying she didn't mind. He had planned to courteously wine and dine her before dishonouring her in this gracious Hammersmith house yet she was humouring him. She sat stiff-backed in her chair, wondering whether to continue doing so or fly into the night. A niggling thought nudged in on her. He had said 'we must travel'. Did he intend to accompany her home? Or did he simply mean he had to return to Mayfair and was keen to get going?

The main course of slivers of succulent-looking beef with horseradish and numerous dishes of roasted vegetables arrived. David paced restlessly as their plates were filled.

An impatient grunt or a dismissing flick of his hand answered the servants as they nervously indicated various dishes for his approval. He was abrupt with them, yet mannerly, Victoria realised, observing that he wanted them gone but muttered thanks before they left.

He sat down close to her again and refilled her empty glass. Victoria stared at it, horrified. She hadn't realised she'd drunk all of the cool, fizzy wine. It was then she realised that it had indeed warmed her. A slender hand felt her complexion, sensing the burn through her fingers.

Smouldering blue eyes caressed her face. He cut his food and a fork moved to his mouth. The back of a long finger skimmed to and fro against a pink cheek as he slowly chewed. 'I told you it would warm you. Are you feeling more relaxed?' he asked huskily.

His knife indicated her dinner, insisting she eat. Cutting into her food, she managed a small smile and nod. She did, indeed, feel a little more at ease, and hungrier. Her plate received her full attention as she ate some of the delicious meal.

To avoid his steady sapphire gaze, her eyes travelled the room. It was expensively furnished in the same highly polished mahogany wood as graced the drawing room. Swags of rich rose velvet draped the lofty, wide windows and covered sofas set against the walls. Her eyes flicked upwards to the richly carved ceiling. It was certainly a much larger and more sumptuous house than her papa's Hammersmith residence had been, as she recalled.

'Would you have liked living here, Victoria?'

Victoria recognised the smile in the soft query and sensed the glow in her cheeks increase. She sipped from her wine glass and nervous grey eyes met his over the rim.

'Don't answer,' he told her gently. 'It wasn't fair…and it's of no consequence. Neither is your innocence.'

When she simply raised her glass again in an unsteady

hand and drank to avoid commenting, he asked quietly, 'Do you know what I mean when I say it's unimportant, Victoria?'

She shook her head, seeming intent on draining her glass, but their eyes were inextricable.

'I mean that, virgin or no, I would never have harmed you. I had no intention of staying here. I did intend making you stay a night or two—as a consequence of trying to cheat me—before taking you home.' He leaned back in his chair and his mouth twisted wryly. 'This…' he moved his head to indicate the house '…it's nothing. Just a theatre. It was all just a game. You won.'

Victoria's empty glass plonked heavily on the table. 'I won…?' she echoed, having difficulty focussing through the wine-induced haze.

'You always win…'Twas ever thus,' he mocked himself. 'Have you had enough to eat?'

Unable to trust herself to speak, Victoria simply nodded and retrieved her glass as a way of avoiding doing so. She frowned at the empty goblet.

'I think you've had enough champagne, Victoria,' he fondly chided as he walked to the bell-pull.

Through the muzz in her head, Victoria heard instructions given for the coach to be brought round. He turned and smiled and from a long way off told her he would be but a moment and left her alone. Within what seemed mere seconds, he returned with her cloak and bonnet and a pistol.

Victoria squinted at it. Even with the fog in her brain she realised it horrified her. She blinked weighty lids at it. 'What…what's that for?' she finally managed.

'Protection,' he said with a caressing look. 'Don't worry. There are few incidents of robbery along the Cambridge Road at present. And my man Bennett is one of the finest shots in the country. So am I,' he added, as an afterthought, 'if I can stay awake…and avoid distraction. I've no intention of losing you to some wastrel out to find himself a dubious infamy and his doxy a few baubles.'

Victoria carefully stood, bracing one hand on the table and the other against her chair-back. She tilted her chin, took a confident step forward…and made a hasty grab for the chair. David separated her from the furniture, steadying her against his hard body while wrapping her into the heavy black cloak. He made a gallant attempt at the bonnet, gave up after a few seconds, and tossed it aside. 'I never liked it, anyway,' he muttered as he swung her up in his arms.

'I can walk, David,' she protested into his collar, yet her head lolled immediately against his shoulder and her arms crept about his neck.

'Say that again.' He nuzzled softly against her cheek as he descended the stairs.

'Put me down; I can walk,' she sighed against his cravat, and then yawned.

'Not that. What's my name?' he growled as he strode past a bland-faced butler, down the stone steps and crunched on gravel to the coach. He set her down by it.

Victoria immediately rocked towards him and her arms fumbled back about his neck.

Inclining close to capture her wine-sweet lips with his, he ended the caress abruptly, too soon, demanding against her pulsing, sensitive mouth, 'What's my name?'

'Lord Hardinge?' Victoria slurred solemnly, wondering why he was asking her silly questions instead of kissing her in that wonderful, drugging way that focussed her mind and stilled her spinning head.

Sitting in the carriage alone, feeling hot, Victoria jerked the window down and a gust of cooling air stroked her flushed face. A hand went up to steady her bonnet and discovered it wasn't there. Angling her head to see the horses, she noted that David and the grooms stood by them, deep in conversation. She watched, frowning, as David raised the pistol and cocked the chamber, squinted along the barrel and then deposited it into his greatcoat pocket.

The night air was dispersing a little of her inebriated daze and she tried to clarify how she came to be sitting in a carriage when the last thing she clearly recalled was eating soup from a silver spoon.

She was going home! She had it now. She was being sent home and he was going to journey with her to Mayfair.

She was aware he was approaching the carriage and she sank back into the cushions as he entered.

He settled opposite her with a sigh and dark eyes immediately locked onto hers. Smiling to himself, he glanced at the open window. 'You look as though you've sobered up a little, Victoria.'

'Yes, I have,' she stiffly, carefully enunciated, then gripped at the seat as the carriage pulled away and her upper body swayed in a graceful circle.

'Pity…' David murmured; with a glamorous white smile that, drunk or not, made her stomach flutter. Then he laughed and settled back, stretching out long legs in front of him.

Victoria peered out at the dusk as they hurtled through the night. She hadn't been aware that horses could go so fast with just coach lamps to light the way. A gust of bitter evening air had her again reaching up for her bonnet to shield her chilling face with its brim. She tutted impatiently while feeling about on the seat for it and David watched.

'Are you cold?'

'A little,' she haughtily allowed. She had been wondering for the past ten minutes or so where they were and how long it took to journey from Hammersmith to Mayfair. She was sure by now he should have been delivered home, for it looked more like countryside than town speeding past her blurry vision.

He reached across and snapped the window shut. As he

started to move back, she was gathered into his arms and he sank back in his seat with her.

'I can't simply look at you all the way home, Vicky,' he said softly as he curbed her tardy, wine-sodden reflex to push him off. 'Come, it will be warmer to sit together, in any case.'

'You soon will be home,' she accused with a catch to her voice, realising that that made her feel sad and, what was more, tears were imminent.

David tilted her face, noting her hastily closed eyes and suspiciously dewy lashes. Settling her in front of him on the upholstery, he abruptly swung his long legs up onto the seat, bracing one foot against the carriage side to shift and find the best position. Victoria was then deftly tumbled against him so she lay with her breeze-loosened hair pitching over his torso. Muscular arms banded about her, anticipating objection.

Victoria felt the muzz returning to rotate her head and the warmth and comfort were so tempting. When cool fingers smoothed her salt-damp cheeks, she nestled her face into soft wool and her fingers crept into the warmth of his coat.

'Are you nearly home?' she gasped, and sniffed against his shoulder.

'I'll be home when you are, sweetheart,' he soothed her, and dropped a kiss on crumpled black satin hair. He leaned his head back against the carriage with a sigh that was never completed but metamorphosed into a rueful laugh. 'Don't do that, Vicky.' He caught at her small hand as it trailed a wandering path inside his coat. 'It's not that I don't like it…but it might make me have second thoughts about Hammersmith.' He linked his fingers into hers and his thumb traced her palm, making her nestle her head further beneath his chin and turn her body into his.

'Do you remember when we journeyed back from Brighton together, in Wainwright's carriage, and he travelled in Dickie's with your aunt? Matilda had rather over-indulged on barley wine that evening, as I recall, or I'd never have managed to wangle us being alone.'

Victoria sighed her recollection of the event.

'Do you remember what we did?'

There was a tiny pause then a virtually imperceptible nod against his shoulder.

'Shall we do it now?'

Even inebriated, the memory made Victoria's lids flick up in shock against his coat. She remembered…oh, she remembered. She had never been kissed so many times, or caressed in so many enchanting ways, or felt so deliciously wanton…or chagrined when he'd eventually put her away from him…for her own good, he had said. The most cherished part had been feeling so absolutely adored. How many times had he told her he loved her…that he would always love and care for her…?

'No!' Her refusal was declared vehemently into his coat.

'Why not?' he asked softly.

'It's different now…it's not the same,' she slurred, endeavouring to beat the throb in her head which defeated both her reasoning properly and breaking free of his bewitching, warm control.

'What's different?' he persisted as his hands began a slow, coaxing massage along her back.

'Stop it!' Victoria gasped, trying to twist away and flee to her own side of the coach again.

But he kept her close, then lifted her over him so satin curtains of long, thick hair draped her white face and pooled on his shoulders. 'What's different, Victoria?' he softly demanded, glittering dark eyes trapping frightened, evasive ones. 'Tell me…'

'You don't love me now,' she defeatedly cried, and immediately tried to dip to seek the shelter of his shoulder, but he held her still.

'It's different because I don't love you?' He choked a laugh. 'Not because I'm a repulsive degenerate who makes your flesh crawl?'

'You are not!' Victoria spontaneously championed, her eyes rushing to meet his. 'I've never said that.'

'I've never said that I don't love you now.'

He held her braced above him with one hand while the other smoothed her cheek and gathered her silken hair back from her heart-shaped face. He lowered her slowly until her lips were mere inches from his. 'If I tell you how much I love you…' he paused to touch his mouth to hers '…will you remember it in the morning?'

Her lids flicked up and tipsy, glossy eyes reproached him. 'You're…you're just saying it…you're lying to seduce me…'

'I could have done that in leisurely comfort in Hammersmith, Victoria, and without needing to lie…or flatter…or indulge you in any way.'

She stared at him, urging her brain to function.

'Well? It's true, isn't it?' he said, smiling at her forced concentration.

'I'm not sure…I can't think properly,' she wailed.

He lowered her completely, settling her against his shoulder with her body turned into his. 'Go to sleep. I'll tell you again in the morning,' he said huskily against her hair.

She snuggled close…then closer still as she heard him laugh and say tenderly, 'I love you, Victoria.'

Chapter Eleven

The two men locked eyes pugnaciously.

It was true what Beryl had said, then, was Samuel Prescott's fighting thought. Hartfield's beautiful, revered mistress had been coerced into vice in a last-ditch bid to keep the estate for them all. That was why she had disappeared to London looking so forlorn and with barely a day's notice.

He recalled this noble brute from the day of the funeral and hadn't been deaf to awed whispers about his money and notoriety. Neither had he been blind to the nature of the glances the man had slanted Mrs Hart's way. Even proper manners and finery couldn't camouflage lust where Samuel's practised eye hovered. This blackguard had obviously had his evil sport and now couldn't wait to rid himself of her! She was dumped before the sun was even up on a new day! Samuel's hands balled into brawny fists.

The antagonism was not lost on David. He carefully shifted a drowsing Victoria in his arms while his cool, arrogant gaze slid into Hartfield's hallway and settled on disembodied flames wavering above the ghostly outline of a candelabra. 'Are you going to let me pass? As you can see, your mistress is in need of her bed.'

'I can see my mistress is in need of her *sleep*,' Samuel snarled, jerking out beefy arms to remove the precious burden. Oh, he might appear all lofty elegance and smooth sophistication but his reputation was as black as hell. And it was to there that Samuel silently, savagely cursed him.

David's eyes narrowed and his lips strained over set teeth. He exacted absolute deference from his employees and it was willingly given. This man had a lot to learn. At any other time and place he would have gladly tutored him. In a perilously quiet voice he enunciated, 'Move yourself out of my way before you rue the day you were born...'

'Samuel, a guest for our chamber...I mean, a chamber for our guest, please.' Victoria's sleepy, wine-husky voice sighed through David's dulcet threat. Her manservant received a sweetly tipsy smile. 'I believe you have before met Viscount Hardinge...that is, Mr Courtenay....' She hesitated, frowning in concentration.

'Try David...' The amused advice was murmured against her cold ear, then a delicious, discreet kiss warmed it.

Samuel's hostility soared, his generous mouth clamping so tightly, it began disappearing into ruddy cheeks. Not only had the villain ravished her, he had plied her with strong liquor too! In seven years he had never known Mrs Hart take more than a few sips of alcohol on special occasions. Judging by her mellow manner, she'd no memory of what degradation she'd endured. It was for the best, raced through Samuel's anguished mind. Ignorance was indeed bliss. He glared belligerently at this detested guest. Oh, he wasn't frightened of him! In fact, he'd be more than happy to rearrange those regular features to match his deviant character.

After a final resentful moment stationed in the doorway, Samuel executed a stiff sidestep, allowing David entry into a sombre Hartfield.

'Thank you...' David clipped sarcastically, making immediately for the stairway. Then, 'Follow with the light,' was grated imperiously over a shoulder.

With a large palm shielding flaring wicks, Samuel loped obediently after him. But only to ensure Victoria's safety in the dark corridors. He would have gladly watched, nay, aided, their lecherous lodger in tripping and breaking his decadent neck over the gloomy banisters.

Balancing Victoria in his arms, David found the handle and a booted foot sent the door swinging inwards. He approached the high four-poster, a sturdy, solid shape in the milky moonlit chamber, and sat her gently down on it. He carefully eased her cloak from her shoulders, aware of trustful eyes, luminous black in a silvered face, gazing up at him through draping, dusky locks. Yielding to temptation, he dipped his head, touching his lips to hers.

Weak, flickering light was immediately strengthening. 'Wait by the door,' he gritted. Samuel's insolent rejoinder was intentionally audible.

'Do you want your aunt to come to you, Vicky, to help you undress?'

A polished ebony pendulum of hair answered him. Then, with a contented sigh, she drooped sideways onto the feather mattress.

A slow, indulgent smile and head-shake accompanied David's removing her shoes and settling her under the puffy quilt. After a tiny hesitation he again succumbed. Slender arms stretching out invitingly made it impossible not to. He skimmed his lips on hers, steeling himself not to linger as she nestled uninhibitedly closer. An abrasive cheek caressed her soft, pearly complexion while small fingers were unlocked from about his neck.

Having shut Victoria's door noiselessly behind him, David turned and gave Samuel his leisurely attention. The man was glowering up the two or more inches into his face. A look of expressionless contemplation was returned; it effortlessly transformed into a special smile that chilled the burly man to the marrow. 'We'll leave the matter of your insubordination till daylight. For now…where is a bed for what's left of this night?'

'There isn't one,' was Samuel's surlily smug retort. A dangerous flare to the Viscount's eyes and nostrils had him grudgingly, truthfully expounding, 'The only bed made up is in with Mrs Hart's father. We keeps a pallet prepared in there for when Mr Lorrimer's ailing and needs attention overnight. There's no other ready.'

'Well, show me to it,' David prompted with icy calm, while inwardly wondering whether a night in the stables wasn't really more to his taste.

David shifted, grunted and then yanked at the insubstantial blanket. He resettled into the lumpy mattress with a sleepy sigh despite grey morning light battering his eyelids. Relinquishing this meagre warmth to rise and close the annoying chink in the curtains was weighed against persevering for another hour in an uncomfortable half-snooze then abandoning the idea of rest altogether. He guessed the time to be approaching five in the morning; soon the servants would be about creating noise and more distraction.

His mind again veered to Victoria. Somnolently he calculated how many paces…how many walls…how many doorways separated them. His body heat furnaced, making the need for the blanket superfluous after all. It was irritably flung back as needling perspiration rimmed his brow and top lip and his loins pulsed with such energy that the vibration quaked his entire body. A booted foot stamped down on the mattress and he shoved backwards, instinctively seeking the cool wall.

Instead he tormented himself with thoughts of his bed at Beauchamp Place: almost seven foot square, and cushioned with the finest array of downy mattresses, silks and linens money could buy. The last time he'd slept on anything this crude he'd been at school. His mouth tipped wryly as he turned restlessly on the unsprung pallet and then started fully awake.

The white-gowned apparition leaning over him mirrored his surprise by jumping back and wringing together freckled hands. Then one went to settle a nightcap on its bony head while it again crept close. 'How much?' it suddenly croaked.

'How much?' David parroted in confusion, blinking to clear his vision.

'How much will you pay me, then, for my daughter?' Charles Lorrimer demanded, while eyeing him craftily through droopy, mottled lids.

'How much do you want?' David asked, levering himself upright. His stubbled, gaunt face grazed massaging hands as he laughed silently, helplessly into them. He wearily took stock: he'd got a maddened servant who wanted to knock him senseless and a senseless old man who wanted to sell him his daughter and an unrequited passion for that daughter that was likely, in any case, to drive him equally insane.

'Fifty-five guineas,' Charles Lorrimer eventually calculated.

'Why that amount?' David asked with vague interest.

'It's for hounds,' the old man emphasised as though irritated by the need to explain. 'The better the hounds, the better the hunting, and I've a mind to ride out this morning. I'd course some hare and shoot a few brace of pheasant to hang for a fine dinner. You can come.' He magnanimously bestowed his invitation.

David inclined his head in gracious thanks.

Scuttling back to his bed and perching upon it, with his cold feet held away from the chilly, polished wood floor, Charles then allowed, 'You seem a nice fellow.' He sighed

in resignation. 'I suppose I should be nice too and tell you.'
A dramatic pause this time, then his feeble frame inclined
forward and he hissed on a single breath, 'My daughter's
a beauty but she's a wanton.'

'A wanton?' echoed back immediately.

'Such a disgrace, I'll own,' Charles said, wagging his
head sadly. 'But she *was* seduced by a villain.' His nightcap
recommenced bobbing in emphasis. 'The wretch set out to
ruin her, you know. Such was his hold over her…and her
shame…that I had to send her away to take vows…to cool
her fever and beg forgiveness for her sins.'

'Take vows?' David echoed, his eyes seeming an incredibly vivid blue in his whitening face.

'I suppose she's still there…at the Sisters of Mercy at
Baldock. No…no,' Charles dismissed, with a tut and a
wave of a skeletal hand. 'Sometimes, I'm forgetful…and
confused,' he amiably disclosed, 'but now I recall. Daniel
was to fetch her. And discipline her for me. She's a bad
girl to cause her papa so much trouble.' He eyed David
consideringly. 'I'll own you're the sort of steady fellow to
keep her checked and docile. Not like that other one…'
Folding in half again, he whispered, bulging-eyed and con-
spiratorial, 'Always fighting and carousing and such scandalous breeding!'

Having frowned lengthily at David's hunched shoulders
and dishevelled appearance, he concluded, 'But he was
quite a fine figure of a man and so elegant and handsome
with it. You should watch out for him. He was a most
insistent rogue and might come back.' With surprising agil-
ity he had, within a moment, swung his feet onto the bed
and scrambled beneath covers which were pulled right up
to his ears.

David sat staring at his hands, a muscle twitching in a
shady, concave cheek. It was probably just senile rambling.
Had it ever come to such lunacy, Victoria would have got

word to him somehow. But then two weeks after being banished from Hammersmith with a flea in his ear, he'd been on foreign soil. His fingers gripped until the knuckles gleamed bone and were abruptly yanked apart. The past was best forgotten… What point was there in dredging up all the heartache? No recrimination… They had a future to share.

Aware of Charles Lorrimer's steady, slow breathing, he pushed away from the bed and walked to the window. Widening the gap in the velvet curtains, he braced broad palms against the sill, looked out into the emerging dawn, and smiled.

So this was her Hartfield. His roving sapphire gaze took in the quiet pastoral scene. It was as she had described: undulating parkland, woods fringing the horizon and off to the right a glass-smooth lake glinting mercurially as the sky brightened. He glanced down, closer to the house, at the neat box-hedged herb garden and spied the blonde girl who had accompanied Victoria and her aunt to London hurrying along the gravel path with a washing basket beneath one arm. The servants here were obviously few and versatile, this one encompassing the duties of laundry and lady's maid.

Reluctantly abandoning the charming rural vista, he collected his neckcloth and tail-coat from the chair where last night they had been casually discarded. They received an automatic neatening shake; the rest of his crumpled attire got a rueful glance coupled with a perfunctory brush with a hand.

Out in the dim corridor, he instinctively squinted at Victoria's doorway. A lazy smile emerged as he spied Samuel's bulk overflowing from a boudoir chair that looked on the point of collapse. The servant's head was lolling against the wall as he snored, his arms crossed belligerently over his chest.

David paced quietly closer and gazed down into weather-roughened features: brow corrugated and jaw fiercely jutting even in sleep. The man must have been on guard all night. David nodded in appreciation. Loyal and protective. He liked that. He liked that very much. Incompetent. He wasn't quite so impressed. Leaning across, he silently opened Victoria's door an inch, then shut it again with an audible click.

Samuel shot upright so violently, the dainty chair nearly flew out from under him.

'Fine morning...' David cheerfully greeted while shrugging with deliberate leisure into his coat. He straightened his cuffs before smiling and strolling past to the stairs.

He'd break every bone in his body...he'd tear him limb from limb...

'Are you sure there was no message, Samuel?' Victoria repeated breathlessly, insistently.

'No, ma'am...no message,' was Samuel's mild affirmation. And after that, he savagely promised himself, he'd wring his elegant neck, cut out his black heart and feed it to the crows.

'The Viscount said nothing at all before he left?' Victoria quavered. 'Nothing?'

'Er...he said it was a fine morning, ma'am, nothing else.'

'A fine morning...' Victoria repeated, in little above a whisper. She turned quickly away. 'Thank you, Samuel.' Having squeezed shut her aching eyes and drawn a huge, steadying breath to compose herself, she whirled back. 'I believe we are low on logs in the morning room, Samuel. Would you fetch more, please? Then Mr Lorrimer requires assistance to take some air after breakfast. 'Tis a fine morning...' The words faded as she recalled who had already issued that happy verdict on this awful day. 'My father would benefit from half an hour in the sunshine…' she bravely croaked on.

Samuel inclined his flaxen head at his mistress but his eyes were attached to her strained white face. He'd travel to London, if need be, and kill the swine. That was what he'd do. Not only had the bastard seduced and abandoned this wonderful woman, he'd not even manners enough to thank her for her hospitality before haring back to the city and his iniquitous pleasures.

'Don't fret so, Victoria.' Her father's thin tone floated over from the window seat just as Samuel quit the dining room on his stomp to the woodpile.

'I'm not fretting, Papa.' She approached him and an unsteady white hand patted his thin forearm. 'Samuel will take you out for a stroll later…' She peered up at scudding clouds. 'The sky is clearing and—'

'That strange fellow in my bedchamber has only gone to do a bit of business… He'll soon return,' her father confidently said.

Victoria stared at him, amazed. He seemed perfectly sure…perfectly lucid. 'Did he say so, Papa? Did you speak to him before he left?'

'Indeed I did. He seems nice enough. He's gone on an errand for me.'

'For you?' Victoria queried disbelievingly but with a smile imminent.

'As I say…he's a good chap. He's gone to buy me hounds…so we can hunt.'

Victoria closed her eyes, shielding despair and grinding disappointment. Her eyes and head felt heavy from the wine she'd drunk and the deep sleep she'd finally started from at nine o'clock. Beryl had been upbraided for not waking her sooner. The blame had then been laid firmly at Samuel's door by his erstwhile lover. Her manservant had apparently given strict instructions that the mistress was to get herself awake when she would.

'Beryl said you were home...' Matilda burst out as soon as the dining-room door was shut behind her. Drawing her away from her father, Matilda whispered, 'You are back so soon. What...what occurred in London? Why are you back so soon?' Pale eyes probed Victoria's wan countenance. 'Surely not...surely not discarded after just one night... What of the debts?' she hissed, horrified.

'No, Aunt Matty,' Victoria hoarsely, hysterically denied. 'Not *even* one night. I believe I have been returned unsuitable... As for the debts...' She glanced about, blinking away the heat in her eyes, then looked at her aunt as though to say more. It was impossible. Gathering her grey skirts in shaking hands, she muttered incoherent excuses and left Matilda staring after her.

Victoria sank slowly to the turf and automatically began picking out the seedling dandelions between the flowers. She squeezed shut her eyes to stem the tears. Fool! she silently berated herself. Don't let it hurt so! You can't pretend ignorance of his character. How many scandals do you need? How much sordid gossip...before you believe him the reprobate everyone whispers about?

She bowed her head and murmured aloud, to engraved granite, 'Oh, Danny... Help me, please. What am I to do? I don't want to leave Hartfield...to leave you...'

'Best ask your flashy lover for a few trinkets you can sell, then,' came a sneering female voice from behind.

Victoria gasped and twisted about. She recognised the woman at once even though the last time she'd spied her they had been in a murky dockside street rather than a bucolic churchyard. 'Who are you? What do you want?'

The woman merely crossed her arms over her voluptuous body while raking Victoria with spiteful almond-shaped eyes. Close to, she *was* very attractive, Victoria acknowledged, with her deep green eyes and pale gold curls peeking out beneath her dark bonnet. She judged her to be in her early thirties yet her complexion was clear and smooth, a sullen droop to her mouth the only flaw.

Victoria felt a clogging weight plummet from her throat to settle in her stomach. Of course! This woman must have somehow discovered the Viscount's whereabouts and followed him. Was he so very sought-after that women customarily hounded him after just one night away? This one had the look of a woman scorned, Victoria realised, chilled, and was possibly out for revenge.

Hysteria bubbled in her throat. Well, this stranger wasn't alone in feeling spurned and vengeful. She had been subjected to a few honeyed words herself. Intoxicated she might have been last night, but she knew she had not dreamed his wooing kisses and declarations of love whilst wrapped against him in the coach. And now he had abandoned her without a by-your-leave. Escalating fury ground her teeth and clenched her fists so tight, her nails scored ridges into her palms. She was heartily sick of it all.

'If you have come here seeking the Viscount, I'm afraid you are out of luck. He did stay overnight but departed early this morning. I imagine he is now at home. You will have more chance of running him to ground in Mayfair.'

'Thanks for the tip,' the woman scoffed. 'I might just do that. And from what I've heard of his lordship he might just let me.' Victoria's slender figure received a disparaging, summarising scrutiny. 'Managed to keep him just the one night, did you?'

Victoria sprang to her feet, infuriated. 'The Viscount is kinsman to my late husband and was thus accorded hospitality.' As the information was icily conveyed, the fact that she felt compelled to justify his presence at her home incensed her further. 'Now, if you have any purpose here other than to ambush Lord Courtenay, state it. If not, go. You are trespassing…'

'I'm Petronella Vaughan…' No more was offered apart from a self-satisfied smirk.

'And…?' Victoria quizzed, frowning. 'What am I supposed to deduce from that? If you are one of the Viscount's infamous courtesans—'

A shriek of lusty laughter interrupted her. 'Wouldn't I just love to be! I'll own I'm ambitious…'

'I'm afraid the name means nothing to me,' Victoria snapped. 'I am rarely in London and know none of the gossip…'

'Well, know this,' the woman spat through her teeth. 'You owe me…' She stabbed a finger at Daniel Hart's grave, about to say more, just as the churchyard gate whined open and Alexander Beresford's stout figure appeared.

'We'll speak again,' the woman threatened. Within a moment she had wrapped herself concealingly into her cloak and was hurrying into the valley towards the village of Ashdowne.

Victoria walked the gravel pathway to meet Alexander Beresford, shaking with a nauseating sense of foreboding. Her preoccupation prevented her instantly seeing his leer and pebble eyes brazenly sliding over her body.

He knew! Did everyone hereabouts know her business…know the Viscount had rejected her? Courage failed her. She swept past him at the gate and on down the slope towards Hartfield. 'If you wish to speak to me, Mr Beresford, come along to the house. There's a chill to the air and I wish to be indoors.' The brusque words trailed over her shoulder at him as she increased her pace towards her home.

Victoria turned from the library window some ten

minutes later. 'I can't imagine why you are here, Mr Beresford; there can be little for us to discuss.'

'I disagree, Mrs Hart. I'm sure we might now find a… *mutually*…beneficial topic,' he insolently insinuated. 'As for why I am here…I came at your aunt's behest. Yesterday she gave into my safe-keeping some items of jewellery she was keen to sell. I am now returned with the good news that Squire Lennox is interested in purchasing for his lady wife the emerald and diamond ring.'

'That's my aunt's betrothal ring!' Victoria exclaimed, shocked.

'I've no idea…' Alexander dismissed, gesturing apathy. 'In any case, your aunt has just agreed the sale.' He paused. 'She also let slip you had returned from your very brief *sojourn* in London. Thus, I thought we might have a little chat. You were gone barely one night, then?' A snide smile and heavy-lidded appraisal accompanied the remark. 'I indeed expected your return; but not quite so soon. The Viscount's *ennui* is becoming legendary…'

'I have no wish to detain you now you have finished your business with my aunt, Mr Beresford.'

'Your aunt has kindly invited me to dine, to celebrate the sale of the emerald. If my acceptance will be putting you out, of course…'

Victoria blanched, reddened, excused herself and swished furiously from the room.

Her heart was hammering with rage and despair, and the mundane worry that there might be very little in the kitchens to provide a decent meal for the family, let alone a despised guest. She had no wish to feed Alexander Beresford one crumb from her larder, but the invitation had thoughtlessly been issued. And she would definitely not allow him the satisfaction of thinking it beyond their means to adequately accommodate one extra mouth.

She hastened into the kitchen to find Edith, their cook, seated at the table supping a dish of tea.

'Why is the range not high? Why is the meal not underway? Where are the girls?'

Plump shoulders were raised and a grey head wagged dolefully. 'I's been sat 'ere this past ower awaitin' that Samuel. Gets me some fish outta the lake or a chicken from the coop, I says. "Yes", 'e says, and that's the last I sees of 'im. An ower ago, were that. Now what's I s'posed to do with a bit o' left-over mutton if'n 'e don't turn up with a nice roaster or a coupla trouts? And Mrs Sweeting's been in 'ere 'n all, saying as 'ow the late master's man o' bizniss be sittin' down too. I tell you, Mrs 'art, I's sorely tempted to take meself off somewhere where me uses be better appree-shated and me colleagues o' more assistance. I—'

Victoria held out a silencing hand. She breathed deeply, calmingly. 'Are the vegetables prepared?'

Several chins dropped to Edith's chest in answer.

'Is there a fruit tart of some sort ready?'

Another nod.

'So we are in need of meat. What can you do with what we have?'

'Can 'ash it, I s'pose, and you'll get a coupla forkfuls each…if'n one o' those skiving girls gets themselves back 'ere with some 'erbs to bulk it out.'

'I shall get you some herbs, Edith. Please stoke the range and set to at once.'

She was slowly going mad, she was sure of it, was Victoria's placid self-assessment as she made for the kitchen garden. Her head still pulsed from her hangover, her stomach was still in angry cramps from her confrontation with Alexander Beresford and the woman in the churchyard. On the periphery of her mangled mind niggled the servants' disobedience. Even if they were now aware of her poverty and shame, surely they had not so quickly withdrawn respect and loyalty? Samuel she would have trusted with her life. But where on earth were they all? As though in answer to this conundrum, Beryl clattered down the back stairs.

'We was looking for you ma'am,' the maid burst out, freezing Victoria's ready rebuke on her parted lips. 'We believed you to be up at the chapel. It's Mr Lorrimer. He went up for his afternoon snooze and rolled out of bed and cracked his head and a nasty bruise he got, too, but Samuel's managed to soothe him and now he's fast asleep.' She gulped in breath. 'I'm just getting the mop for Sally to clear up, 'cos there was another little accident, like…' She delicately coughed. 'Probably the shock, 'cos he's been real good in that way of late…'

'But he's not badly hurt at all?' Victoria demanded urgently.

'Oh, no, ma'am. In fact, he managed a giggle when Samuel slid on the wet floor and went down a crash too.' Beryl bit her lip, trying to disguise her own humour at the memory of it.

Victoria passed a tremulous hand over her face. She felt like screeching hysterically herself. Instead she said formally, 'Thank you, Beryl. If you would carry on, then, please.'

Victoria exited the house by the side door. It led directly to the walled garden via a gothic arched portal. Having fought with the rust-swollen latch to creak open the ancient, paint-peeling gate, she ducked through the low opening. She wiped gritty, umber flecks from her fingers to her skirts while following the shingle path through the box hedging towards the stumpy rosemary bush. Silent, unstoppable tears streamed down her face and she simply blinked through them, unable to summon enough energy to wipe them away.

She had been on the point of misjudging her dear servants. A gurgle of watery laughter escaped her. She was no judge of character at all. Had she not once believed Alexander Beresford a kind and decent man? The only man worthy of such praise now lay in Hartfield's churchyard and was unable to help her further.

The setting sun slanting golden warmth at her wet face reminded her of the lateness of the hour and the need to return Edith her herbs. She began breaking off a variety of fragrant clumps and dropping them by her feet.

'Don't we have a gardener, Vicky?'

Victoria swirled around, her heart lodging in her throat. She squinted against the tears and low yellow rays impeding her vision and made out the tall, athletic figure on the shingle path. He looked unbelievably distinguished and attractive and with an anguished cry she spontaneously flew at him and began pummelling small, grubby fists against his arms, his chest, anything she could reach while her sobs crescendoed. 'Go away!' she screamed, swinging this time for his face. 'Go on…go away…you always go away…you always go and leave me…'

She was picked up bodily and embraced so close she could barely breathe. Another futile struggle ensued and then she yielded and buried her wet face into verbena-scented skin. She felt large hands slide up her back, just one bridge her neck beneath her tousled hair and stroke in a slow, mesmeric rhythm. But it was the murmured soothing endearments that made her determined to prise herself away. She wriggled her arms free, pushed once, then lashed them about his neck in an unbreakable coil as though to prevent him ever leaving again without her.

'I take it you missed me, Vicky,' David choked. 'God, if I'd known, I'd have woken you and taken you with me. I thought you'd be sleeping off a hangover all afternoon. How long have you been up and about?'

She hiccoughed against his shoulder as her breathing steadied.

Long fingers threaded through her hair to her scalp and cupped it tenderly. 'Does your head hurt?'

She simply nodded her head in his hand, incapable of speech.

He relaxed his hold on her a little but she refused to loosen hers on him. She clung to him with such tenacity, he had to support and lift her again. Warm lips stroked a damp cheek through silky matted hair. 'What's the matter? This isn't just about me going to town to attend to business for the day. What's happened? Is it your father?'

She shook her head with a huge indrawn, shuddering breath and drank in the solid, reassuring feel of him, the fresh scent, the soft graze of his fine clothes.

Her composure steadily strengthened; so did her mortification at behaving with such lack of decorum. Sliding her arms quickly from about his neck, she sought firm ground and stepped back. She tried to turn immediately away but he caught at her wrists, keeping her facing him. One hand followed her evasive face and, between holding it still and picking away veiling strands of hair, he read her expression.

'You thought I'd gone away for good, didn't you?' he accused with soft, bitter wonderment. 'You thought, despite what I told you last night, that I'd returned to London and drinking...gambling...
whoring...didn't you?'

'Yes,' she breathed, wrenching free of his clasp. 'That's *exactly* what I thought, Lord Courtenay. Especially after one of those...*women* came searching for you.' She stepped back along the shingle path and automatically dipped to gather the herbs. 'I have to take these in to Edith. We are late with dinner this evening and we have a guest...'

'Me...?' he ironically guessed.

Victoria coloured. 'No. But you are very welcome, of course...'

'Of course...' echoed back drily. 'A woman came here

searching for me?' His disbelief was vaguely amused. 'Did she leave her name?'

'Indeed she did, my lord,' Victoria frigidly told him, yet for some reason could not, immediately, tell him what it was. 'Petronella Vaughan,' suddenly burst from her.

David stalked her along the path and with a cool smile grabbed at her wrist and spun her about to walk with him towards the house.

'We'll talk about it later,' he said.

Chapter Twelve

'He's back, then.'

'I reckon he's in love with her!'

'I'll wager he'll marry her!'

Three pairs of eyes were peering discreetly out of Charles Lorrimer's bedroom window through a veil of velvet curtaining.

'Such as he don't even know what love is. He'll never marry…'less he needs an heiress sharpish.' Samuel scathingly dismissed the serving maids' romantic fancies. Both young women craned their necks to catch the last glimpse of their beloved mistress being led by the masterly Viscount from the herb garden.

'The man's a rogue and a philanderer,' was Samuel's next pious pronouncement. 'And she'd be best off without him.'

Sally and Beryl turned, as one, from the window and exchanged a look before both glowering at him.

'I'd say that be true of someone else not a mile off. And that it takes one to know one,' Beryl sniffily said on exiting the room, blonde head held high.

Samuel offered his betrothed a sickly smile.

Sally returned him a pursed rosebud mouth and narrow-eyed glare. Tossing brunette curls, she also swished haughtily from the room, mop in hand.

Samuel's grin drooped. He looked towards old Mr Lorrimer, satisfied himself that the man was sound asleep, then he too went to discover just what was going on.

Alexander Beresford turned casually from where he sat chatting to Matilda while patiently awaiting his supper. Of a sudden, his fleshy bottom lip seemed to hit his barrel chest. He was still gawping comically when he sprang clumsily to his feet.

'Lord Courtenay is arrived and will be dining with us,' Victoria announced breathily, feeling immensely proud of the imposing man standing casually close to her as they proceeded into the drawing room. 'May I introduce you to Mr Beresford, Lord Courtenay? He is…he is…'

'A kind and decent man…?' The sarcasm was barely audible.

'He is my late husband's attorney,' Victoria spluttered on, colouring at such warranted, withering irony. To conceal her confusion she blurted, 'Aunt Matilda, would you arrange for our guests to have some wine while the meal is prepared?' Wide grey eyes expressively appealed to her aunt.

But Matilda seemed as confounded as Alexander, simply gazing glassily at David as though he were an apparition. She started to her senses. 'How wonderful to see you again, Viscount Courtenay,' she smarmed, all honeyed charm.

Victoria chanced a sliding peek at David's face. He hadn't forgotten either that the last time he and Matilda had met the woman had famously snubbed him at Emma's ball. He bowed gallantly…too low. That private amusement was about him, Victoria noted, anxiously nibbling at her lower lip.

Realising she was still clutching a handful of mixed

herbs, she withdrew a few paces. 'I shall just see how Edith is doing with dinner…' With a final explicit look at her aunt to play hostess, she was backing out of the drawing room and speeding towards the kitchens.

'Oh, I'm so sorry, Edith, but there is another guest to dine with us.' Having catapulted into the kitchen and plonked the culinary bouquet down on the scrubbed pine table, she became aware of four sets of eyes pinned on her.

Beryl reacted first. 'Told you so,' she muttered smugly to her trio of colleagues.

'Samuel, please find some wine, and serve it in the drawing room.'

'Perhaps, ma'am, I should get to the lake and net out something to put on the table for dinner…'

'Shoulda done it owers ago…' Edith darkly muttered.

'I been attending to Mr Lorrimer.'

'That's enough,' Victoria rebuked, but pleadingly, with a slender, massaging hand at her brow. 'Yes, thank you, Samuel; some fish would be a great help.'

'I got some gooseberries 'ere somewhere.' Edith was into her stock cupboard, sorting through the preserves. 'Gooseberry sauce 'ud go a treat wi' trout or pike and…' The rest was lost as she disappeared further into the dim recess.

'Beryl, perhaps you would serve some wine…' Victoria knew her voice was shrill and that she was being too polite and grateful with the servants.

'You come along with me to your chamber, Mrs Hart, and we'll find you a pretty gown and tidy your hair. Sally will fetch some wine.'

The two young women exchanged a smiling nod with an air of camaraderie.

Suddenly comprehending Beryl's mild criticism, Victoria glanced down, horrified, at her appearance. Her plain grey day- dress was crumpled and a few spikes of rosemary clung to the hem. Her fingers checked trailing ebony tresses, attempting to neaten them. A blink of her damp lashes had her trying to inconspicuously scrub at tear-stained cheeks with a gritty, grubby hand. How useless and feeble she must seem! What a fright she must look too if the servants needed to bring it to her attention!

'Had I known it would all turn a'right, Vicky, my dear, I should never have invited that tubby solicitor to dine. I only did so to put an eligible man in your way...yet look what you have again found for yourself!'

Victoria twisted on the bedroom stool, almost sending the hairbrush flying out of Beryl's hand. Beryl calmly held her glossy dark head still and went about her business with pins and brush.

'Oh, Aunt...your beautiful betrothal ring. You must ask Mr Beresford to return it. I know you have sold it simply to raise some funds to help us all out but we shall manage...'

'I believe we shall...now,' Matilda said with an explicit smile. 'But it doesn't matter. These bony old fingers are past adornment. I should have liked to keep it as an heirloom for Justin...but it has been a long time...too long...' After a wistful sigh, she changed the subject abruptly. 'Come, we must hurry downstairs. You look a picture,' she interjected, waving away Beryl and her combs. She nodded with great satisfaction at Victoria's shimmering reflection: her glossy hair spiralling almost to the centre of her graceful back, her classic sculpted face softened by curling ebony tendrils, the longer of which draped to fragile white shoulders, and the taut lilac silk accentuating the curve of her breasts.

'Do hurry! The entertainment is too good to miss. The Viscount, I believe, holds no high opinion of fawning Alexander, yet he in turn seems to think the sun might rise tomorrow out of his lordship. Their conversation is a joy!'

Impatiently, she pulled Victoria off the stool and towards the door. Beryl bustled after them tutting, a perfume bottle in her hand aiming a flowery mist at her mistress.

'All the excitement has made me quite ravenous. What's for supper?' Matilda asked as they made their way downstairs in a cloud of rose petals.

'Not a lot…' Victoria ruefully admitted, and made a turn towards the kitchens to check on the meal's progress.

Matilda restrained her with a firm grip on her elbow. 'Beryl will chase them all up,' she decreed, with a fierce squint at the young serving maid, while steering Victoria in the opposite direction towards the drawing room.

'I must just quiz you, my lord, on another tale that reached my ears some years ago. It had you rescuing a well-known gentleman's son from ruin at the tables! Is it true you took his place and turned his last ten counters into one and a half thousand pounds?' Beresford's gushing adulation was ill at ease with his scepticism but certainly allconsuming: he hadn't noticed the ladies' entrance. David was also oblivious to Victoria's arrival due to positioning himself as far from his irritating interrogator as possible in the hope the man would leave him in peace. He was thus standing with his back to the door, pensively studying the smouldering logs.

'And I believe you allowed him one thousand of the pounds and took only five hundred for yourself.'

'The man had a consumptive cough that could clear a room,' David recounted wearily, still staring into the fire. 'Seemed little enough to pay him off with to keep the Duke of Wellington seated and his fifteen thousand pounds within my grasp.'

'*Is* that true?' escaped Victoria in disbelief. 'It's just gossip, surely…?'

David pivoted on his heel, took a few steps forward, then stilled and stared. Deep blue eyes engulfed smoky grey as he once more approached and halted just a little too close for propriety. 'You look absolutely ravishing.'

She blushed in thanks for his husky compliment. 'Is it a story?'

'Do you want it to be?' he tendered softly. 'Tell me what you wish to hear and I will say it. Whatever pleases you, Vicky.'

Her eyes rose, her blush heightening, as last night's bitter words were so sweetly offered back to her. Becoming conscious of Alexander Beresford's scrutiny and that he was actually tipping forward to try and catch their muted conversation, Victoria included him and Matilda in it. 'I must check if Papa is yet awake and will be coming down to dine with us all.' There was no need. Samuel entered the drawing room as she turned to leave it.

'Dinner is served m'm,' he intoned, bowing low. 'Mr Lorrimer is dining in his room.'

David offered her an elegant arm and Alexander scrambled to show equal gallantry to Matilda.

The servants had excelled themselves! It was obvious from their florid faces that they had toiled fast and furious in the hot kitchen. Edith had now discarded her cook's pinafore and donned one of Sally's black skirts to assist with serving. And that was unheard of. Edith's only domain was the kitchen; something she was wont to frequently drum into her colleagues. Victoria smiled her silent, gracious thanks and as one they bobbed, faces bursting with pride at the sight of their beautiful mistress on what, they had collectively decided, was the affluent arm of Hartfield's saviour.

The fruits of their labour decked the laden table: vegetables garnished with nuts and sauces, pickles, two sizeable trout smothered with gooseberry glaze. The sideboard displayed cheeses and sweet tarts for dessert. The mutton hash was there too: spiced and livened with onion and herbs, as was a plump jointed chicken covered in a creamy caper sauce. How Samuel, Sally and Edith between them had managed to achieve all this in one and three-quarter hours was beyond comprehension.

Victoria peered closely at the crispy roasted hen; a rogue feather *was* among the capers. She glanced up to discover Samuel's gaze roosting on the same spot. Their eyes briefly held before he smoothly began serving wine. He deftly removed the steaming dish of poultry to precisely position a wine carafe in its stead. When the chicken was resettled on the table the quill had disappeared, eliciting a muffled giggle from Victoria, and a sideways smile passed between them.

The sort of vivacity she had enjoyed seven long years ago scintillated within her, and she instinctively sought David's face across the flickering candle flame. She was rewarded with a slow, intimate smile before his deep blue eyes rose to Samuel and they shared a stare of grudging respect tinged with antagonism. Victoria paused to watch while reaching for her wine glass. On raising it to her lips she found it empty. A wobbly goblet finally caught Samuel's attention and had him speeding towards her…with the water jug.

'As fine a dinner as I believe I have ever tasted, Mrs Hart,' Alexander Beresford huffed, squashing back in his chair and blotting at his mouth with linen. 'You are lucky to have kept on such a talented cook…'

'Indeed…' Victoria politely agreed, yet uneasy with the implication that Edith might choose to leave her and the reasoning behind it. But she was feeling too content—quite light-headed despite Samuel's prohibition—to take umbrage. And Alexander's praise was indeed deserved. The meal had been superbly cooked and presented and more than adequate in quantity.

'We've been plagued with an unseasonably hard frost

these past nights, my lord,' Alexander commented in a tone mellow with satiety. 'Are you travelling far to lodgings this evening?'

'The Swan at St Albans,' David answered succinctly, studying his goblet.

'Oh, but we can put you up for the night again, Lord Courtenay,' Victoria spontaneously intervened, keen to be hospitable, but mostly desperate not to let him so soon slip away.

She watched long, inky lashes slowly rise to reveal wry humour.

'Oh, I promise a room to yourself and a good night's sleep this time....' Belatedly aware of her infelicity curling a leer into Alexander's claret top lip and rendering her aunt drop-jawed in horror, she floundered wretchedly on. 'I mean…that is to say…I shall have one of the servants air you a chamber and make up a proper bed…'

'I don't think that would be wise,' David intervened, smiling gently at her scarlet-faced confusion.

She tensed anxiously, instinctively knowing the whole of her future happiness hung on his next words. And with that awesome insight came another that drove home so hard, she actually winced. *I want him to love me as he did seven years ago, because in all that time I've never stopped loving him. And I wish he had no money for then debts and duty and relations would be irrelevant… We would get by. All I need is his love and fidelity…*

'I believe it's bad luck for the bride and groom to too often associate in the evenings before they wed. Seems a stupid superstition…' David's mild words penetrated her poignant self-perception.

'Wed…?' Alexander and Matilda echoed as one.

'Victoria and I are to be married on Saturday.' He delivered his proposal, his candle-flaring eyes not once flinching from hers. 'Preparations for the marriage kept me in town for the best part of the day. That and getting my attire back in some sort of respectable order.' He brushed an imaginary speck from an immaculate black sleeve. 'Oh, and this…' He stood, strolled around the table, and placed a small box in front of her on the polished mahogany. Victoria stared at it with a thundering heart, her fingers refusing to relinquish her goblet stem, her tongue the roof of her mouth. Beseeching grey eyes sped to his. The casket lid was immediately snapped back and a magnificent teardrop diamond blazed a rainbow.

David removed the crystal glass from her grip and her plain gold wedding band from her finger. Sliding the diamond to replace it, he raised the glistening stone to his lips. 'A symbol of what's past and all that I regret, Vicky,' he said, a deep throb to his quiet sincerity.

'How wonderful!' Matilda squealed, finally finding her voice.

Alexander Beresford simply stared and as Victoria's glowing grey eyes met his, angry colour mottled his skin. He had much preferred her in the role of the Viscount's discarded fancy…and his own prospective paramour, Victoria perceived. She gazed again at her magnificent engagement ring and it immediately put her in mind of her aunt's.

'My congratulations. You will wish to be alone, no doubt.' Having offered his stilted words, Alexander shoved back his chair.

'Mr Beresford…before you leave, the matter of my aunt's emerald ring must be resolved.'

'The matter has been satisfactorily resolved, Mrs Hart,' the man bluntly supplied. 'My thanks for a fine dinner. I shall set on the road before the ground gets too solid.'

'Oh, please wait.' Victoria quickly stood to detain him. 'My aunt is willing to return to you Squire Lennox's cash.

He need never realise the sale was agreed,' Victoria reasoned imploringly.

David moved towards the door as Alexander did, cutting off his exit. 'That sounds a fair offer, Beresford,' he said evenly, his quick intelligence immediately comprehending Matilda's hare-brained fund-raising. A cynical smile preceded, 'Had you earmarked for yourself a commission on the deal?'

Alexander's floridity furnaced but he refused to say more. After a stiff bow to the ladies he took a purposeful step towards the exit, yet maintaining a wary distance between himself and the Viscount.

David unfurled a lean hand. 'I'll take the ring, Beresford.' When Alexander pursed a mutinous mouth, long fingers snapped and beckoned impatiently.

The man delved into his pocket, slapped the tissue-wrapped ring into David's palm, and barked, 'My money…?'

Matilda was already speeding up to him, withdrawing a bundle of notes from her reticule as she went.

With a snatch and the cash scrunched in a hand, Alexander was immediately striding from the room.

'I fear we may never see him again,' Matilda observed, smiling broadly. She bestowed a proud, affectionate look on her newly betrothed niece, judging her never more exquisitely beautiful than at that moment with her smoky eyes heavy with serenity and her delicate, high cheekbones afire beneath her fiancé's steady, smouldering gaze.

'Well, what a day! It has quite wore me out. What you young people have to bear in mind is that I'm not as energetic as I once was.' She trudged backwards towards the door. Her lack of vigour was abruptly disproved as she whisked up to David, removed her ring from his hand with an impish beam, then sped back to the exit. An exaggerated yawn soon re-established her weariness and then she was gone.

As the door closed, Victoria realised they were at last truly, acceptably alone. He had promised to marry her in front of witnesses. It was a marriage contract as surely as if signed and sealed. And he knew that as certainly as she. Her rich, honourable hero had, against all odds, rescued them all. Relief and happiness sent a surge of spontaneous tears to prickle her nose and eyes. 'Thank you,' she whispered, suddenly shy and searching for distraction.

He held his hands out to her and without hesitation she flew into his embrace, her slender arms about his waist, hugging him close. 'Oh, thank you, thank you…'

Long fingers slid into her hair and tilted her face up to his. 'That's not what I want to hear, Vicky. I haven't gone without sleep, gone without seeing you all day, dealt with bankers, lawyers, clergymen, the licensing magistrate, to come and have you thank me…or feed me a good dinner.'

'Did you enjoy it? Truly?' Victoria demanded, shining-eyed, glad of a neutral topic while she composed herself. 'It was a rushed affair and the servants worked so furiously but I was worried…'

'It was just fine.' David interrupted her by laying a finger on her mouth. It sensuously skimmed sensitive scarlet lips while blazing blue eyes obsessively followed its movement. 'What do I want to hear, Vicky?'

Pearly eyelids drooped with the mesmeric stroking. 'That I will again ask you to stay the night?' she sighed against his finger.

He grunted a laugh and dipped his head. A leisurely, loving reward replaced his finger, moistening and parting her mouth. Eventually he said huskily, 'No…but it's a very tempting offer, sweetheart.'

'Have you really done all that today? Seen all those people so we can so soon be married? What shall I wear?'

'Victoria...' he gently threatened. 'There is something I want you to say first or I won't marry you...'

A startled, reproachful look elicited a defeated, wry smile. 'Well, I'll admit that's a lie, but, nevertheless, I'd like you to say...'

'I love you, David,' she whispered softly against his cheek before he could finish. 'I love you so much. And I must thank you...I am grateful.'

Unsteady hands cupped her face and turned her shy, radiant countenance up to his. 'I would have settled for David... You truly love me? Even knowing of the...the debauchery...the life I've led? You're not saying it from pity or gratitude? You still truly love me?' he demanded hoarsely, disbelievingly, while his thumbs quaked at her face. His sapphire eyes tracked her from head to toe, devouring the purity of her expression, the allure of her body's slender beauty.

His humble, childlike astonishment was so total and so unexpected, the poignancy wrenched a silent sob from Victoria's blocked throat and a slow, salty trickle from a sheeny eye. 'Of course I love you,' she choked. 'I thought you had already guessed. I've always loved you, David...always. Even long ago during those bleak days when I swore I hated you for abandoning me...'

The rest of the dulcet reassurance was smothered as his mouth swooped, welding to hers, forcing her head back against his possessive, cushioning arm. As though immediately regretting his raw passion the kiss was curtailed. But his lips couldn't quite break contact and stilled against her quivering mouth. He was about to apologise, Victoria realised, glimpsing his squeezed-shut eyes and tortured expression. In solace, she tendered her own inexpert version while whispering, 'I'll get used to it, David. In fact, I quite liked it this time...'

She felt him smile against her sweet, naïve comfort.

Once more he seized sensual control, his mouth slanting, fitting expertly over hers in a slow, seductive assault that liquefied her limbs and swirled her mind. Tapered fingers slid about his neck, clinging to his nape to keep her upright. Muscular arms enclosed supportively about her hips and shoulders, and long fingers curved up into sleek jet hair.

'You liked that better, though, didn't you?' It was murmured throatily with very real male contentment. 'I think I ought to leave now, Vicky,' he said, the look in his eyes giving the lie to the valiant statement.

She shook her head, clasping tighter to his neck, innate femininity grazing her body enticingly on his as she pressed closer.

'I can't stay…it's torture,' he explained and complained in one voice. Unlocking her imprisoning fingers, he held her away from him by her wrists. 'There's only one arrangement I'll accept to stay…sharing your chamber this time…'

Victoria's weighty lids flew wide. 'But…'

'Exactly…but…' It was his turn to reassure and his knuckles brushed against her rosy cheek.

Drawing her into a close, comforting embrace, he rested his jaw against a shimmering crown of satin hair. For a moment they remained silent, simply savouring, protracting their peaceful joy. Then, turning her with an arm about her shoulders, David steered them towards the door.

In the hallway sconces flared and sputtered, throwing shadows all around. By the great oaken doors, David inclined towards her and with a wry self-mockery just pecked her cheek. Victoria slyly tried to catch his lips in a mischievous tormenting that harked back seven years and elicited a playful, groaning restraint. And then her gaiety faded away. 'Will you come back tomorrow?'

His eyes held hers steadily, reflecting candlelight. 'Will I?'

'Yes,' she told him trustingly. 'Come early and we shall have a picnic lunch…by the lake.'

'Are you going to show me Hartfield?'

She nodded.

He sobered.

'We have things to talk about, Vicky. A moment ago you said you believed I had once abandoned you. I want to know why you thought that.' As she immediately frowned and began to speak, he laid a silencing finger on her lips. 'Not now. Nothing is spoiling this evening…no seven-year-old spectres are allowed. But we must discuss things.' To cheer her wistful, far-away expression, he added lightly, 'Where we're going to live is another topic.' The ploy worked: startled from her solemn reverie, she immediately began to quiz him.

He kissed her into silence, then murmured against her lips, 'Tomorrow. You've got the advantage on that score at the moment. And that's not fair. Losing isn't something I'm used to.'

Victoria swayed against him. Encircling his neck with alluring arms, she tantalised his lips with her tonguetip, employing a little of the eroticism she had just learned. As though unable to withstand it longer, his response was immediate, groaning and wolfish.

Now she was first to control and withdraw. 'I'm sure you'll *get* used to losing, David.' She teased his arrogance, before backing away to the stairs.

The commotion had Victoria folding upright in bed. It sounded as though someone was in great pain and yelping. She threw back the bedcovers and shapely bare legs were swung over the side of the mattress. Within a second she was on her way to the window for the noise seemed to be issuing from outside. On yanking apart the curtains, bright morning sunlight streamed onto her face, warming her body through her broderie anglaise nightgown. A tut and a sigh acknowledged she had again overslept.

Her attention was drawn from lucid skies to the garden. She watched in amazement as Samuel charged along the laundry pathway like a man demented: he was crouched to the ground, arms outstretched, yet, amazingly, almost running as he disappeared in the direction of the kitchen.

Victoria knuckled sleep from her eyes and groaned. Chickens or geese were obviously out of the run. Perhaps a fox in the night had scattered them. Samuel had no doubt decided on a mischievous morning rounding them up. Would never a day pass without some chaos erupting in the servants' quarters?

Snatching up her flimsy robe, she was struggling into it and belting it tightly as she raced down the stairs with her loose black hair streaming over her shoulders.

She burst into the kitchen crying, 'What in heaven's name is all the noise about? *What* is going on…?'

The sight of her fiancé, coffee cup midway to his mouth and a black puppy rolling playfully on his hessian boots, froze her, drop-jawed, to the spot. At that moment Samuel came strolling through the kitchen doorway with another dark, furry bundle secured beneath a brawny arm. Without pausing and with a gruff, 'Morning, ma'am,' he turned about and strolled right out again.

David's gaze, replete with an odd mix of humour and ardour, took in the dishevelled, ravishing state of her. His intense blue gaze became heavy-lidded as it discreetly tracked the creamy flesh exposed by her gaping robe and then lowered to a tiny waist accentuated by the firmly cinched belt.

Victoria put a hand to her hair and to her state of undress…but there was nothing she could possibly do to improve either. 'I…I…wasn't expecting you…' she excused and accused in a wail as her cheeks flamed.

'You said come early…' he reminded her in a voice of velvet gravel.

Victoria felt her face stinging beneath his unwavering scrutiny. What a wild hoyden she must seem, haring about the building in such an undignified manner. And he looked so immaculate! And so handsome! His dark hair, highlighted by dusty morning sunbeams, adopted a bronze sheen where it curled over the collar of his tailored dark green riding coat. Gripped in long fingers was a crop. It and the coffee cup were abruptly discarded onto the kitchen table as he walked towards her.

A large hand rose to comfort her rosy complexion before gathering a thick dusky tress and slipping its silky texture across his palm. 'Do you look like this every morning?'

'No!' she gasped, hurt.

'Pity…' he said, dipping to lingeringly touch his mouth to hers. 'I'd like you to remedy that, Victoria.'

'You…you didn't sleep well at the inn…I can tell,' she breathed. ''Tis why you're here so early. You'd have been better served staying,' she said, keen to distract his attention from her unkempt appearance, yet unwittingly having the reverse effect with her artless comments.

'You're right, I slept ill,' he agreed gently. 'But better than I would had I stayed here with you…' A finger traced the drape of her hair against her delicate bone structure. 'You obviously got your beauty sleep.'

She smiled, her eyes still entrapped by his. 'I…I'll just get dressed. I'll be but a minute…'

'If you must…' he sighed. He returned to the table for his coffee and crop, allowing Victoria the opportunity to nimbly extricate herself from the kitchen. It was only as she was flying back up the stairs that she remembered the puppies and wondered how on earth Hartfield had suddenly acquired them.

* * *

'You bought my papa a present?' The wonder and appreciation in Victoria's tone occasioned a smile from David.

'He seemed keen on having hounds. I thought they might occupy him now you're to be married and won't be dedicating so much time to relations.'

It was a subtle ruling; nonetheless, Victoria acknowledged it with tilted chin and arched dark brows.

David laughed and, avoiding the remnants of their picnic lunch, reclined onto the spread rug. They had chosen an area of springy turf to settle on, close by the lake and bordering woodland that afforded privacy from inquisitive eyes.

The mid-June afternoon was pleasantly warm with a hazy sun that from time to time escaped the cottony clouds to slant gold onto the water.

A razored blade of grass was drawn between thumb and forefinger on its way to slot between even white teeth; then David's hands pillowed his head. 'The bitch in whelp at the Swan seems a docile, obedient sort of animal. I'm sure her pups will follow. Your man Samuel seems good with them; no doubt he'll train them…'

'No matter your motives, Papa is thrilled; and very little pleases him lately. It was very kind and thoughtful of you to remember him.'

He raised himself on one elbow and looked at her through a mesh of dark lashes while lazily expelling the grass onto the ground. 'That sounds like me, Vicky,' he said with studied irony, before a hand snaked out and drew her off balance.

As he rolled expertly to cover her, a muscled thigh wedged instinctively between the softness of hers, parting them, yet she remained unprotesting and wide, trusting eyes gazed up into his handsome, angular face.

David smoothed away stray ebony strands from her face

with reverent fingers. Satisfaction thickened his tone to honey as he murmured, 'You're not frightened, are you? I've been haunted by the fear you would flinch from me now…consider me a sickening rake…'

'I love you, David,' was her simple answer as her head angled away from the tartan rug so her lips could prove it.

'And I love you, Victoria Lorrimer,' he said with a certain amount of wry self-mockery. 'No doubt that's why I'll put up with your flirting and teasing and return you to the house this afternoon as righteous as when you left it.'

Gossamer lids shielded eyes brimming with very female gratification as Victoria savoured the influence she wielded over this rugged, powerful aristocrat. Her arms encircled his neck, pulling him tormentingly close. 'I'd expect no less from such a kind and decent man,' she taunted, and then started to laugh. She laughed with such infectious joy, he started chuckling too.

Jerking her upright, he settled her on his lap. 'Don't push me too far, Vicky,' he softly warned, not wholly in jest. 'I've been a long time without you…too long.'

It was the catalyst that brought them both to brooding a little. Yet neither wanted to speak first and risk ruining this wonderful afternoon.

'Why was that horrible woman here yesterday?' Victoria broke the silence and the first niggling anxiety came tumbling out. 'I recall seeing Petronella Vaughan in London, at the cock-fighting with that ruffian, Toby. And she stared at me that night in such a hateful way. She came here looking for you, didn't she? I know she is one of your mistresses.' The accusation ground out, she chewed at her lip while vainly trying to slip off his lap.

'Petronella Vaughan is Toby's sister. She was Daniel Hart's mistress, not mine.'

Chapter Thirteen

'That's a lie!' whiplashed out of Victoria. Fighting free of his embrace, she faced him, fiery-eyed, on her knees.

'It's the truth, Vicky,' he corrected her. 'Had the blasted woman not come here meddling, you need never have known about it. It was only when sorting out Daniel Hart's financial affairs and draper's bills came to light that I became aware of their liaison myself. Petronella has been dunned for settlement.' He stared at the horizon, unwilling to go into detail, especially as the unpaid merchant happened to be his ex-mistress's father. David had settled the account personally, yet insisting on strict anonymity. He wanted Petronella to believe the draper had given up the chase, not that she'd netted a replacement punter.

His eyes focussed on Victoria's shocked, blank gaze. The revelation of her late husband's paramour hurt her; she was withdrawing from him because of it and that rendered him teeth-grindingly furious. 'Petronella was kept by men in London and Hertfordshire. But I wasn't one of the fools.'

Victoria choked back a retort about his claim to such hauteur.

'You had a platonic marriage…were no proper wife to

the man. Why should his mistress worry you? It's childish to have expected him to live like a monk.'

'I am not childish…' she snapped, incensed by his patronising tone. 'And I guessed that Daniel had…lady friends. Although we never discussed it, I'm sure he knew I was happy he gained such comfort elsewhere. I certainly didn't expect him to live like a monk…'

'While we're talking of a cloistered life… Your father mentioned something very odd…that he'd sent you to a nunnery at Baldock seven years ago.'

'And so he did,' Victoria allowed in a quivering whisper. Nausea bubbled in her throat at the vivid memory of the freezing gothic edifice, the damp, sour smells and withered, crow-like nuns that even now could creep her senses. The two weeks she had been incarcerated in a spartan cell had crawled by like two years.

His daughter was steeped in sin, Charles Lorrimer had confided to the sisters. Her soul's salvation was imperative, he had ruled, and so an indefinite purgatory had commenced. Little that was edible had come her way, yet by the beginning of the fifth day, when her body was racked by cold and hunger, even the unpalatable coarse bread and revolting lukewarm gruel had been welcome. But of all the privation it had been the austere silence, the withdrawal of any human compassion and comfort that had almost broken her.

Despite shivering, she managed to tilt her chin and re-count, 'At first Papa simply banished me to our home in Ware. When he realised I was unrepentant and would never disclaim you, I was sent on to Baldock. But why dwell on it now, all these years later, as though it matters? It bothered you little at the time, when I wrote and told you…begged you to come for me. You didn't even acknowledge my letters before leaving the country—'

The damning accusation was curtailed by a gasp as she

was hauled against him. Blue eyes blazed from a bloodless face. 'Letters? I received not one word from you after you returned to Hertfordshire. Not one word! You barely waited a month before marrying that old man. I was coming back for you, you knew that. I swore, no matter how your father received me, we'd be together. I loved you, dammit! You must have known I needed money before offering for you again.'

Their breathing came in shallow, matching pants as they locked eyes then scanned beloved features, as sure now as they had been seven years ago of the other's fault. Corrosive memories, partially submerged by time and tears, now boiled to the surface and refused to simply drift away.

'Yes, I knew that, and had I believed you would return I would have waited. I would have suffered so for a year or more with just one small sign that you hadn't after all regarded me as some novel infatuation. You asked yesterday why I accused you of abandoning me, yet you must already know: when I wrote in desperation offering to elope with you, to stay with you unwed, to do anything you wanted...' She choked a bitter laugh welling in her sandpaper throat. 'Yes; I would have agreed to be your mistress then. At eighteen I loved and trusted you so much I was prepared to risk everything: losing my family and friends, my reputation... But I heard nothing other than a report that you were travelling in Europe. You ignored me and went gallivanting abroad!' Victoria forced out through a clog of pulsing agony in her throat, 'I never heeded gossip about you then...that you were heartless and wild and dissolute. It's only recently...'

'It's only recently you do,' he finished for her, and grunted a hard laugh that was utterly devoid of humour. 'Goddammit...!' The blasphemy was so guttural and savage, she flinched and twisted away, her eyes squeezing shut. His face sought sheltering hands. 'I swear to you,

Vicky, I never received one letter before I went overseas.' The oath was slowly, vibrantly ground out through his fingers. 'And as for gallivanting...' An amused amazement pitched the words apart. 'Would you like to know how pleasurably my time was spent?

'Wellington was recruiting for a mercenary willing to risk death or torture behind enemy lines. He wanted back one of his generals who had stupidly allowed himself to be taken by the French. My brief was to rescue him if possible, kill him if not, for he held secret information. Three officers had unsuccessfully attempted the mission. The last poor soul was sent back to the allied encampment in several pieces. The French were by then so prepared for the clandestine forays that it had become almost a macabre game.

'At that time fighting was the only skill I possessed. It seemed the answer to my prayers: I was desperate for money...and enough money that your father would never again turn me away. I *was* coming back to buy you...it was the only way.' A hand swiped his jaw and he gazed off into the distance.

'The reward was grown exorbitant...ten thousand pounds...because no further volunteers were forthcoming and because the government believed it would always go uncollected. It was a fool's errand. No one...not even Dickie...considered it possible either the general or I would return. But I knew I'd return.' He twisted a mirthless smile and his voice softened. 'And when I did I wished I hadn't, for they'd been right after all...it *had* been a fool's errand. The day we set foot back on Dover beach Dickie told me you'd married. Did you take them to the post yourself? The letters?' he abruptly, obliquely demanded.

Victoria's face was chalky, her mind numb as she struggled to absorb such devastating news, and her response trickled out, slow and murmured. 'No...I couldn't escape my father's vigilance. Neither could Matilda. For he kept us apart. In his eyes she was equally guilty: a neglectful chaperon who had allowed me too much licence when out socialising. Daniel took the letters and promised me they had been despatched.'

David indicated disbelief and despair with a savage, cynical jerk of head and hands.

'No…it wasn't like that,' Victoria cried. 'Daniel displayed no dislike of you and no real wish to marry me. He did so simply to save me from such a dreadful fate. He was so…' *'Kind and decent'* died on her lips.

Absolute proof of her husband's carnality left her unmoved. It was his choice of sly-eyed partner that astounded her. She continued quietly, 'Daniel first suggested we wed as a ploy to bring me home from the convent. Even then Papa was showing signs of insanity. He was unyielding. Neither my emaciation, my distress nor Daniel's logic moved him. In his mind it was settled and sensible. Either I married his friend or I returned to Baldock.' She sighed. 'It *was* oddly sensible. Daniel and I both knew I needed protection from Papa's derangement. Daniel had sworn never to remarry for true love: that hallowed place in his heart was reserved for Sarah, his first wife. But he held me in great affection. And I was but eighteen and it seemed you no longer wanted me…'

She was spun about by the shoulders in a steely grip that sent her head swaying back, exposing an arc of ivory throat. 'Don't ever say that,' he exploded through barely parted teeth.

But the haunting memories demanded exorcism. Reflexively, she swiped out at his face, in a way mentally practised and perfected over seven years. A cracking blow caught a lean cheek, angry colour tracing her handprint.

Retribution was swift and unexpected. Tipped off balance, she sprawled back onto the rug. Within the same second her mouth was bruised beneath a punishing kiss and predatory hands were stripping her clothes from her body before she had dragged in breath enough to protest.

His hot mouth skimmed from hers, steaming against the exposed thrust of her petite breasts. The pull of ravening lips on creamy flesh was fractionally less than rough and had her gasping. Small hands bunched into spontaneous fists against his torso…but refused to defend her. Slowly they uncurled to lie against ridges of muscle, to clutch, to slide over and explore the contours of a broad back while her breath wedged dizzyingly in her throat. She seemed to float in an odd limbo, awaiting pain or pleasure yet helpless to deny either.

'David…!' His name finally tore from her in pleading censure as her bodice was parted and her skirts raised with such practised speed that she felt virtually naked, yet hadn't shed an item of clothing. Mild summer air cooled her feverish skin; a grazing palm and long, hard fingers splaying to torment both breasts scorched back an exquisite throbbing heat that coursed through her veins like quicksilver.

'Please, David…not like this!' Even as the words sobbed out against his neck, her body was arching pliantly into the skilful seduction.

His mouth and hands stilled, clenching, trembling against her body, a noise of anguish deep in his throat. Her panting, parted mouth was covered by his slanting, hot and moist, across it and he tempered his angry passion with shaking, rigid discipline until he was kissing her with a sensual sweetness. Rolling onto his back, he held her fast to his chest, burying tortured features in tumbling ebony hair. 'God, I'm sorry, Vicky. I'm so sorry for everything,' he choked.

Soothing fingertips swirled softly against the inflamed satin skin of her back where her dress was lost. On sensing her relaxing, snuggling into him, he rasped, 'If I'd known how you suffered then, how you wanted me, I would never have gone away. I would have come for you penniless,' he stressed hoarsely against her cheek. 'I would have killed anyone who tried to stop me...and that includes your father and Daniel Hart. I was hurting too. When I returned from abroad, I believed you'd simply bowed to your father's wishes and easily forgotten me. I thought that you considered me a wastrel. I was in black despair. I felt like death. I tried to find it when they welcomed me back into the army. But for Dickie and his crazy, selfless vigilance—he was always too damn close—no doubt I would never have survived to take up my birthright when Michael died. I never wanted it. But reinstating the Courtenay estates and wealth seemed a punishing task. So I came home.'

His voice softened in wonderment and self-perception. 'Everything I've striven for, the whole grand show of property and wealth, was for your benefit. To flaunt at you what sort of wastrel you'd turned down.'

She ground her face comfortingly against him. 'I missed you so much, David. My grief frightened Daniel...he just didn't know how to console me.'

She was immediately enfolded heart-stoppingly close. 'Neither of us has anything with which to reproach the other,' he said earnestly, urgently. 'We survived all the horror because fate decreed that this be our time...our destiny. It's best we don't talk of it. Nothing can be gained by dwelling on the past and what can't be changed.'

Ignoring his own counsel within seconds, David gritted, 'God! When I think...had those letters been delivered, we could have been married seven years! We might now have had our own family about us...!'

'I must have misdirected them. Anyway, you said you didn't want a family,' was achingly whispered into his shoulder.

The recollection of that antagonistic afternoon elicited a wry, unseen smile. 'I was smarting that afternoon, too,

Vicky…from the moment you made it clear you didn't want me to make love to you. I would have married you within the hour, you know, but for wounded pride. And I've always wanted our children, although it's true I've never wanted an heir for the Courtenays. But then I'm not a Courtenay. I'm actually a bastard, and that makes me feel better.' He stopped her shocked gasp with his lips.

Sitting up with her, he casually smoothed down her skirts and neatened her gaping bodice, talking to her to distract her from her fiery embarrassment. 'My choice is your lilac dress.' His nimble fingers fastened small pearl buttons.

She looked enquiringly at him.

'You asked me yesterday what you should wear to marry. I'd like you to wear that silk dress.' He grazed his lips lightly on hers. 'There's no time for a wedding gown, I'm afraid. I've no intention of delaying for a team of seamstresses to perfect their art.'

He gave her face a last lingering caress and was on his feet in a lithe second and strolling to gaze out over the lake.

After a few moments spent tidying together the bits and pieces of their picnic, Victoria joined him and slipped a hand into his, clasped behind his back.

'I should like my friend Laura to be my matron of honour. Who will act as your groomsman?'

'Dickie's visiting his parents in Bath. I'll ask Sir Peter and hope he'll be agreeable.' His thumb idly fondled the soft palm cupping his. 'I shall need to return to London before we wed. There are various matters…'

'I don't want you to go back there,' Victoria countered fiercely, making him slant a frowning look at her. 'And I don't want us to live there. I want to live here at Hartfield. I'll give you Hartfield as a wedding gift,' she decided, solemn and gracious, 'so you won't ever feel beholden to me for providing our home.'

'I don't mind feeling beholden to you, sweetheart,' he said gently. 'But I'll be damned before I'll be beholden to your first husband, no matter how well the man treated you. If you don't want Beauchamp Place or Hawkesmere, I'll build a new estate in Hertfordshire. Reasonably close by so you'll be able to visit your family at Hartfield. I did promise to maintain it,' he reminded her with a rueful smile. 'But for us I intend a home exclusively ours.'

It was a velvet-voiced promise coupled with a searing look. Her breasts reflexively swelled, tingled; the memory of recent bitter-sweet passion, of her semi-nudity, of her longing for more made her blush and stutter, 'Hawk…Hawkesmere? How could we live there? You no longer own it.'

'I never said that, Vicky,' he mildly contradicted her. 'It was seized by the bank against unpaid debts. But I bought it back about four years ago. I don't know why for I rarely use it. Possibly that's simply to avoid setting eyes on my strumpet mother. I've let her back into the dower house.'

His satirical remark was overlooked. 'You let me offer you Hartfield for hunting and shooting when…when you had that vast Berkshire estate at your disposal? You could hunt there with scores of people if you wished!'

'But I don't wish. I've no happy memories of the place. In four years I've hosted no more than a half-dozen routs. No doubt the wildlife is now as abundant at that accursed pile as it is here.'

'I…I should like to meet your mother, David.'

'No.'

'Why do you hate her so? You allow her to stay at your home, at your expense, yet you make no secret of despising her. That shouldn't be: she is your mama, after all. I'm sure she cares for you…in her own way.'

A grim laugh preceded, 'She certainly introduced Dickie to some of her *own ways* during school holidays when he came to stay. I once stumbled across them…quite literally…in a barn. By then, I understood the "Courtenay Courtesan" well enough: a strapping blond fifteen-year-old stood no chance of eluding her rapacious clutches. I thrashed him anyway. Fifteen years on I still feel guiltier about the beating I gave him that hot August afternoon than I do about rarely visiting my one surviving parent.

'Oh, the Duke of Hawthorne died last year in his seventy-first year. He has a widow and legitimate heirs who are either ignorant of my connection or choose to be. But I accept now that he was genuinely fond of me: he bequeathed me some touchingly personal mementoes. He was a kind and decent man, Vicky,' he said, with a wry smile at the horizon. His voice became husky with emotion he no longer strove to conceal. 'With his money and faith and my tireless ambition I showed us both that I could be a nobleman's son as well as a harlot's.'

After barely a moment's heady silence, he had regained his ironic impartiality. 'So…we're back to my dear mama. My Berkshire neighbours describe her as a virtual recluse. She'll no doubt survive another score or more.'

Victoria's slender hands comfortingly squeezed his. She chanced a glance up at his impassive profile. 'After we are married, I *shall* meet your mother, David,' she announced firmly.

He strode abruptly away from the sun-glinting lake, forcing her, hand imprisoned in his, to skip and trot after him back to their lunch.

With David carrying the picnic things, they started wading back, through long, clinging grass, towards Hartfield.

'I'm not discussing it further,' was his tardy, autocratic ruling. Anticipating her pique, he deftly deflected it. 'Why don't you want me to go back to London?'

Unwilling to voice jealous suspicions that he might allow himself to be waylaid in Cheapside, and, furthermore, irked that he wanted confirmed what she was sure he already knew, she remained stubbornly silent and turned to gaze over the undulating verdant landscape that comprised Hartfield's acres.

'Are you worried Petronella might come back?'

Victoria gave a brief nod; it was the truth, after all, if not her prime motive for wanting him to stay in Hertfordshire.

'You won't have to deal with her, Vicky. I'll see to the scheming...' His abuse tailed off into a smile. 'Daniel Hart left her nothing but outstanding debts...she's only out for dibs. I'll deal with her.'

'I think that's what she's hoping...that you will deal with her,' Victoria muttered caustically.

'You have to trust me now, Vicky,' he said quietly, making Victoria marvel at his acute hearing...or perceptiveness. 'You told me once a husband should have his wife's respect and I want yours. I want your trust and your respect, just as you have mine.'

'Will you be visiting Cheapside when you go back?' spilled out helplessly.

'Have you a message for Emma you want me to deliver?' He blandly met her question with one of his own.

Victoria dug a forceful heel into the springy turf and swished to glare...to accuse him of being deliberately flippant.

He meandered on alone a few paces before pivoting and continuing backwards. Well aware of her seething indignation and its source, he halted. 'Well, have you? I've no other need to visit that part of town. Since you went to London looking for me the only time I've been to Cheapside is to visit you at the Worthingtons'.'

She slowly approached him, storm-grey eyes scanning his face for deceit.

'Where else have you been, then?' she burst out audaciously.

'Nowhere.'

Her darting, doubtful eyes prompted some self-mockery. 'I've told you, Vicky, you're ridiculously civilising. Ridiculously satisfying, too,' he allowed with a wry smile. 'You're all I want. Retiring from London to live a sedate country life with you is actually wonderfully appealing.' He transferred the wicker basket and a liberated arm pulled her close.

'In that case,' Victoria said contentedly, hugging into him, 'I would like you to take a letter to Emma; although if I know Emma she may not be as surprised as she ought to be at our news.'

'There's something about Miss Worthington's acerbic wit that Dickie finds fascinating. It's as well they're not to attend our wedding. It might not be the quiet, dignified affair I'm hoping for.'

'There will be gossip of our unseemly haste, you know,' Victoria mentioned on a sigh. 'We will scandalise society by marrying so soon after Daniel's death.'

'Scandalising society is what I do best, sweetheart,' David replied drily. 'Society expects no less of me. In fact...' he adopted a contemplative look '...perhaps we ought to really flout protocol by waiting the customary year to wed...by which time you'll be well on the way to producing our first-born.'

'David!' Victoria shrieked, giving his arm a spontaneous slap.

'Actually, it's not inconceivable, Vicky. If it's what you want, I'll pander to etiquette and postpone the wedding...but the wedding night goes ahead as planned on Saturday.'

'You just wouldn't dare...' she primly provoked him.

'Invite me to stay here tonight,' he challenged softly.

She tilted her rosy face to his, about to bluff, but the words died on her lips. Their eyes merged, strained and her heart fluttered crazily behind her ribs. It was all she could do to shield her confusion with his shoulder. 'Well, really...!' she muttered, with an outraged laugh.

'Come, be fair, sweet,' he gently mocked. 'It's been seven years...'

'You may kiss your bride..' Jonathan Woodbridge announced, beaming over knobbly knuckles.

Victoria turned a blissful, radiant countenance up to her husband's and thought she had never seen him look more heart- stoppingly handsome...or youthful. Languid cynicism was nowhere to be seen.

With unabashed adoration and pride in brilliant blue eyes, David inclined towards her and a reserved peck threatened to become embarrassingly more. On hearing her aunt's delighted squeal, Victoria gripped at his charcoal velvet sleeve. 'Please don't,' she whispered against his warm, sensual mouth. 'I do believe Aunt Matilda might start to clap!'

The newly-weds turned to the congregation. Victoria's shining eyes swept over the few friends and neighbours who had managed to attend at such short notice. They settled on her papa, dressed in his finest and dozing on the wooden pew, a black furry coil by each of his feet.

'Oh, I told him to leave the pups outside,' she whispered to her husband on a giggle.

They made their leisurely way from the chapel, passing an abundance of stone urns frothing with scented summer flowers. Drawing level with Hartfield's servants, Victoria bestowed on them an exclusive, fond smile. Samuel beamed back, Edith nodded sagely to herself, and Beryl and Sally, as one, dipped heads, dabbed eyes then clung to each other's arms.

On stepping from the sun-gilded chapel vestibule into balmy June air, rice and petals suddenly showered down, making the newly-weds duck and share a smile. Villagers whooped and cheered, laughing children skipping forward to shyly scatter painstakingly collected fragrant posies onto dry earth.

As soon as word had spread of Mrs Hart's nuptials, and the eminence of her prospective bridegroom, plans to honour the occasion had begun. The consensus of opinion about Ashdowne was that there was none more deserving of such marvellous good fortune.

Most local families had at one time benefitted from her generosity. Tenants' hardships were never ignored by the young mistress: a bushel of apples, a churn of milk, a plump hen brought along by Samuel Prescott when none was to be had at home.

Yet no one sought to take advantage of her humanity despite knowledge of her forbearance on late rents. Or perhaps because of it. Her philanthropy was too precious to be tested and each knew his neighbour's wrath would be lethal should her sympathies be withdrawn because of calumny. For fair she might be, fool she certainly was not.

During the late master's sickness it had become common knowledge that Hartfield would founder were it not for the canny thrift and selflessness of the young mistress up at the big house.

As a widow, her threatening financial ruin had prompted many a villager to sadly ponder when government by an assuredly less caring landlord would begin. Yet even thus burdened, the lady was charitable. Lace had been sent by Mrs Hart only last month to prettify the Harvey girl's dimity bridal gown. And fine it looked too, despite many a respectable matron reckoning it better employed trimming the layette as it never could trim that swollen belly.

Sheila Harvey waddled forward, one sturdy hand mid-back, the other strewing lilac by the churchyard gate.

Labourers ranged against the drystone wall lobbed saucy advice over their wives' chatter. The urbane groom received these helpful tips with a suppressed smile and a gracious dip of his gleaming chestnut head.

Gay, gregarious guests began trailing the shingle path towards the house, yet Victoria hesitated. She was put oddly in mind of a sombre procession some months ago. No sun or joy was to be had during that hard march back to Hartfield.

Tapered white fingers touched her dewy spray of pastel roses laced with fern. Appealing eyes rose to her husband's face as her arm slipped from his. He glanced towards the headstones, then a small smile accompanied an indulgent, sanctioning nod.

David turned away to Sir Peter's congratulatory handshake and back-slapping and his wife Laura's delicate peck, while his new bride gently laid her wedding bouquet on her dead husband's grave.

Squinting hazel eyes watched the poignant gesture. A puckered brow furrowed further and a rough hand raked through unkempt brown hair before swiping a bristly chin. The stranger's eyes were held by the dainty figure in lilac silk and the tall, distinguished man who watched her so proprietorially. The couple commenced walking with their guests towards the big house in the distance and his hazel eyes were with them every step. As conversation and laughter wafting back on a balmy breeze became ever more muted, the man stepped from behind the shielding oak. Skirting trees and bushes for cover, he ran in the same direction as the wedding party.

'I believe this to be as unconventional a marriage as ever could be, sir,' Victoria solemnly judged, then concealed her impish smile with a sip of wine.

'I assure you, my dear, this alliance will be anything but…' David softly countered, helplessly rising to the bait.

'A viscount married to an impoverished widow, a wedding breakfast served on the lawn, all levels of society mingling and dancing until dusk, boisterous village children frolicking with two madcap black puppies… Not to mention the bride's father a-snooze in a chair under the influence of a summer moon, or her aunt a-snooze under the influence of barley wine…' Victoria tutted at the catalogue of chaos yet had never felt more serenely happy as she surveyed her tenants, her servants and legitimate guests celebrating their marriage. It seemed as though every local family had come to bless them and had thus been casually invited to partake of a little refreshment before departing. Only none had gone away.

Musicians and a superb feast had been supplied by the proprietor of the Swan tavern—who also had been reluctant to return to his posting house.

Edith's ruffled feathers had soon been smoothed when Victoria had explained that, far from doubting her ability to provide an equal buffet, David and she wished all the servants to have a holiday on the occasion of their mistress's wedding.

Long, firm fingers covered Victoria's soft, slender ones resting lightly on the banquet table. 'Would you like to dance again?'

She slid him a smiling negative look. Lacing her fingers round his, she abruptly raised their joined hands, declining Laura's mute invitation for them to join in the Barley Mow with her and Squire Lennox. Edith grabbed Samuel's brawny forearms where his shirt-sleeves had been flung back, urging him to partner her in the set.

'Would the Duke of Hawthorne have liked to see his

noble son married amid such happy disarray?' she mused, not wholly mocking.

'He would have liked to see me so happy,' David mildly remarked, 'or I knew him, after all, not at all.' He looked at her with heavy-lidded black eyes and smiled as he watched his sensual scrutiny stripping her of mischief. A sweet self-consciousness stung colour into her porcelain complexion and silky, dusky lashes fanned the sudden shyness in her eyes.

'Now…how to get some peace and quiet, for the hour is getting late…'

David gently broached the subject and watched her fine-boned face positively glow. But she raised limpid eyes to his and gave her answer with a diffident smile and the single word, 'Yes.'

A large hand cupped one side of her fiery complexion, his thumb smoothing a cheekbone, his fingers shaking slightly as the strength of his love and need became enervating. He was about to speak when something glimpsed at the corner of his eye caused him to frown.

If the man was too timid to join in with the others, why didn't he simply take himself off instead of lurking about in the bushes? If he was up to no good, he would be well advised to conceal himself professionally. He made a mental note to find Bennett and get him to check him out.

Glancing away, sapphire eyes were drawn to a beautiful, demure profile and all thoughts of a stranger's odd antics were lost. Anticipation of his wedding night rampaged through his mind, battering his body into a state of throbbing urgency, no matter how hard he tried to impose further patience and distraction. David guessed it to be close to ten of the clock and he wanted Victoria to himself. His whole being felt riddled with an inflexible tension.

With a subtle, pre-arranged signal to his groomsman, Sir Peter and Laura Grayson were soon courteously carrying out their duties. Within moments the first of the revellers came to congratulate the blushing bride and graciously patient groom before departing merrily across the fields.

'Of course they can accompany you, Papa,' Victoria reassured her father. 'See, Samuel already has them safely on leads.'

Charles Lorrimer's weary sigh of contentment preceded his finally allowing his son-in-law to help him into Sir Peter's coach. Samuel followed with two exhausted, panting puppies, one beneath each strong arm, leads dangling superfluously from velvety throats.

Matilda approached her niece unsteadily. Her face looked wine-blotchy even with moonlight *maquillage*. Dabbing at her eyes, she hugged Victoria and then unceremoniously crushed her new nephew to her bosom too. Once aboard the coach with the others, a discreet yet determined hand-flick from the bridegroom had the conveyance, at last, swaying away.

At Sir Peter's insistence, and with David's blessing and eternal gratitude, just a skeleton staff were to stay at Hartfield while the rest of the household sojourned at Sir Peter's residence until Wednesday.

With a firm arm about Victoria's shoulders David turned them towards the house, mentally noting that he owed the master of Willowthorpe a great favour.

'Would you like some wine, Vicky?' David asked in a strangely formal tone.

She glanced over at him, from where she was relaxing into the drawing-room sofa, and as the decanter chimed discordantly against a glass she realised he was, unbelievably, in need of reassurance that she was ready to retire. His touching restraint subdued a natural nervous anticipation of her first night spent as a proper wife. With a private smile, she rose to slip a comforting arm through his, hugging into his side.

'No, thank you. I'm a little tired. It's been a hectic... exciting...perfect day. But now I want to go to bed,' she murmured, laying her face against his charcoal velvet sleeve to conceal the blood suffusing her face.

David's eyes closed and he said on a groaning laugh, 'Me too.' He abruptly abandoned the glass and decanter and pulled her around in front of him. As she tilted her face to his, sapphire eyes adored every plane, every hollow, her complexion's usual alabaster tone peachy in the candlelight.

'Did I tell you how beautiful you look today?' he asked hoarsely.

'Several times.' She subtly thanked him with a dip of burnished ebony curls and a whimsical lowering of dusky lashes.

'You look rather ravishing yourself,' she murmured, her soft mouth slowly curving and ten fingers sweeping over the luxurious pile on his dark velvet sleeves. A solitary digit flicked through the ruffles on his snowy shirt. It trailed up an amethyst silk cravat to absently polish a candle-sparking diamond. 'Thank you for making today so marvellous: for allowing the local people to stay awhile and celebrate with us. I...I admit I wasn't expecting you to. I thought you might be annoyed so many came and wish to limit the celebration to those few formally invited. I had no idea the villagers would find out so quickly or stay so long.'

'Is that what you thought?' he asked softly. 'That I would deny your tenants paying wedding-day homage to the finest lady in the land? Adam Holdbrook told me they so style you. And also that you've tolerated his rent arrears. It's quite a sum. Had you attempted to call in that debt before travelling to Hammersmith last week?'

'No,' Victoria said simply. As she watched pride and

love and desire fire his eyes to brilliance, she added lightly, 'Something in me always trusts your integrity. Even when I'm defenceless or I hear scandalous gossip I can't extinguish the faith that you are an honourable man. I've kept and cherished that faith for seven years. Had I ever truly believed you would mistreat me, I should never have journeyed to Hammersmith. I just knew you'd rescue me, David. I just knew it.' She went onto tiptoe and soft lips caressed a hard cheek. 'You're your father's son. My trusty hero…my one love…my kind and decent man.'

Chapter Fourteen

Viscountess Courtenay turned her lovely face to the heavens and admired the stars bejewelling a lapis lazuli sky. So many and so bright…as though each one had buffed up for her perfect day.

And so it had been. From the minute of her early morning rising, through the fuss and excitement of her maids and Matilda dressing her and getting her to the chapel, to waving the last of her guests on their way home, everything had been idyllic. And now… A slender hand trailed her throat at the thought of her husband's imminent arrival in her chamber…in their chamber, she corrected herself with a small smile. The yearning for him to come to her made her eyelids droop and caused her to sway dreamily.

As she glanced down at her skimpy negligée a sudden twinge of modesty made her don her more substantial cotton wrap over the froth of snowy satin and lace.

This morning Matilda had miraculously produced this gossamer scrap with an elaborate flourish. A blush had then rejuvenated her wrinkled cheeks as Victoria had raised amused brows, tacitly enquiring as to its provenance.

With a swing of loose, silky black hair she turned daintily from the velvet-skied panorama at the very same moment that a male voice whispered urgently, 'Victoria!'

An indrawn rush of breath signalled a reflexive scream.

'Don't s-scream! For God's s-sake don't s-scream. You'll get me killed…' The muffled moan was in an eerily familiar voice.

'Justin…?' exploded from Victoria in a murmur of disbelief.

He stepped close to the guttering candle by the bed so she could properly see him. Not that she would have recognised him, even in daylight. She would have passed her cousin in the street without a second glance. It was his slight speech impediment which reintroduced him after eleven years' absence.

'Justin…?' she again queried croakily as an air of surreality took hold and she glided closer to him. 'Why on earth didn't you send word you would be coming? Why are you creeping about? Where in God's name have you been for so long?'

'I look awful, I know,' he gruffly, obliquely volunteered. His fingers raked his tousled hair as he anticipated her distaste at his dishevelment. 'I had to c-come and tell you, and today in c-case he finds out. God only knows what he'll do to me. I thought if I came and told you…you m-might be able to b-break it to him g-gently. But I'm to b-blame and I'd b-better own up.' He grunted a noise hinting at guffaw and groan. 'I've heard he's unfor-forgiving to those that cross him…and a crack shot and nifty with a b-blade, too, and he's s-sparred with Ajax…'

Victoria sped towards him then and shook him into silence. She squinted up into his forlorn face, noting the lines of maturity and worry scored around his mouth and the deep furrows tracking his forehead. But his hazel eyes and matted, mousy hair were achingly familiar and further interrogation died on her lips. She hugged him round the neck. 'I imagined you dead and felt guilty for doing so. Aunt Matilda always believed you simply at sea and that you would one day return... Oh, no! You have just missed her... She has only just departed for Willowthorpe...' Victoria cried in anguish.

'Thank God!' Justin declared with such guttural vehemence, Victoria stepped back to stare at him.

'Have you been at sea?'

Justin looked about miserably before nodding. 'I ran off. I c-couldn't see Mama s-scrimp and s-scrape to buy me a c-commission. I decided to s-start at the b-bottom.' He twisted a smile at his rapt-faced cousin.

'And how did you do?' she whispered.

'A commission would have been easier,' he said with fluent irony, and turned away to stare out of the window.

Because, even with this astonishing turn of events, she couldn't put her husband from her mind for more than a few seconds at a time, Victoria bubbled, 'Come, I have someone wonderful I want you to meet. Today I was married to a most fine gentleman and I love him so much.'

Replete with sudden overwhelming joy and gratitude at this marvellous addition to her previously perfect day, she turned in the doorway, embraced him again and said, 'Oh, I can't tell you how glad I am you're here.'

'Try telling me instead, my dear,' invited a coldly ironic voice.

Frowning at the disturbing edge to her husband's voice, Victoria nevertheless greeted him with soft pleasure. 'Oh, there you are, David. We were just coming to find you.'

'Indeed?'

One silky, single word, yet it erased Victoria's smile. 'I know how bizarre this must look, David, but—'

'On the contrary, my dear—' he sliced through her explanatory preamble '—it's the sort of scenario I'm well used to. I was reared watching grubby strangers sidling from Hawkesmere's bedrooms.'

David's glittering blue gaze flicked back to Justin, noting his nervous twitching and his eyes darting about for escape routes. The mangy little weasel looked and acted guilty as hell. And his wife looked…so beautiful and innocent and utterly desirable that he felt the heat and tension suddenly shift from his torso to his loins. Clenched fists shoved into his pockets to try and disguise his discomfort…and impede their use on this stranger who was…who was what? Intending to cuckold him? Was that what he really believed?

I want your trust and respect, just as you have mine. The words hauntingly mocked him. He'd told Victoria that mere days ago, while rambling through a halcyon meadow. He suddenly felt every kind of idiotic, jealous fool for allowing insidious childhood memories to make him ever suspect that this unsavoury-looking specimen might be a love-lorn beau. Perhaps he was a bashful tenant with no sense of protocol. Or perhaps, if he asked, he might damn well find out.

'Aren't you going to introduce us, Victoria?' His tone was cool and controlled and vastly at odds with the blistering blue gaze wandering her slender, night-robed body, causing her to blush.

'Yes, yes, of course,' she agreed in breathy confusion. 'My cousin, Justin Sweeting, has arrived. He is Matilda's son, and she has departed for Willowthorpe without realising him here. She will be beyond upset to have missed him.'

'Indeed, she will,' David endorsed, all smooth sympathy. 'I myself am beyond upset…that he didn't accompany her. But no doubt he has some perfectly reasonable explanation for secreting himself in your room rather than make his presence known to me.' A deal of the scorn was directed at himself: he'd forgotten to get Bennett to accost the interloper earlier in the evening. Had he done so, none of this damnable lunacy would have come about. The irony choked a harsh laugh in his throat.

The chilling sound transformed Justin's uneasiness into real apprehension: the belated realisation hit home that stealing into Victoria's room for a private tête-à-tête had been hideously ill-conceived. He commenced a surreptitious slink along the corridor wall, intending to put as much distance as possible between himself and the frustrated bridegroom. Two brown hands stuck out, shaking, in front of him. 'L-listen t-to m-me. I—I'm s-s-sorry. I—I c-c-can explain,' he stuttered helplessly.

'I hope I can take your word for that,' David drawled as he approached Victoria. A firm arm about her slender shoulders immediately drew her close. He felt her light tremor and then the pressure of her innocently tantalising body seeking warmth and comfort from his. An involuntary groan made his wife tilt her face up to his with sweet concern, and his other arm enclosed her too. They shared a private smile before his narrow-eyed attention sliced over her glossy, dark head at yet another of her vexing relatives.

'Perhaps we should all remove to the parlour and you can let me know what major catastrophe forced you to skulk in my wife's bedroom.'

As Justin scuttled past David towards the stairs, Victoria tightened her fingers about her husband's broad palm and made immediately to follow.

The rather lengthy lapse which kept Justin kicking his heels in the hallway, awaiting the arrival of the newly-weds, went unremarked upon. The rather hectic flush enhancing his cousin's beautiful face went, intentionally, unobserved. Justin stared determinedly along the shadowy corridor. Then, on David's brusque instruction, he meekly entered the nearest room.

'I...I'd s-sooner s-speak to Vicky alone, my l-lord,' Justin pleaded as he perched, fidgeting, on a fireside chair in the small parlour. 'I-it after all c-concerns her late h-husband's affairs.'

'Which are now mine.' David slickly denied him. Whipping a high-backed chair from the breakfast table, he spun it about and seated himself astride it. 'I'm all yours,' he dulcetly drawled, euphemistically challenging his dismayed cousin-in-law to give him one good reason why he shouldn't knock his teeth down his throat.

A frantic, hangdog look arrowed Victoria's way. A helpless shrug met his entreaty; but she smiled encouragingly for him to begin as she settled in a chair opposite him by the hearth.

Justin raked back a tangle of mousy corkscrews from his brow. He stared into rusty-black embers flaking ash into the grate. He squinted at the candles, guttering in their sockets on the mantel. He tried to whizz his eyes past glittering arctic-blue shards that pinned him to his chair…but his flying gaze was caught and held fast.

Dark brows languidly rose in a deliberate display of impatience.

'I stole the money collected for the insurance premium on the dockside warehouse,' streamed out perfectly pronounced.

Victoria simply frowned and then, as comprehension dawned, she jerked forward to the edge of her seat, mirroring her cousin's pose. 'You stole the insurance premium that would have compensated for Daniel's goods destroyed in the fire?'

Justin wobbled his head up and down. 'I—I s-swear I never knew your h-husband had a s-stake in the d-depot. I—I was out of c-credit. So I g-gambled a b-bit b-but landed even d-deeper in Queer S-street. I—I s-secured a position with a shipping c-clerk. The p-policy renewal was my duty, and the f-fifty guineas was so t-tempting. It was only m-meant to be a little l-loan until the b-bully boys were off my b-back. I just never got a ch-chance to pay it b-back in time. The f-fire...' He swung his head wretchedly. 'I've b-been in hiding s-since M-March.'

Victoria's appalled gaze flew to David; but his expression seemed no different now than it had been before he'd learned he had discharged over forty thousand pounds of her debts because of her cousin's fraud. He settled backwards on the dining chair, rested his hands on its back and perused them thoughtfully.

Justin's hazel eyes sheepishly strayed to Victoria. 'S-Sorry, Vicky,' he mumbled. 'I'll p-pay b-back...' He fell silent, gesturing despair.

A sardonic blue gaze bored into the side of Justin's head. 'How many centuries do you intend to survive?' The derision contained more than a hint of genuine humour.

Fighting to surface through a quagmire of numbing shock, Victoria finally forced out, 'Have you any idea, Justin, exactly how much that theft of fifty guineas devastated us? How vulnerable we all were? The cost of it all...?'

A grimy, grimacing face dropped into shielding hands. 'I don't think I want to know. It must have been a g-good few th- thousands, I'll warrant.'

'Try forty...' A mocking smile acknowledged Justin's immediately revealed expression of profound horror. David's blue gaze skimmed on towards Victoria, but her pallid, heart-shaped face was averted immediately, allowing their eyes to barely graze.

'How much did it cost you, Vicky?' he demanded softly. 'More than money? More than Hartfield? More than you're truly willing to give?'

'No!' she cried, swinging to face him in a ripple of ebony silk. 'No, of course not! I'm just so sorry that you...that you paid so much...so generously...for what was, after all, a disaster of my own family's making.' Small white teeth clamped on her unsteady bottom lip while she sought more words to express her chagrin. Instead of uttering them she, and the parlour's other two occupants, stared at the door as, impossibly, Matilda's voice became audible amid clacking footsteps.

With a curse and a gesture of sheer exasperation and disbelief David flung aside his chair and was, within a moment, in the hall.

'Ah…you are still up,' Matilda greeted him. Then, with a discreet cough, she added, 'I imagined you might have already retired.'

'Me too…' David said with such arrant sarcasm in his tone and smile that Matilda stared at him, slack-mouthed.

'Is Vicky there?' she finally enquired, recovering composure and peering past his obstructing muscular breadth into the lighted parlour. 'Her papa is being the most tiresome creature imaginable.'

Matilda swept past him and into the room. She peeled off leather gloves which were then tossed theatrically onto the polished mahogany breakfast table. 'He's forgotten his spectacles,' she announced. 'It matters not that he'll not read nor see anything much till daylight; he wants them now and no other time will do. Samuel is having a devil of a job trying to restrain him at Willowthorpe. Determined to march back in the dark, he was, to fetch them, if you please, and walk those infernal mongrels with him.'

'They're thoroughbreds…' David neutrally imparted from his stance by the doorway. He leaned back against the frame, seeming quite nonchalant with his long, black-clad legs casually braced and his arms crossed over the pristine ruffles of his shirt. He threw his head back and his hands shoved into his pockets for a brief instant. They withdrew almost immediately and one began idly loosening his silk cravat, while the other eased the knot between his eyes.

It was that quiet, telling gesture that at last jolted Victoria from her trance, to quickly offer, 'I'll fetch them. They're probably hidden in the side of his armchair.' She glided towards the door, her mind dominated by the chaos she knew her father was capable of wreaking. And Sir Peter and Laura had so kindly, so considerately offered him their hospitality. In a way she wished he had returned with Matilda, then she could, as usual, have taken the brunt of his choler on herself.

As she drew level with David he caught her wrist, preventing her leaving. The mingling of bleak humour, murder and tenderness in his eyes made her disregard all propriety, all duty. She swayed against him, muffling a sob with his shoulder.

Soothing fingers threaded through her hair, lovingly cradling her against him.

Matilda watched them fondly. A little wedding-night tantrum never hurt any new bride, was her sage thinking, and she felt it prudent to let them in on that. She would have added to her nuptial wisdom but a movement by the fire caught her eye and had her curiously approaching, candelabra aloft.

She squinted down at her prodigal son, who in turn did his best to conceal his identity by wearily hanging his head.

'Justin!' she screeched, plonking down the candles on the mantel so swiftly that the flames elongated almost to extinction. 'What do you mean by arriving unannounced? You've missed the best of the day. We had a feast... dancing, and now you come when there's nothing left to do but retire for the night.'

Lifting a tangled lock of hair from his eyes, she waggled it about. 'Were you beset by highwaymen? Is that why you look like the cat dragged you in? Is that why you're too late for the celebrations? And how did you find out about the wedding, in any case? It's all been so rushed and hushed. Well, no matter. It was very clever of you.' She twisted about to share her maternal pride with the newly-weds before recommencing her interrogation. 'Well, did you follow your papa's salty steps into the navy? I guessed you had that brine-lust rampaging in your veins too, and couldn't wait longer. But what you have to bear in mind, Justin, is that it's been eleven years, and I've been a bit worried…'

Justin suddenly sprang from his chair, making Matilda leap back, and then the two of them were locked in an embrace which carried them about twice before they broke free.

'Now come along,' Matilda sniffed, all businesslike, pressing her eyes with her fingers. 'This won't do. Charles wants his spectacles or he'll bleat the night through and keep us all from our beds.'

Justin trailed after his mother into the hallway, unsure where he was headed, but certainly glad to be putting distance between himself and Lord Courtenay.

His mother determined his destination for him. 'You shall sojourn at Willowthorpe with us all, Justin. How thrilled dear Laura and Sir Peter will be with this news.' She swished back to David and Victoria and offered them both a shrivelled cheek. Satisfactorily saluted, she was, within a moment, heading off towards the drawing room with Justin in tow, and a cheerful aside that had David grinding his teeth again. 'Come, do hurry. Sir Peter's coachman will think I've decided to overnight here…'

It wasn't until the sound of the great door being slammed echoed through the building that Victoria stirred. Disengaging herself, she backed away, suddenly awkwardly aware of her *déshabillé*. But her onerous duty to family members, still undischarged, disturbed her the most.

'Matilda is so pleased to see him.' She quietly broke the heady silence. 'She would be devastated to discover he had so jeopardised us all…'

'I know.' David watched her intently: her fingers twisting together, her lowered face, the way she was distancing herself from him. He silently cursed as he dropped into the chair Victoria had recently vacated.

Picking a log from the basket, he sent it into the dying fire a little too forcefully. The crash and sputtering blaze drew Victoria's immediate, startled attention. And from there it was but a little way to entrapment by those demanding dark eyes. Long, lean fingers slowly extended, inexorably inviting her towards him.

Victoria hesitated, without knowing why she did, and her heart started a slow, hard hammering.

'Please…' David coaxed softly.

She went to him at once and slipped a hand on his. He brushed a thumb across the platinum wedding band and glistening oval diamond before catching at her wrist and urging her down. She sank between his spaced feet, kneeling in front of him with her loose black hair and the whiteness of her skin and nightrobe honeyed by leaping flames.

'Do you want me to apologise?'

'Why?' Her head tipped back and forlorn grey eyes met warm blue. 'It is I who should apologise, David, for the…the devious behaviour of one of my own relatives. And all for fifty guineas! Forty thousand pounds for a paltry…' She quavered into silence, blinking rapidly at the fire, then whispered, 'I'm so ashamed!'

David's hands fastened about her waist and he abruptly lifted her onto his lap, settling back into the armchair with her.

'Well, I think I ought to apologise, too,' he said with gallant soft humour. 'You know I was sorely tempted to hit him, don't you? And just for one insane moment, when I saw you embrace him by your bedroom door, I imagined he might be an admirer…'

A slender finger was placed on his lips and she nestled

her head against his shoulder. 'I'm beginning to wish you had hit him. God knows, he deserves it.' She stared into the fire for a moment then whispered, 'I'm so sorry, David. He's ruined our perfect day.'

David gently turned her face up to his. 'No, he hasn't. He hasn't ruined our day…or our night. Initially you were very pleased to see him. So that pleases me, and I'm glad I've met him.'

Her lids flicked up, grey eyes searching his face for irony.

'It's true…' he said with a slow, heart-stopping smile. 'I would have preferred he'd arrived at the appointed hour with the rest of the guests…but that's families for you, Vicky: they can be the most tiresome lot.'

A fond finger caressed her cheek. 'While we're talking of kith and kin…your father's affliction will never cure, you know; would that it might. There's another forty thousand for such a physician…' He smiled at her expression, then added gently, 'But you don't have to cope alone now, sweetheart. It's my problem too.'

His trailing finger lulled her as she stared solemnly into mellow flames. 'I'm only just fully appreciating what you've had to contend with for years. When Daniel was ill too it must have been quite hellish.' His lips replaced his finger at her face. 'You're amazing, you know. You're beautiful, courageous, loyal, selfless…and that makes me ashamed when I think how easily I've neglected my own mother. I've felt no twinge of filial duty. And whatever my mother is…or was…I should have.'

She twisted on his lap, hugging him about the neck, enveloping him with soft, rose-perfumed skin and silky black hair. 'You're always so…so…honest, David, and so generous. And I feel so lucky to have you. I don't know how ever we…I can repay you.'

'And that's the main reason I must own to feeling

ashamed, Vicky,' David said hoarsely. Gently disengaging himself from her embrace, he cupped her fragile face with a determined hand, so she was unable to avoid his penetrating gaze. 'I make you nervous sometimes, don't I? Frighten you a little? Even now, when we're married, you retreat from me.'

Her eyes welded to his, watching pain darken the midnight velvet of his eyes, yet she could not sincerely deny it.

'I'm not blaming you, Vicky,' he huskily reassured her. 'I'm begging forgiveness. For from the moment you were back in my life and I realised that, incredibly, I still wanted and loved you there was a subtle need to punish you. Not only for seven-year-old wounds but for new hurts and slights. I'd believed myself content, yet could no longer ignore just how sordid and shallow my life was.

'I was loath to admit to such regrets because I was convinced you were disgusted by me but tolerated me simply out of duty to your family...to provide financial protection. I couldn't bear that...not with you. I wanted you to love me back. So I hurt you back in, I imagine, the self-deluding way of all arrogant, frustrated males—by preying... controlling...conquering.

'I'd believed myself invincible; I can brawl, fence, shoot, yet you slew me that night in Hammersmith. I'll never forget the sight of you standing in that room, so proud yet vulnerable, full of courage yet trembling. When I got close and saw your eyes huge with rage and fear...and hurt...I knew I had succeeded...but lost. Your grief was so raw, I felt like dying. For you wouldn't have been so sad if you hadn't after all cared for me a little...'

Victoria flung her arms back about his neck and her warm tears trickled between them, dissolving that last subtle barrier.

'Had I not coerced you, you wouldn't now offer to repay

me. And that's what frightens *me*, Vicky—that you might still believe there exists between us some venal contract.'

She combed her fingers through his long hair. 'All I give is freely given, David. No terms, no bargains,' she choked in a voice husky with emotion. 'If your truthfulness…your generosity…your restraint is depraved then I want more. I love your immorality. I love everything about you. You suit me perfectly. You're the most kind and decent man I've known in my life. She sniffed a little laugh, then said brightly, 'So, you truly don't mind losing all that money?'

'You're my wife…I accepted your debts when we wed…of course I don't mind.' And because he knew the matter needed airing before she would allow it to be buried, he said lightly, 'Besides, what else would I do with it? Buy a dress coach and matching two pair? Gamble it away at White's? Install a whore or two each end of town?'

He stood abruptly with her in his arms, then placed her back on the chair and sat on the edge of it. Soothing fingers slid along her jaw to spear softly into ebony hair and make her look at him. 'You said you loved my honesty,' he reminded her wryly, lifting a pale, slender hand and touching the palm to his lips.

'There's something I have to tell you about that, Vicky…why it's unimportant and I don't want you to dwell on any of it. For it's all as nothing and long finished. The fire a man cools in his loins can be insignificant and separate to what burns in his heart.' Then, on a wry smile, he added, 'In fact it's almost as though the two parts are destined never to unite. At times, I've hoped they might, to fill the emptiness, but…'

'You're lonely?' A husky catch to her voice displayed her poignant concern.

His mouth trailed a lingering reward across her upturned face. 'Not now. Now I've got you. But, excepting Dickie, I've remained unattached most of my life. Apart from a blissful six-month interlude seven years ago, that is, when I first felt that heat in my chest and discovered it to be infinitely sweeter than any harlot's artifice.'

She moved a small hand to rest it against his breast, the pounding rhythm beneath it quivering her fingers, then angled back her face to look into his velvet eyes. 'And I started that blaze in your heart?' she demanded softly.

His dark head inclined until he was smiling against her mouth. 'You managed to set two fires at the same time, sweetheart. Quite a trick. Magical,' he whispered, and their laughter dissolved in a kiss.

Chapter Fifteen

'Look at me, Victoria.'

Silky, dusky lashes fanned his cheek as she did his bidding.

'What's the matter?' David murmured as coal-black eyes probed hers. 'Are you nervous?' he asked gently on a feather-light kiss.

'No.' She smiled brightly up at him, her hands sweeping up satin-coated muscle to rest lightly on his shoulders.

That's a lie! she wailed inwardly. Tell him what bothers you. But she couldn't! Everything was now so right between them. She couldn't bear it if he again deemed her childish.

Yet the more she reasoned it irrational, the more anxious she became. The contours of her husband's firmly muscled naked torso braced, barely touching, yet infinitely purposeful, over her fragile, lace-webbed nudity both fascinated and alarmed her.

Gentle fingers smoothed her face, sank into thick tresses to cup her scalp as they had so many times before. But it was different now…now they merely touched as an overture to…she knew not what.

And therein, she abruptly perceived, lay the heart of the

matter. What dismayed her was ignorance of what was expected of her…of her wifely duty. And duty was something Victoria had never previously found daunting.

Scarcely half an hour earlier she had revelled in lingering, passionate kisses by the parlour fire, never wanting them to end. She wouldn't even allow him free of her captivating, questing lips when he'd abruptly stood with her in his arms, twirled them slowly about before the hearth and carried her upstairs.

Strangely, it was only when he'd courteously left her for a few moments to prepare for bed that insidious niggles had stirred. As she'd lain alone for the final time on cool, crisp sheets, they had begun writhing in earnest. And now verbena-scented warmth from a male body, along with a faint, heady fragrance of cigars and alcohol, conspired to increase her diffidence.

Only a few days ago he had teased her about producing their first-born, obviously believing she knew how that would be achieved. She was, after all, twenty-five years old and had lived with a husband, if not a lover. David no doubt assumed that she was cognizant with the theory of conjugal duty, if not the practice. Yet, with excruciating embarrassment, she'd realised she had no idea what would happen next. The sum of her knowledge, gained from adolescent girlish chatter, was that she would remain a virgin until she had lain naked with a man.

'Will you talk to me for a while?' She introduced a gaiety into the suggestion, desperate to gain time to conquer her idiotic insecurities. And they were idiotic! She loved him utterly, with all her being, and trusted he adored her and would thus be patient, and yet…

'Now…?' The word resonated with rueful query as his eyes flicked to the bedhead.

'I'm worried Justin might do something silly…run off

again…' exploded quietly from her. 'Will…will you promise to say nothing to Matilda of his antics?'

'Right now, I'll promise you anything you like, sweetheart.'

'It's not a joke, David,' Victoria quavered, her dusky head twisting on the pillow, shooting skeins of black silk to embroider pristine cotton.

Barring forearms and hands stirred beneath its luxuriant weight, long fingers threading, twining.

'I know he's been foolish and selfish, but to see him gaoled, or worse…'

'*Are* you nervous, Vicky?' His parted lips traced from brow to jaw, hovering enticingly close to the corner of her mouth.

'And yet he really should not get off too lightly.' She speedily persevered with her one-sided dialogue, yet her lids drooped in response to his subtle seduction.

'I won't hurt you, Vicky…' David vowed softly, a finger trailing a pearly cheek, and urging her back to face him. 'Have you heard terrible tales of wedding-night blood and pain?'

Her eyes jerked to his, unblinking and lustrous with alarm. 'No…I've heard nothing like that. I've heard nothing at all,' emerged in a croaky whisper.

'Nothing at all?' he echoed, with such loving concern in his voice, his tone was equally gruff.

Interpreting the roughness as disappointment, she cried in raw apology, 'I'm so sorry, David…I know it's childish… I'm twenty-five and married since eighteen and I should know better. But…but there's only ever been you who's made me feel…like this…so it's never before bothered me to discover what I must do.' Gulping in air, she slid her hands from his shoulders to the sheets.

He retrieved one and a slow thumb smoothed her tapered fingers before they were raised to his lips. Unhurriedly he replaced the hand on his shoulder, then turned his face, sweeping a soft caress along the sensitive, fine skin of her arm. But he remained quiet, his protracted silence instrumental in prompting her to disclose more.

Bathed by his warm, liquid gaze, she continued more placidly, 'Matilda might have told me…for when about thirteen she told me other…facts…girls should know.' She paused, absently shielding her blushing face with unsteady fingers. 'But when I married Daniel at eighteen they were such horrible, traumatic days. There was no inclination for such talk…and no need. Although Matilda never knew that. Daniel and I were respectful of each other: no mention was ever made of the lack of an intimate side to our marriage.' She hesitated, frowning up at the velvet bed canopy, and moistened her lips with an innocently erotic tonguetip. 'Daniel would have explained, had I asked…he was like a parent, a confidant…'

That was all the unburdening David could stand. With a muttered oath, she was hauled up onto his lap, her shivering form enclosed within the solace of his arms. Leisurely thumbs tracked her satin-sheathed spine, trailing delicious ripples of sensation in their wake.

'Please don't talk of him, Vicky. I'm eternally grateful he cared for you so well, but even so…I'm jealous he had those seven years. They were mine.'

The fears he really wanted to allay were put aside for a moment.

'I said earlier that we'll share the burden of your family; that includes that fraudster cousin of yours. I'll do my utmost to keep it all from Matilda and I'll endeavour to thrash out some sort of deal with investors if uninsured losses become a problem. And I definitely won't let him get off too lightly—even if recompense means he works his fingers to the bone as a stevedore alongside Toby. Does that put your mind at rest?'

She nodded, grazing her smooth brow against his shaven jaw.

'As to what else worries you...there is nothing else to worry you, Vicky,' he murmured with gentle gravity. 'Making love isn't just another onerous duty to be discharged, you know. It's something wonderful for us to share. Just as we'll share the not so wonderful moments,' he said, his lips stroking at her hairline. 'And I want you to confide in me...talk to me about whatever troubles you. Anything at all...even facts girls should know. It's only fair: I shall want to confide in you.'

After a pause he offered with sweet self-consciousness, 'It's only fair, too, that I tell you a secret as you've told me one. Can you guess how long I've loved you?'

'Seven years,' was whispered against his abrasive skin.

'No...' He smiled against her face. 'No...much longer,' he said with an appealing bashfulness. 'I might have been about seven, though, when it started; when I first vaguely understood that all the raucous carousing in the house was about sin. To hide from my parents' disgrace, I'd crawl beneath the bedcovers and in that spectral realm between awake and asleep there was something magical. Neither real nor imagined but a flower-scented, soft darkness that lulled me.

'As I grew older and bolder I thought it all forgotten. Just a faceless fairy-tale companion for nursery days. For that's all it had been, just an essence...a hint of someone.

'Then one tedious afternoon seven years ago Dickie and I decided that the staid society at Almack's deserved our irreverent company.' His voice began to sound as distant as his memories as he recounted, 'I remember the assembly room that evening being noisy—music and crowds—and very bright, yet as I turned and saw you I was enveloped in peaceful darkness and the scent of rose petals...I recognised you straight away.'

Victoria withdrew her face from his and dewy pools gazed into his far-away blue eyes.

'You see how long you've comforted me, Vicky… You can't withdraw now. I couldn't bear it.'

She lovingly emphasised how willingly that comfort was bestowed by tightening her arms about his chest, laying her face against his shoulder and rubbing with innate femininity against his torso.

'And as for you knowing nothing of what pleasures we'll share tonight…tomorrow night…every night, into our dotage,' he tenderly teased with a kiss on her warming cheek as a solid knee slid subtly between hers and he casually positioned her hips, 'that makes me feel more proud and humble than I could ever express. Do you believe that?'

An ivory brow again swept over his shady square jaw in answer.

'This is new for me too, you know,' he said in a voice rich with sincerity yet harbouring humour. 'I've never made love to anyone in my life either and at nearly thirty-one I definitely should know better.'

Ebony hair caped her alabaster back as Victoria tipped her face up to his, dark brows winging sceptically, her confidence steadily strengthening.

'It's true,' he stressed, with a boyish smile that flipped her insides. 'There's a world of difference between coupling with a woman and making love to her.'

'How do you know?'

'Well, I don't, of course,' he glibly owned. 'I'm hoping now to find out. To learn about loving…just like you…just with you.'

Victoria's grey eyes locked onto his, searching deep into his soul, and found nothing other than truth and adoration…and desire. Even as she watched, it was kindling into a blue flame that scorched through her gauzy nightgown and stirred her to her female core.

'You love my honesty…' he murmured against her flaring skin as his lips touched her cheeks, her brow, her fluttering eyelids.

She was barely aware of the whisper of lacy satin on sleek skin as her nightgown floated away from her body. A moist throb between her thighs grew in intensity, trembling her limbs and making her rock against him.

'You like it when I kiss you, don't you?' he murmured while his warm mouth skimmed tantalisingly close to her lips.

She nodded against his face, strangely unable to form words, her breathing was now so shallow.

'Well, we'll start there, with what you like…' he decided, capturing her mouth in a drugging, wooing kiss of such infinite mellifluousness that Victoria felt she might drown in it…never again surface…seek daylight.

'And we'll see how we go on,' he eventually concluded, sheer contentment in his voice, his smile as her parted lips tracked his.

He watched her vigilantly, rewarding each shy, exploratory touch with further tender wooing, deftly defeating her inhibition. His hands shook with the restraint of caressing so gradually, so lightly, when what he really wanted was to plunge headlong into her…make up for seven long, barren years.

Torture…no penance, he mocked himself, and never was purgatory so enslaving…so bewitchingly sweet. The first unselfish physical union of his life. But he serenely accepted that, unto death, the die was cast; he was about to prove to them both he never lied.

Epilogue

'Thank you, Samuel. Has Mr Beresford gone?'

'Yes, ma'am,' Samuel confirmed. 'He said as how just to bring you this.'

Victoria gave silent thanks for Alexander Beresford's tactful withdrawal as she took the small package and looked at it curiously. She and David had thankfully seen very little of him since their marriage.

When alone, she broke the seal and removed the wrapping paper. Her fingers stilled as she recognised something of her own making. Shaking fingers retrieved two letters from her lap as though they were as fragile as wafer. She unfolded the single sheet of parchment with them.

The sight of Daniel Hart's spidery scrawl brought spontaneous tears stinging to her eyes and she hastily folded the paper to prevent spoiling this precious message from the grave. She blinked through a mist at the name and direction on the letters.

Had her writing altered? Was it young then and mature now? Would it look the same if now, seven years later, she wrote 'The Hon. Mr David Hardinge, Falconer's Mews, Chelsea'?

She knuckled wet from her eyes and began to read:

Well, my dear, did he marry you? I think he must have for I left strict instructions that Beresford only deliver this, my final bequest to you, three months after you again changed name...title, too, I hope. And, if I can at all trust this faltering judgement of mine, I feel sure that duty did override disquiet and you invited him to see me laid to rest. As a consequence you must now have that true happiness I could never give you. I know only love will again make you a bride: if I can claim any merit, it is that I have provided satisfactorily for you. Your selfless duty to your family should never force you to seek security in wedlock. Please God, I'm right; that certitude is all that allows me peace...

Victoria raised glossy, distant eyes at that irony and a small smile twisted her soft lips before she recommenced reading...

The purpose of this letter, of course, is to beg forgiveness for, as you will now know, I'm so sorry, my dearest Vicky, but I lied. I never did despatch those letters. I have kept them...and now return them.

So; to the motives for my bitterly regretted arrogance. It is a story fraught with prejudice and greed. My failings, I'm afraid, not my cousin's...who, you might now be aware, is in fact no blood relative at all. He can lay claim to far more august stock than I.

But, to my shame, but not wholly for bad reasons, I did not want him to have you then. I believed, despite your loyal championship of David Hardinge, all the scandalous gossip I heard. Personally, I bore him little ill will, even envied him, as most men did. But I had appointed myself custodian of your virtue, your sweet person. Relinquishing you to such a reprobate was beyond my courage, as was honestly telling you so.

You see, at times, I swear I feel more father to you than Charles himself.

But now, as I battle for breath and strength to finish this letter, I wish…oh, how I wish I had left well alone and allowed you your very feminine intuition where he was concerned. For I discovered three years ago and four years too late that you were right. He is an honourable man; he does truly love you. Giving you into his care would have been a father's finest hour.

My come-uppance is a tale filled with dignity… restraint. Your husband's, I'm afraid. Would that such principles were mine. My part was no more than a base, greedy speculation: I had high hopes of a quick handsome profit from eastern wares conveyed home by the cheapest route and vessel. Venality inevitably leads to disaster and so it turned out. The wreck of a merchantman limped home after heavy weather and all I had to show for my avarice and coin was a load of sea-stained silk and perished spices. Bankruptcy, squalor for us all, seemed certain, auctioning off the ruined goods a fruitless exercise…

Your husband bid for my worthless stock. He persevered even after I deliberately drove up the calls. He was in it to mock and shame me before all those gawping bystanders, or so I thought, and would callously withdraw once he'd had his sport. Never once during the transaction did he look my way or falter; never once did he seek recognition or gratitude when the deal was signed and sealed. Never once since has he been near nor by. Even a chance meeting and he accords me no more than a flick of dark head and azure eyes.

My credibility and capital were thus restored at his own expense—for all present speculated yet dared not ask why such a financier bought flotsam that day. On

reflection, the awesome truth in his motives made me
sick with a guilt I believe has never truly left me.
 He loved you still and so unconditionally, so abso-
lutely, that he would allow me dignity and shelter too
because of it. You must ask him, Vicky, my dearest,
what ever he did with that cargo of salt-water...

The laboured words trailed into bare parchment.

Victoria stared blankly; dear Daniel's strength had finally
failed him. She stood and walked to the window, for it
seemed about that time. She gazed out into the russet-skied
harvest evening. A wistful smile met the sight of her papa
and his companion.

They walked slowly, the woman aiding his progress with
a thin arm through his. She pointed out the beauty in the
full-blown roses trailing the arch and Charles cocked his
head obligingly to look. Still elegant and very charming,
Victoria had said to David of his mother when the dowager
had arrived last week to stay a while. And he had given
her one of his smiles that let her know that but for her
whim...

Her grey eyes drifted past to what she really sought. Two
robust black Labradors bounded up then circled her father
gently, as they had been taught. Charles patted at each
sleek, dusky neck before the dogs chased back at their master's signal.

Victoria watched, quietly fascinated, as always, by her
husband in all his powerful, masculine splendour. He
walked with an easy stride, gun slung casually over one
shoulder, his vented coat flapping about long, muscular
legs. Dark chestnut hair whipped about his face in the light
breeze, trailing lengthily over his collar. He laughed at
some comment from Samuel, keeping pace with him, ham
fists full of game.

David scanned the house, as he always did, shaking back

hair from his searching blue gaze until their eyes met for that infinite moment. Then he was angling away to the entrance.

She found him in his study, as always, poring over the architect's plans. Stealing quietly up behind him, she dropped a kiss on his dark, glossy head, combing her fingers through soft hair to cup his cheek. A large hand covered hers, removing it so he could touch his lips to the pulse in her wrist.

'Alexander Beresford came while you were out shooting.'

'Yes, I know. Samuel said.'

'He wouldn't stay…he simply left me something.'

'I wonder why…?' David mused drily while tracing a boundary line with a long blunt finger.

'Wonder why? Why he wouldn't stay?' At a sideways smile from her husband she softly chided, 'You know why. He believed you about the building somewhere.' She barely paused before withdrawing the parchment from her skirt pocket. 'I'd like you to read the letter he brought…it's from Daniel.' She sensed him stiffen but he said nothing and merely placed a broad palm on the parchment to keep it flat on the table in front of him.

Victoria wandered away to the window to stare out while he read. With her eyes on the sunset, she knew the instant he finished it.

'Is it true?' she asked quietly. 'Did you rescue us then, too?'

'Yes.'

She turned towards him, her eyes stinging with tears. 'Why did you never say? You could have told me that when first I arrived in London.'

She watched his elegant, patrician fingers smooth the parchment, then fold it, his expression a little abashed. 'He credits me with too much. It started in jest…Dickie and I mischief-making. But ended in earnest. At the time I never pondered my motives. Just a whim…'

'You did it for me.'

He laughed self-consciously. 'Yes, Victoria, I did it for you. But at the time I chose not to realise and Dickie, bless him, opted not to tell me.'

'Sometimes, David, I think if I love you any more I'll burst…and yet still I manage to.'

She walked back towards him, her heart quickening in rhythm with her womb. She knew now she couldn't… wouldn't wait longer. She was as sure as she was ever likely to be. As she neared the desk, he shoved back his chair and pulled her onto his lap. She sensed the arousal in him, his breathing slowing, the rough gentleness in his hands. And as always felt her own melting response. She smiled serenely and turned her attention to the charts on the table. 'How long before we can move in, do you think?'

He choked a laugh. 'The shell of one wing is barely set, Vicky. Besides, I thought you were reluctant to leave Hartfield.'

'But I've changed my mind, David,' she softly decided, sweeping a slender finger over the proposed eastern wing of their grand house. 'I'm glad we started here. I like this bit very much.'

'Guest rooms, servants' quarters, the nursery…' he readily listed.

'Yes…I know.'

She felt the sudden stillness in him. The vibration in the hands that held her.

'If I draft in extra labour, that wing might be habitable in…six months?' he tendered hoarsely.

'That would be fine,' she confirmed. They turned simultaneously, faces already angling.

'I want Dickie to be godfather…' David murmured against her lips.

'I want Emma to be godmother...' she countered.

'I want a quiet life...we'll ask the Graysons,' he said, silencing any objection with a sublime wickedness peculiar to such a kind and decent man.

* * * * *

A Regency Invitation

to the House Party of the Season

Nicola Cornick, Joanna Maitland, Elizabeth Rolls

On sale 3rd December 2004

Available at most branches of WHSmith, Tesco, ASDA, Martins, Borders, Eason, Sainsbury's and all good paperback bookshops.

Susan Wiggs

THE CHARM SCHOOL

From wallflower to belle of the ball...

"...an irresistible blend of *The Ugly Duckling* and *My Fair Lady*. Jump right in and enjoy yourself." —*Catherine Coulter*

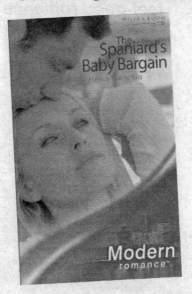